Handbook of the

BIRDS OF CYPRUS

AND MIGRANTS

OF THE MIDDLE EAST

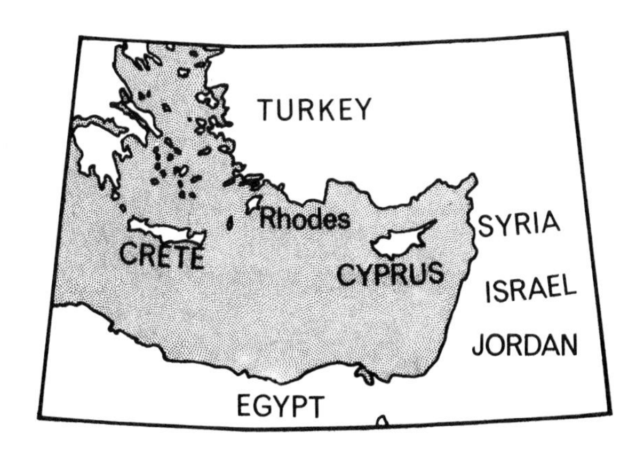

A

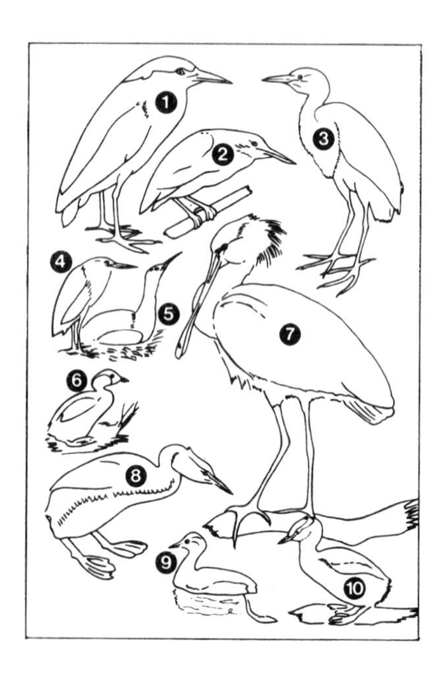

Plate 1. Frontispiece

1. Night heron
2. Squacco heron
3. Buff-backed heron
4. Little bittern ♂
5. Little bittern ♀
6. Little grebe
7. Spoonbill
8. Great-crested grebe
9. Black-necked grebe
10. Slavonian grebe

C.E.Talbot Kelly '70

Handbook of the BIRDS OF CYPRUS

AND MIGRANTS OF THE MIDDLE EAST

by

DAVID ARMITAGE BANNERMAN
O.B.E., M.A., Sc.D. (Cantab), Hon. LL.D. (Glasgow), F.R.S.E., F.Z.S.

Honorary Associate, British Museum
Honorary Curator, Royal Scottish Museum
Vice-President, Royal Society for the Protection of Birds
Gold medallist of the British Ornithologists' Union

and

W. MARY (JANE) BANNERMAN
O.B.E., Honours graduate & Reid scholar
London University

1971

OLIVER & BOYD

TWEEDDALE COURT, EDINBURGH

OLIVER AND BOYD
Tweeddale Court, 14 High Street
Edinburgh, EH1 1YL
(A Division of Longman Group Ltd.)

First published 1971

ISBN 0 05 002445 0

Filmset by St. Paul's Press Ltd., Malta
Printed in Great Britain by
T. & A. Constable Ltd., Edinburgh

FOREWORD

Dr. and Mrs. Bannerman need no introduction as they have already made their mark by their book *Birds of Cyprus* which has been a source of information to all persons interested in the avifauna of Cyprus. Members of the Cyprus Ornithological Society found this book most useful in their field meetings and many of the data which appeared in the 1st list of Cyprus birds issued in 1963 were taken from the *Birds of Cyprus*. It has contributed considerably in promoting an understanding about birds among the local population of Cyprus.

I am therefore greatly honoured to have been given the privilege to write a Foreword to this *Handbook of the Birds of Cyprus*, which should be equally valuable as a means of identification not only in Cyprus but also all over the Middle East, for the birds described in it are common to all the countries of the Eastern Mediterranean. This Handbook which was prepared with my warm approval and that of the Cyprus Ornithological Society has been written in close cooperation with Sgt. Peter Stewart one of the most knowledgeable and dedicated members of the Society, who put all his notes as well as his Check List which will be published in 1971 at the disposal of the Authors.

The book, which comes at a time when the Government of Cyprus is making efforts to promote a sense of responsibility for nature conservation, will I am sure prove invaluable in supplementing these efforts. At present over one fifth of the Island is declared a Game Reserve Area and several birds are on the "protected list". The attention of the Government has been directed to promoting the love of birds among school children and this Handbook should prove invaluable to those who are entrusted with this task. Every school library should have it on its shelves.

G. S. SAVVIDES
President
Cyprus Ornithological Society

Sovereign Base Area Administration
Dhekelia
27 August 1970

AUTHORS PREFACE

The authors of this Handbook are no strangers to Cyprus. We first came to the island in 1954 at the invitation of the (then British) Cyprus Government to make a survey of the bird-life and to prepare a book on the subject. We began our work in the island in the outwardly peaceful days of 1954, to be interrupted by the Eoka emergency which put a stop to our activities for more than eighteen months. We returned in 1957, and again in 1958 for a third period before the publication of our book, *Birds of Cyprus* towards the close of the year. During these visits we had gained first hand knowledge of almost the whole island, latterly under most difficult conditions.

Our book was primarily an historical account of the island from an ornithologist's standpoint, and of all those who had worked on our subject from earliest days. We believe it fulfilled the objects which the Government had in view and brought the knowledge of Cyprus ornithology up to date at that time. It will remain as a monument to the many distinguished Ornithologists of early days who had worked in the island, of whom we have given biographical sketches in our previous book. It had the disadvantage of being a large heavy volume of 455 pages with many coloured plates and text figures and suffered from some errors which are all too prone to occur in pioneer work, when collating the work of predecessors, for ours was the first book on Cyprus birds ever to have been attempted. These mistakes have now been corrected in the pages which follow.

The new Handbook has been prepared for the convenience of visitors to Cyprus for use in the field, as well as at home. In it we have given mostly newly prepared descriptions of *all* birds which have been seen at least ten times. The more rarely-recorded species, which bird watchers and others are unlikely to encounter, are relegated to an Appendix which, however, is more than a bare list. Pictures in colour of 184 different birds are depicted on the twenty-seven plates, thirteen of which with 143 figures in colour are entirely new.

Cyprus is especially famed for the great number of birds which pass through the island on their way from Europe and western Asia to winter in Africa and which return the same way in the Spring. In addition Cyprus with its great diversity of scenery, its salt-lakes, fresh-water reservoirs, maritime plains, foothills and forest-covered mountains reaching in Mount Olympus 6403 ft in altitude, harbours a particularly interesting resident bird-population, with a number of endemic forms, as well as attracting a vast number of winter and summer bird-visitors and thousands of passage migrants annually. For many years only a handful of ornithologists worked in Cyprus, some even before the days of binoculars. Now an increasing number of people are interested and knowledgable about ornithology, and since our larger work appeared in 1958, the Cyprus Ornithological Society under its President, George Savvides, has done much valuable work, particularly in the field, and in the formation of Nature Reserves.

A word must now be said about that Society with which we have worked in close and friendly collaboration. It will be referred to for short in the text of the Handbook as the C.O.S. The Cyprus Ornithological Society owes its existence in the early days to the enthusiasm of its founder members Fl. Lieut. W. R. P. Bourne and Captain (now Major) P. C. T. Wildash who between them, together with its first Secretary and Treasurer, the late Captain Robin Dove, Royal Ulster Rifles, tragically drowned in Ireland after seven years active service in Cyprus, set the Society on its first legs, publishing regular "Bulletins" of its activities. The first-named eventually brought out a Check-List of Cyprus birds in the 15th Bulletin in 1963 in which the work of its members since its formation was tabulated. It was a useful start. In its first days the Society was composed mainly of young National Service recruits, and a few regular officers in British regiments on active service, especially during the emergency years and a few civilian residents in Cyprus with an interest in birds. Since those days there have been many recruits to the C.O.S. and a much wider membership has resulted, embracing more civilian residents of British, Greek and Turkish nationality as well as Army and Air Force personnel fresh out from the United Kingdom. The distinguished President of the Ornithological Society, George Savvides O.B.E., Area-officer of the Sovereign Base Administration, Dhekelia, is especially concerned with conservation for which he has already done so much. Indeed it is to that aspect of its work that the Society should devote much of its energy not only for the sake of the birds but of the great number of tourists from overseas with interests in Natural History, who so signally contribute to the island's economy. An island geographically situated on one of the great bird migration routes to Africa is bound to attract scores of tourists whose interests are bound up with the birds and flowers which this beautiful island can offer – but they will not choose Cyprus for their holiday if they are to be met by a barrage of guns, (the number of gun licences is already far too great for so small an area), and are unable to find any peaceful spots in the island in which to watch the wonderful bird-life, uninterrupted by shooters.

Nature Reserves which have been formed in several areas – and we may hope in due course on the Karpas Peninsula – if properly administered would assuredly pay the Government of Cyprus a handsome dividend, and bring the right sort of tourist to the island! It is to the credit of those who have guided the C.O.S. during the last ten years that the

Society has flourished as it has, and especially to its energetic Secretary Peter F. Stewart who in addition to his onerous duties as Sergeant in the R.A.F. found time to ring literally thousands of birds and who has now capped his work at the ringing-station at Akrotiri and the part-editing of the Bird-Reports, by compiling, with the assistance of his Danish friend Steen Christensen, a revised *Check-List of Cyprus Birds* to be published in Cyprus, in 1971. It will contain, among much else, full migration and ringing data accumulated since the Society was formed. We cannot sufficiently express our indebtedness to Sergeant Stewart for placing his *Check-List* unreservedly at our disposal for use in our Handbook, and to the President of the C.O.S. for welcoming our project so warmly. We paid the island another memorable visit in the Autumn of 1969 when we were most cordially received and made many new friends.

The 143 new illustrations in this book on thirteen plates are the work of the highly-skilled bird artist Miss Chlöe Talbot Kelly and have been prepared with a view to assisting identification of the birds in the field. We are grateful to her for the care she has bestowed on her subjects which will surely enhance her already international reputation. We have included once again the fourteen beautiful pictorial plates by David Reid-Henry which so much enhanced the value of our larger work – a style of painting in which he has no equal. The work of these two distinguished artists will speak for itself. The woodcuts and line drawing which illustrate the text are by C. F. Tunnicliffe, R. A. the late G. E. Lodge, Roland Green, Chlöe Talbot Kelly, D. Reid-Henry, Eric Gorton, and Peter Clancey. Those by D. Reid-Henry were first published in Cave and Macdonald, *Birds of the Sudan*, 1955 (Oliver & Boyd), and it is with much pleasure we acknowledge to these authors their very great kindness in permitting us to include them here.

To the trustees of the late Colonel Meinertzhagen, for permitting us to use certain line-drawings from his *Birds of Arabia* we express our grateful thanks – and to the artist, Mr. Roland Green.

We would also wish to thank Mr. George Savvides for writing the Foreword to this new Handbook. Under his Presidency, as well as its new Secretary, and with an increasing number of Cypriot members, the C.O.S. will give a splendid lead and encourage an even greater interest in the well-being and study of Cyprus birds.

Its former Secretary, Mr. Peter Stewart, has already left the island for other fields of activity after ten years service in Cyprus, but his valuable ringing work is being carried on, and the interest in migratory movements through Cyprus maintained. We would urge those who have the facilities for doing so to pay more attention to the *resident birds*. There is still much to be done in the field especially with regard to the breeding biology of many species on the lines so well begun by Mr. J. F. R. Ashton-Johnson of The Royal Ulster Rifles, whose field notes we have used in this book.

We wish to make it clear that while this is essentially a work on Cyprus, the birds which fill our pages are largely passage-migrants, common not only to Cyprus but to the *whole of the Middle East*. Bird-lovers, or more scientifically-minded ornithologists, visting the countries of the eastern Mediterranean, whether it be northern Egypt, Sinai, Israel, Lebanon, Syria or Turkey as well as some of the Greek islands such as Crete or Rhodes, will find eighty per cent of the birds dealt with in our pages; while it would be unfair to call this a handbook of the birds of the Middle East, with its strong bias to Cyprus, it covers so many of the birds a visitor to any of those countries or islands may see, that it will prove useful, as a source of identification and guide to migratory movements, to others besides those for whom it has been primarily written. We have only recently been counting up the latest list of the *Birds of Greece*, the Ionian Islands Crete and Rhodes (1969) and find that the authors list 380 species of which 342 have occurred in Cyprus. Likewise in *List of the Birds in Turkey* (1956), 392 species are described of which 302 have occurred in Cyprus. We have now had an opportunity to count the number of species in *Birds of Lebanon and Jordan* and the proportion found to occur in both Lebanon and Cyprus is even closer than in the first two books cited. *Birds of Lebanon* is a useful companion volume to ours. A new List of the birds of Turkey has been published as we go to press, too late for use to have been made of it in this handbook.

To our publishers Messrs. Oliver & Boyd of Edinburgh, especially to the Managing Director Michael Wayte, and to my old friend and collaborator in the course of producing thirty books, Tom Jenkins, – who has designed and edited the work – we owe a great debt for the interest they have both taken, and the care bestowed on its publication and promotion.

We are greatly indebted to the George Lodge Trust for bearing the initial publishing costs of this volume, the major expenses of which will eventually be borne by ourselves. We owe a special debt of gratitude to the Trust's chairman, General Sir Philip Christison Bt., G.B.E. for the interest he has taken in our handbook and his faith in its success.

We would like before ending this Preface to express our gratitude to our valued friend of earlier days, John Reddaway C.M.G., O.B.E., Administrative Secretary, Cyprus, during the last British Administration, for his untiring efforts to interest His Beatitude President Makarios and the Cypriot Government in our new Handbook which we hope will encourage many bird-lovers to visit this lovely island and see for themselves the wealth of bird-life which it can offer.

Bailiff's House,
Slindon,
Sussex,
England.

D. A. B.
W. M. B.

A NOTE ON CLASSIFICATION

In the *Birds of Cyprus* (1958) the classification adopted was that in former general usage, based on Hartert's classic work *Die Vögel der Palaarktischen Fauna,* for the reasons given on p. X of our larger book. Since then, by general agreement, Dr. Wetmore's classification has been universally accepted by ornithologists, and has been followed in the non-passerine groups in the still unfinished *Check-List of the Birds of the World* by J. L. Peters.

A revised *Classification for the Birds of the World* by Dr. Wetmore appeared in *Smithsonian Miscellaneous Collections* Vol. 139 No. 11 1960 and is the classification adhered to in this new book on Cyprus birds, with the exception that the Old World vultures are retained in a separate family Aegypiidae and, in the Order Passeriformes, the buntings are retained in a separate family from the Fringillidae. Other proposals advanced by Dr. Amadon, Dr. Mayr, and others for the regrouping of the Passeriformes have been advocated in *A New Dictionary of Birds* (1964) but have not yet been universally accepted.

A Handbook on Cyprus birds is not the place to argue the merits or otherwise of the new arrangement proposed, but the senior author finds himself in much closer agreement with the families as listed in Dr. Wetmore's Classification, and rebels against including the thrushes, warblers and flycathers in a single family Muscicapidae. Nor does he agree – particularly in view of Dr. Wetmore's note in the *Condor** on the systematic position of the Corvidae – in placing the crows at the end of the List. We feel that in view of the diverse opinions held by leading ornithologists on the arrangement of the Passeriformes in America and in Europe that in a small work of this kind it is best to stick to the grouping to which we have grown accustomed. *We adhere therefore to Dr. Wetmore's Classification of 1960,* and are confident that the non-interruption of the families and sequence of the Passerine birds as there set out – to which *Dr. Wetmore himself still adheres* – is preferable to retain in this small book.

In the following pages we have listed the Orders and Families as the principal divisions, omitting the headings "Super-Order" and "Super-Family" as unnecessary in this work. In our text, when the geographical race which occurs in Cyprus is certainly known, we have used trinomials to indicate the subspecies, but when it is the typical or nominate form which occurs, we have employed a binomial heading, thus saving space,

---

*Vol. 59, 1957 pp. 207–209: The Classification of the Oscine Passeriformes.

rather than repeat the specific name twice. The species name is here the important factor. If the bird is an endemic species, restricted in its species or sub-species to Cyprus, the fact is indicated in the text, but it must be noted that those engaged in systematic research often fail to agree on this question.

CONTENTS

COLOUR PLATES

Order PODICIPEDIFORMES

Family PODICIPEDIDAE

The grebes form a cosmopolitan assemblage embracing many species. They are remarkable for the formation of the legs and feet, the latter having each toe separately lobed and the tarsus flattened. The bill is straight and pointed, the body is covered with dense silky plumage and the legs are situated far back on the trunk. A tuft of downy feathers represents the tail. The wings are relatively weak, but once launched in the air grebes can fly strongly.

Four members of the family now figure on the Cyprus list, three of which are breeding species dependent to a great extent on the annual rainfall and consequent state of the reservoirs and marshes. Several species resort to salt water in the winter and may be seen off the Cyprus coasts but in winter plumage they are far from easy to identify, especially when bobbing about in the sea.

GREAT CRESTED GREBE

Podiceps cristatus [Plate 1, frontispiece]

A long slender bird with a long neck and tapering body measuring from bill to tail when the neck is outstretched some 19 ins (48 cm). In winter dress it is mostly greyish-brown above including the neck, the head with a black crown, a white streak in front of the eye and blackish ear tufts; the cheeks and throat are glistening white and so are the entire underparts. The very short tail, no more than a tuft, is brown, the feathers being soft and not stiffened. The bill is strong, dagger-shaped and pinkish horn; the eye is crimson; the legs and feet olive and greenish yellow.

In breeding dress a bright chestnut tippet edged with black is assumed; young birds are remarkable in appearance having

the head and neck striped black and white.

To Cyprus it is a regular winter visitor in small numbers and passage migrant, to be seen on the larger sheets of water such as the reservoirs upon which it formerly used to breed, as well as round the coast and in the harbours. It is seldom seen in summer nowadays. When in flight a large amount of white is apparent on the wing, the bird flies fast with outstretched neck and rapid wing beats and the uninitiated will have difficulty in recognising it as the same bird seen swimming on a placid surface. It dives for its food. We have little doubt it may breed again in the few suitable spots which Cyprus has to offer now that protection has been afforded it in specified places in the breeding season. Its courting actions are so remarkable that they have been the subject of a little book. The nest is a floating mass of dead reeds and the three to four eggs of characteristic shape are chalky white.

The bird is strongly migratory in small parties which cross the Mediterranean in March and September.

BLACK-NECKED GREBE

Podiceps caspicus [Plate 1, frontispiece]
(*P. nigricollis auctorum*)

This is a smaller grebe than the last species described, no more than 12 ins (30 cm) in length, with a much shorter slightly upturned bill towards the tip, and more stumpy appearance with thicker neck. In winter the bird is easily confused with the Slavonian grebe but in breeding plumage the black neck and remarkable tufts of golden-brown feathers on either side of the head enable it to be readily identified.

The black necked grebe has bred frequently in Cyprus in the past, a colony of eighteen nests was discovered on Kouklia reservoir in 1913 but in the years since then great ecological changes have taken place and the bird has not been known to nest for many years. Always dependent on plenty of water there is little hope of its returning as a nesting species, and it is rarely seen in summer.

As a winter visitor it occurs from early autumn to March, the numbers increasing after Christmas when it is present some years in small numbers at Kouklia, Larnaca and Athalassa and in small numbers on pools around the island. It would seem from published notes in recent years to be irregular in its appearance both as regards numbers and time, but must be reckoned one of the more numerous of its family in the island which would assuredly breed again after a wet winter given the peace it would need. A record number of seventy-five birds was counted on Larnaca salt lake on 15 January 1962.

It is a colonial nester anchoring its nest to vegetation growing in shallow water and laying three to four eggs which it covers up on leaving the nest.

SLAVONIAN OR HORNED GREBE

Podiceps auritus [Plate 1, frontispiece]

In our *Birds of Cyprus* (1958) we recorded this grebe in brackets being then uncertain if it had been correctly included by earlier writers. We reported a bird believed to have been of this species in Morphou Bay in December 1957, as seen by a competent observer, but were in doubt again as to definite identification.

Its close resemblance in winter to the black-necked grebe, from which the stout straight bill of the Slavonian distinguishes it from the slender slightly up-tilted bill of the black-necked species causes these two grebes to be easily confused even by competent observers at close quarters.

There have, however, been several sight-records since that date, one in December 1967 at Akrotiri, which definitely establishes the Slavonian Grebe as a scarce winter visitor, by no means annually observed. When on migration this grebe is reported to travel singly or in small scattered flocks and when on the move a flock has been known to break up. It is most likely to be observed off shore, if in the Cyprus area. On long journeys, when flying overland, the birds are known to rise high in the air, following the course of rivers.

Under the surface the Slavonian grebe is superb, darting about skillfully and rapidly after the small fish which form a part of its varied diet.

Although the Slavonian grebe has on a

number of occasions been reported from the Mediterranean, it has seldom been recorded from northern Africa and is then more rarely encountered west of Sicily than to the east of it.

LITTLE GREBE [Plate 1, frontispiece]

Podiceps ruficollis

The Dabchick as this grebe is often named in the British Isles is by far the smallest of the four grebes which figure on the Cyprus list being little over 10 ins (25 cm) in length. In Spring garb it is brown above with a green gloss on the head, a black chin, throat and cheeks rufous and the underparts white. The gape and base of bill bright yellow and the eye red. In winter the colours are duller, a rather pale brown and white bird. Young birds have conspicuous white markings on the head and the chicks have dark streaks on the sides of the face. The bill is dark coloured and is both short and thick.

Its status in Cyprus in former days was that of an abundant breeding species some fifty to sixty nests having been found on one occasion on the reservoirs at Acheritou and Kouklia between 23 March and 9 April at the beginning of the 20th Century.

A very different tale must be told to-day, regular nesting having virtually ceased. A return to breeding was indicated in 1967 when 70 adult and juvenile birds were seen on Kouklia reservoir in early August after unusually high water in the Spring. The high hopes thus engendered were not upheld in 1968 when very few birds were recorded anywhere, even in mid-winter. It is believed it will return to Kouklia as a nesting species now that the reservoir is partly preserved.

In normal years the little grebe is to be found sparingly on Cyprus reservoirs and ponds as a passage migrant or winter visitor, its numbers varying from year to year with varying ecological conditions in Europe or locally. We have found it from the coast to the foothills on reservoirs and ponds. Breeding, when it occured, was from mid-March to mid-May but a single pair bred in August 1967. The nest of dead vegetable matter is built in the water and four to six bluish-white eggs are laid having a chalky surface. It feeds on small fish, larvae, water-snails and mollusca obtained by diving and can remain below the surface for twenty seconds or more.

Ranging through western and eastern Europe and not uncommon in Asia Minor, it is not surprising to find it in Cyprus. It migrates in small flocks and some are apparently resident in northern Africa on the lakes and inland reservoirs.

Order PROCELLARIIFORMES

Family HYDROBATIDAE

There is only one representative of this family in the seas around Cyprus – the widely distributed storm petrel which is one of the smallest of the Tubinares, so called because of the peculiarity of having external nostrils enclosed in a cylindrical tube situated on the dorsal surface of the beak. The two great families Hydrobatidae and Procellariidae into which the order is divided are distinguished from one another by several small characters. In the former group the birds are nearly all small in size, sombrely clad in dark grey, brown or black, relieved in some species by a white rump, in others with a white belly, spending their lives at sea and only coming to land to lay their egg and hatch their young. In flight the wings are constantly beaten, the legs often dangling, their habit of following ships enables them to be seen at fairly close quarters. In parts of the ocean where the species are abundant, they are extraordinarily difficult to identify, the constant erratic motion of the birds against the background of a restless sea, taxing the best field naturalists.

As noted above only the one species, known to our fishing folk at home as Mother Careys Chickens, is likely to occur in the eastern Mediterranean, with the possible exception of Leach's petrel. The two should not be confused for whereas the Storm petrel has a conspicuous pure white rump and square tail, the slightly larger Leach's petrel has a mixture of brown and white at the sides of the rump and a distinctly forked tail. The flight is very distinct and once known should alone identify these very small birds of the Ocean.

Family PROCELLARIIDAE

Embracing some of the larger petrels and the shearwaters, this family is represented in all the great oceans of the world, and shares the anatomical distinctions of the last family as there mentioned; Shearwaters obtain their name from their habit of gliding with outstretched wings over the sea, in rough weather following the contour of the waves, with only occasional recourse to beating the wings. Having webbed toes they can swim easily and settle on the water at will, rising with more dexterity than the gull-family and much less fuss than a grebe. Furnished with long pointed wings they can sustain their gliding flight for hours on end with seemingly no fatigue and very little motion, such wonderful powers of sustained flight are they endowed with.

Vast packs of these birds – especially the members of the genera *Calonectris* in which we place today the Mediterranean shearwater, and the *Puffinus* group, the largest assemblage of all, in which we place the Levantine shearwater – may sometimes be seen sitting on the sea all bunched together like a raft of ducks or coot, when it is difficult to see the water between them, so close do they ride to one another. Both these species are to be found in the Cyprus list, identified as occasional visitors to the coastal waters and probably more often than records to date would indicate. The Levantine shearwaters are none other than the birds which to travellers in the Dardanelles are known as "the lost Souls" for their endless patrolling of these waters, pack after pack flying steadily along – all in the same direction.

No petrel or shearwater has ever been recorded to have come ashore on Cyprus to lay its egg; the most likely place in the Eastern Mediterranean would be the Klidhes islands off the tip of the Karpas Promontory,

White-winged black tern

Greater flamingo

Great white egret

Plate 2

C. E. Talbot Kelly.

but none have been reported and the Cyprian fishermen who annually raid these uninhabited islets for gulls eggs – the last stronghold in these waters of Audouin's gull – would surely know if the shearwaters ever came ashore.

LEVANTINE SHEARWATER

Puffinus puffinus yelkouan

This is a striking geographical race of the well-known Manx shearwater of Great Britain, the Levantine race occurring so commonly in the area between the Black Sea and the Aegean, the Sea of Marmora and the Dardanelles.

This is a medium sized member of the petrel and shearwater family, 14 ins (36 cm) in length, dark brown above (rather than blackish) and the underparts, especially the sides, grey brown as are the axilliaries (rather than pure white below as in its northern relative).

It is more likely to be encountered in small parties well off shore than singly, though odd birds occur, flying rapidly or gliding over the surface of the sea with wings held stiffly, following the contour of the waves. Only a few specimens have ever been obtained but it has been seen off-shore a number of times from early March to early November, mainly in September, once in December.

Its migrations far afield are not well known but it may be this bird which enters the Red Sea and has been reported from the Gulf of 'Aqaba in winter – a route which would take it past Cyprus in spring and autumn to its breeding range in the Black Sea islands.

The much larger Mediterranean shearwater (*Calonectris diomedea*) and the storm petrel (*Hydrobates pelagica*) will be found listed among the rarer visitors in the appendix, p. 213; both have been seen occasionally off shore.

Plate 3

1. White-fronted goose
2. Mute swan
3. Bean goose
4. Whooper swan
5. Common pochard
6. White-eyed pochard
7. Ruddy sheld-duck
8. Pintail
9. Shoveler ♂
10. Shoveler ♀
11. Sheld-duck

Order PELECANIFORMES

Family PELECANIDAE

It has been said of the birds in this family that they are so extraordinary in their appearance that once seen in life they can never be forgotten or mistaken for any other bird. The huge ungainly body, long flattened mandibles terminating in a hook, enormous gular pouch, short powerful legs and broad wings, a truly remarkable combination of characteristics for any bird to possess. On the ground their gait is awkward and they may be said to waddle rather than walk, but both on the sea or lake and in the air they are very much at home, swimming easily with their powerful webbed feet; with head drawn back between the shoulders they are the reverse of ungainly on the wing, flying very strongly and often soaring with alternate beats and prolonged sailing. They feed exclusively on fish and are on the whole very gregarious. They are equally at home on fresh or salt water.

Two species, the white pelican and the Dalmatian figure as migrants, or more correctly, casual visitors to Cyprus; the latter species is the larger and has a crest of loose curly feathers which gives it a comical appearance, but only when at fairly close quarters are they to be distinguished – the white pelican is about 5 ft in length. Both of these pelicans occur on Turkish waters, the white pelican is a common visitor to the Sudan from October to April.

DALMATIAN PELICAN

Pelecanus crispus

Of the two pelicans which visit Cyprus this species is slightly larger than the white pelican (listed in the appendix p. 213 among the rare visitors.) It has the feathers of the forehead ending on the culmen in a concave line and not coming to a point as in the white pelican. Whole plumage white, a full crest of long, soft, pointed feathers, the underparts having a blue-grey wash. Primaries and primary-coverts blackish, secondaries ash-grey. A large straw-yellow patch on the breast. Eye pale yellow, bill yellowish, nail orange; pouch yellowish becoming orange in the spring. Feet lead-grey. Immature bird is brownish with dirty greyish-white underparts. Wing measures 690–804 mm.

The Dalmatian pelican which breeds in S.E. Europe, in the Azov and Caspian seas and formerly at the head of the Persian Gulf, ranges eastwards to China. It is far the most likely of the pelicans to visit Cyprus from time to time, but at a distance, as the birds are more often seen, it is impossible to distinguish from *P. onocrotalus* – for both occur.

There have now been sufficient identifications to enable the Dalmatian pelican to be described as an irregular visitor in Winter and perhaps at other times. The definite records are mostly in November except for the following: fifty birds on 17 September 1957 over Dhekelia, three on 28 March 1959 at Akrotiri and thirteen on 15 March 1967, seen at close quarters on Larnaca salt lake.

For records of the white pelican see page 213 of the Appendix.

Both species are gigantic birds and cannot be mistaken for any other species.

In this century seventeen observations of at least forty-nine birds have been reported during March, June, July, August, October, November and December; mainly October–December when it was found impossible to identify them specifically.

Family SULIDAE

In this group we have one of the best-known sea-birds in the northern Atlantic, the gannet, whose appearance is so familiar to British ornithologists. It breeds on both the eastern and western shores of the northern Atlantic: in Great Britain and the Faeroes in the north-east Atlantic and Canada on the west but nowhere else. Its place is taken in South Africa by the Cape gannet with a blackish tail and in the tropical and sub-tropical oceans of the world by the boobies of which there are a number of species. The only one of these to enter the Mediterranean as a casual winter visitor is the gannet, the British population of which wanders south after the nesting season, especially the birds of the year, to winter off the coast of Mauretania. Very few enter the Mediterranean and even fewer the seas in which Cyprus is situated, though recorded from off Malta, Syria and Egypt as very rare visitors.

They are large birds, recognised by their long pointed black-tipped wings, and a long wedge-shaped tail as well as by the long, stout, tapering bill, bluish-white in colour, sharply pointed terminally and serrated along the cutting edge of the mandibles to enable them to hold slippery fish securely for which they dive from a considerable height plunging below the surface. Adults are white, but immatures may be brown or brown and white depending on their age. Adults take four or five years to assume the immaculate plumage. The skin round the eye is bare. A notable feature is the lack of external nostrils. Feet are webbed as in a cormorant and the birds are as much at home on the water as in the air where they are superb. See Appendix p. 213 for dates of records.

Family PHALACROCORACIDAE

The cormorants and shags are placed in this family and are familiar to most people. Dark birds with dense glossy plumage, they have an unmistakable appearance. The feet are webbed, the short legs placed far back on the body; the long powerful bill ends in a hooked nail which overlaps the lower mandible. The nostrils are reduced to narrow slits. The tail is fairly long, composed of fourteen exceptionally stiff feathers in the cormorants, twelve in the shags. Cormorants will pass inland to fish on inland waters; their flight is powerful and the neck is held outstretched when the bird is on the wing. Members of this family will sit for hours on rocks or fish-traps with wings outspread as if drying them, though it is doubtful if this is the reason for the attitude. More probably the birds enjoy the warmth of the sun on their bodies.

One species of each occurs in Cyprus waters, but only the Mediterranean shag breeds on the sea-cliffs of the island in small colonies. It is the smaller bird 32 ins (81 cm) in length, and is more slimly-built than the Asiatic cormorant which is only a winter visitor from its breeding places in Asia Minor and Syria. In the nesting season the head and neck are white and there is a white patch on the thigh which is very noticeable in flight. The shag, altogether greener than the cormorant, is adorned with a short crest in summer. The Asiatic cormorant measures 3 ft (91 cm) from bill to tail.

ASIATIC CORMORANT

Phalacrocorax carbo sinensis

This is the southern race of the common cormorant and is the breeding bird of the eastern Mediterranean, Asia Minor and Syria. It does *not* however breed in Cyprus, but may be seen irregularly off the coast in winter either singly or a few at a time. It can only be described as scarce. It has been observed from mid-November to 20 April, mainly in February and March. For some reason it has not been reported since 1960. In 1958 there were seven observations off shore involving thirteen birds.

We have seen it ourselves in February when anchored in Morphou Bay and in the same month in Famagusta harbour. Four or five together have been recorded in the month of February off Cape Gata, which seems to be a favoured month for it to appear. It may then be seen fishing off shore or swimming partly submerged in the sea. Once in the air it flies with strong rapid wing-beats, usually a few feet only above the water. Like the next species discussed, it is a superb diver, usually bringing a fish to the surface in its powerful bill before attempting to swallow it.

It is a fairly large bird some 3 ft (91 cm) in length appearing black at a distance with white cheeks and chin; at closer quarters the feathers have a metallic blue gloss on the head and crown and bronze or blue

over the rest of the body. The neck is long and the tail short, the black legs set far back on the body.

In breeding dress in which it is unlikely to be seen in Cyprus, a conspicuous white patch is prominent on the thighs and the head and neck are then white, in contrast to the glossy blue-black body plumage. Very noticeable is the long powerful bill, the upper mandible ending in a sharp hook which overhangs the lower one. Like all its family when on shore or sitting on a buoy or rock it may often be seen sun-bathing with wide outstretched wings.

MEDITERRANEAN SHAG

*Phalacrocorax desmarestii**

[Plate 13, facing p. 65]

Very like the cormorant but slimmer in build and only a little smaller, 32 ins (81 cm) in total length; the shag has brown-black plumage with a very strong metallic green gloss on all the feathers of the upper and lower surface. It has a short crest of the same colour in breeding dress and the yellow at the base of the bill is then brighter than in the cormorant, which can easily be mistaken for it. The shag's eye is green; the feet have yellow webs. Juvenile shags can easily be distinguished by their white underparts.

Unlike the last species it is one of Cyprus's resident birds to be seen on the sea or cliffs all the year round, for while there is some dispersal after the nesting season, the birds are believed not to wander far afield. We have seen them in all the harbours and round the coast in winter, and in spring they congregate at their breeding places, the best known of which are situated at Capes Gata, Aspro and Kormakiti, or again on the rocky N.W. coast and on the Klidhes islands, while there may be others scattered round the coast which are less familiar; for instance the islands in Polis Bay are said to possess a colony. Shags are known to be more particular than cormorants in their choice of breeding places and are partial to ledges in caves as well as cliff sides. They are often reported from Episkopi, Cape Arnauti and the Karpas Peninsula.

The Mediterranean shag has always been recognised as a very early breeder as recorded in our *Birds of Cyprus* (1958) since when several colonies have been visited and fresh eggs found as late as 10 April and young may still be seen in the nest in May as the result of second broods. Three eggs are usual, of a chalky white colour with pale blue undershell. More attention should be given to the breeding biology of this Mediterranean race. Little has been written about it in Cyprus.

*Some systematists consider this is a subspecies of *P. aristotelis*; I do not agree with them.

Order CICONIIFORMES

Family ARDEIDAE

Cyprus has its fair share of this family which includes two closely allied groups, the herons and egrets on the one hand and the bitterns on the other. When we remember that all but the fresh-water reservoirs and largest sheets of water dry up completely in May unless the winter rainfall has been prolific, the list of seven species of herons and two species of bittern is all that we can expect. The salt-water lakes are the main attraction and account for most of the records. Marshlands and reed-beds are very scarce in Cyprus and the paucity of bitterns can be placed to that account.

Herons and egrets are mostly long-legged graceful birds with long straight pointed bills with which they deftly spear their prey when wading in shallow water or searching grassland. Their long toes assist them in wading and when they take flight they do so reluctantly. Unlike the Stork family (Ciconiidae) the heron flies with its head retracted between the shoulders. The night-herons, which have shorter legs than most, have an unmistakable silhouette in flight, with very short rounded wings and short tail. In the breeding season the white egrets are especially notable for their ornamental plumes the possession of which led to dreadful cruelty in the days when "Ospreys", the trade name for the little egret's nuptial-plumes, were sought after by plumage hunters at the time when the adults were rearing their young. Public opinion and the staunch support of H.M. Queen Mary finally forbade the importation of these dorsal plumes into Britain and happily put a stop to this abuse so far as the British Isles were concerned. There were no "egret colonies" in Cyprus, in fact all the Ardeidae which visit Cyprus do so mainly in the winter months, conditions in the island being unsuitable for nesting. Bitterns which prefer solitude and dense reed-beds for breeding, and especially peace and quiet, are unlikely to find any such conditions in Cyprus and consequently the remarkable booming noise which the male common bittern makes when breeding will never fall upon Cyprian ears.

It is a matter of interest that exactly the same species which figure on the Cyprus List do so in Dr. Kasparyan's List of the *Birds of Turkey*. The two bitterns in the genera *Botaurus* and *Ixobrychus* which are passage migrants to Cyprus, are described hereafter, where allusion is made to their retiring ways, facility in climbing among the reeds, and their habit of remaining stock-still if alarmed. They stretch their necks vertically upwards, so that their plumage-pattern including that of the upstretched neck, blends so strikingly with the dead and living reeds, among which they pass so much of their life, as to constitute a perfect camouflage.

The remarkable powder-down patches disposed over the body of the bittern, enable the bird to clean the feathers of its head and neck with its bill when these parts become coated with slime from the wriggling bodies of eels upon which the bittern largely feeds – when these creatures are procurable.

If breeding should ever take place in the island it is likely to be that of the smaller bird, which would have better chance of concealment.

GREY HERON

Ardea cinerea

This well-known bird requires only brief description. Its length, bill to tail tip is 36 ins (91 cm). The general colour of the upperparts is grey including the wings, the flight feathers black. Sides of face and throat are white as well as the long feathers on the forecrown, the rest of the crown black. A white line bordered with black streaks extends down the frontal part of the neck terminating in a bunch of elongated white feathers. The underparts are white with black patches on the sides of the breast. The bill is brown above, yellow below, the cere yellow. Legs and feet are light brown, the eye yellow.

It stands out for its size among the shore and lake birds, often remaining motionless with head sunk between the shoulders. In flight the head is drawn back and the long legs protrude beyond the tail making an unforgettable silhouette. It flies slowly, except when migrating, with heavy flaps of its huge rounded wings. A regular passage migrant in numbers to Cyprus, it is to be seen both on the shore and the lake margins in late March and April, but as the lakes dry up the birds take their departure – a phenomenon which varies from year to year according to the winter rains. This may occur as early as the end of March or as late as the beginning of May. Very few herons are to be seen after the end of June until the autumn migration sets in. From about mid-August till end-October groups of up to 60 birds have been recorded, while in the spring up to one hundred have been seen at once (in March) but such a number is, we gather, exceptional. In the winter months odd birds may be seen regularly frequenting the same places. Breeding in Cyprus is unknown.

Wintering herons have been recorded between early November and late February, the maximum, nine birds, seen at Larnaca in the third week of January 1959. These herons are very scarce in summer, only an odd bird being seen now and again, possibly an ailing individual.

PURPLE HERON

Ardea purpurea

Decidedly smaller than the last species the purple heron measures 31 ins (79 cm) and stands lower than its grey relative and the thinner neck has a more snake-like appearance. The upperparts are grey with long chestnut feathers falling over the mantle, wings grey with a chestnut

Grey heron

tinge, the primaries black. The crown and crest are black, the neck rufous striped boldly with three black lines, those in front terminating in a bunch of feathers in colour black, white and rufous. Underparts are chestnut on breast and sides, black on belly, the thighs rufous-buff. The underside of the wing is rufous, a prominent feature in flight. Eye yellow, bill yellowish-brown; legs and feet brown.

A passage migrant to Cyprus it appears at the same time as the grey heron but in smaller numbers but it does not remain in winter. The European population is also very much less than its grey relative. Birds passing through Cyprus probably winter in the Sudan but until ringed birds are captured it is uncertain how far south they migrate after leaving Cyprus, the difficulty being inhanced by the presence of a breeding population in tropical Africa which are indistinguishable from the European migrants.

The spring migration lasts from the first week of March to the first week of June, with maximum passing in mid-April. The Autumn passage is recorded between

Purple heron

Plate 4

1. Marbled teal
2. Common scoter
3. White-headed duck
4. Gadwall
5. Scaup
6. Goldeneye
7. Smew
8. Red-breasted merganser ♂
9. Red-breasted merganser ♀
10. Goosander
11. Tufted duck

C. E. Talbot Kelly

Plate 5

17 August and 15 October, mainly late August to mid-September in which month flocks with up to fifty birds have been reported on the move on the Northern coast.

Odd individuals are very rarely met with both in winter and summer, as with the last species dealt with, perhaps from the cause there suggested.

GREAT WHITE EGRET

Egretta alba [Plate 2, facing p. 4]

A large pure white egret some 35 ins (89 cm) in length which stands as high as the purple heron. The long dagger-shaped bill is all yellow in summer but in winter the basal part is black. Eye lemon-yellow, bare skin in front of eye green, legs and feet black. Its size separates it at once from the little egret as well as the black (not yellow) feet. In breeding dress a mantle of long disintegrated feathers formed by the elongated scapulars adds to its graceful appearance.

When we wrote the *Birds of Cyprus* (1958) there were few records of this bird but it is now known to be a passage migrant in small numbers at *both* seasons, some of the autumn visitors remaining over the winter months. Often to be observed singly, larger parties of eight or more have been recorded in spring. The latter migration, as observed since the formation of the C.O.S., extends from the second week of March to the third week of May, chiefly mid-March to mid-April. Maximum recorded at once twenty-eight birds in 1958 after a storm. No birds remain in Cyprus in summer. Early autumn migrants have been recorded on 13 August, the passage lasting till the fourth week of November and reaching its peak in October. Sightings seem restricted to the coastal area.

The spring passage is numerically far greater than the autumn. In the twelve years 1957 – 1969, one hundred and sixty three birds were recorded by the Society, one hundred and two of which were seen in March and April. The rest in other months except June and July.

LITTLE EGRET

Egretta garzetta

Distinguished from the last species by much smaller size, black legs and yellow feet. Pure white at all seasons two narrow elongated feathers hang from the nape and are very noticeable in a breeze. Eye yellow and bill always black, long and noticeably fine in contrast to the more stumpy yellow bill of the cattle egret. In length 22 ins (56 cm). A common spring migrant from late March to mid-May, some birds being still present in June. We have counted sixteen on Larnaca lake and larger numbers have been seen elsewhere on other lakes. We have, ourselves, counted several flocks

Little egret

Plate 5 (opposite)

Griffon vulture

Black vulture

of thirty between March and May. The maximum number counted to date is seventy-four at Episkopi by a Service member on the 15 April 1964. Summer records are rare: five only of individual birds in July.

The autumn passage is irregular and fewer birds are seen. In 1964 there were no sightings reported at all. In normal years migration has been observed from 7 August to 11 November. In mid-September the largest flocks of up to sixty birds have been seen.

In our *Birds of Cyprus* we remarked that we had seen two or three little egrets present in Famagusta harbour every day from early December to February but that may have been an unusual year, 1957–58. Wintering birds are definitely rare judging by those which have been recorded in the annals of the C.O.S., where only nine are listed. This is a breeding bird in southern Europe from southern Spain to Asia Minor and many must cross the Mediterranean to winter in Africa joining those birds which breed south of that sea.

Fortunately for the little egret it is not an edible bird although that does not entirely save it from molestation.

BUFF-BACKED HERON or CATTLE EGRET

Ardeola ibis [Plate 1, frontispiece]

In breeding plumage this small heron is pure white except for the crown and nape which are vinous in colour, and the long ornamental plumes on the back and foreneck. The eye is bright yellow, the bill yellow and the legs and feet yellowish-brown. At all seasons the yellow bill is a distinctive character and is quite an inch shorter than the rapier-like black bill of the little egret. It is also much stouter.

In winter the ornamental plumes are absent and the bird is then entirely white except for the wash of vinous which remains on the crown. The bird is 20 ins (51 cm) in length from bill to tail.

The cattle egret, as it is more generally termed today, is a spring passage migrant seen not uncommonly on its northern migration in small numbers mainly observed in April and May, although records of its passing extend from 10 February until 28 June. There are no summer and no winter records. In autumn of recent years, there have been very few seen: five birds on 13 September 1967, six between 22 and 26 August 1969 and one on 15 September 1969. These autumn sightings are of interest as formerly it was believed that this egret omitted Cyprus on its journey south, for there had been no previous sightings at that time of year.

The fact that it has been recorded from islands in the Mediterranean from the Balearics to Cyprus, is remarkable, for there are no known breeding colonies in southern Europe other than in the Iberian Peninsula. In the Middle East it breeds in Syria, Persia and probably Iraq. In northern Africa it is exceedingly numerous, indeed throughout the whole of Africa it is one of the best known, and best loved birds for the great amount of good it does in ridding the land of injurious insects. Luckily that fact is generally recognised.

SQUACCO HERON

Ardeola ralloides [Plate 1, frontispiece]

In summer plumage the crown and neck of the squacco are pale straw-colour, the crest feathers streaked with black, and long feathers, straw-coloured striped black, hang from the nape. The back is buff. The wings and tail are white and so is the chin, upper throat and the belly. The chest is golden-buff. The eye is greenish-lemon; legs and feet yellowish-green; bill blackish. It is 18 ins (46 cm) in length. In size the squacco resembles the little egret, but is easily distinguished by its dark back, and in flight by the contrast between its dark back and pure white wings.

This heron is a passage migrant to Cyprus and is tolerably common in spring when there are freshwater ponds and lakes to tempt the birds to remain in the early summer in the island. In autumn when the return passage takes place, far fewer squaccos are seen, all shallow water is then dried up. Birds have been seen in August and September coasting along the shore. Records are rare during October and it is seldom one is seen as late as 26 October as recorded at the Akrotiri Salt Lake in 1968. The height of the passage lasts approximately from mid-August to mid-September. Numbers vary considerably, the maximum observed being fifty-one birds on 11 August 1962 off Kyrenia.

The main spring passage takes place from mid-March to the end of the last week in May, mainly late March to late May. Maximum recorded thirty birds on I May 1969. Only six summer sightings have been reported – all during 1–26 July.

With an abundance of water in the lakes, 1969 was a specially good year for the squacco with flocks of up to thirty birds recorded during the spring at the Akrotiri Salt Lake. The Kouklia reservoir is also a favourite haunt when as many as twenty birds have been seen there at once. At the end of April and in early May many birds are in breeding dress when they are very attractive. The squacco is not a shy bird and opportunities of watching it at close quarters are not rare.

NIGHT HERON [Plate 1, frontispiece]

Nycticorax nycticorax

This is a stocky small heron, grey and black with short legs. The crown, nape and the middle of the back are bluish-black. A narrow white patch on the front of the head extends back over the eyes in a white line. Two or three long white plumes, very narrow, drop from the nape. The throat, cheeks and belly are white, the wings, tail and the remainder of the plumage grey. The eye is crimson, the bill greenish-black, the legs and feet yellow. The length is 24 ins (61 cm).

In flight the night heron is unmistakable. The wings are exceptionally rounded in shape and very broad. In silhouette the bird then looks short and squat. In Cyprus it is to be seen on passage during both migrations but like so many other birds is more in evidence from mid-March till early June (with maximum late April) than from mid-August to first half of October, mainly first half of September, the autumn migration being on a minor scale in comparison. Some birds appear to stay in the island through the summer months as recorded in 1962, when birds were present from late June to early August.

The night heron has a huge breeding range in central and southern Europe as well as in Asia and Africa. The African population is resident throughout that continent and is augmented in winter by the considerable numbers which cross the Mediterranean travelling in small parties.

LITTLE BITTERN [Plate 1, frontispiece]

Ixobrychus minutus

A very small bird barely exceeding 12 ins (30 cm) in height when standing erect with its neck outstretched, the little bittern is a good example of protective colouration. The male has the crown, back, scapulars and tail black glossed with green, contrasting with a buff neck and frill. There is a conspicuous pale patch on the otherwise black wing. The underparts are buffish, the throat white and on either side of the breast a dark patch. Eye bright yellow, bill yellow except for the brown ridge on the culmen and the legs and feet greenish. The female is much duller with brown uppersurface faintly streaked, and the underparts more streaked than her consort, she shares the dark crown but it is less glossy.

It is a passage migrant to Cyprus regularly in Spring in small parties from late March to early June, mostly in late April to mid-May, exceptionally earlier. The autumn passage had generally been overlooked prior to 1958 when we published our larger book, but there have since been a number of odd records between late August and the end of November, once, on 7 December 1969 in the Akrotiri reed-bed. Mid-summer records are very exceptional but one bird was found alive at Kolossi on 31 July, 1968 sitting by some road water watching the cars go by! It was an adult male. It is much more commonly seen on its way north from Africa, exhausted birds are then reported from time to time picked up on roads or in towns.

Kouklia with its reed-beds is naturally a more favoured spot in which to find it during migration. There have been unconfirmed rumours of its having bred in 1909 but the changes which have taken place mainly to its disadvantage in the last sixty years have been against it. A reserve has now been established at Kouklia during the breeding season, thanks to the C.O.S.

and its wise Cypriot President where it will be free from the endless disturbance afforded the water-birds before that happy event was completed. Quiet, sufficient cover, and plenty of water is sure to work miracles, and of that there can be no doubt.

BITTERN

Botaurus stellaris

The sexes of the European bittern are alike. A mixture of black, orange-buff, brown and white, the birds are so close in colouring to dead reeds and aquatic vegetation that when standing motionless among such surroundings they are wonderfully camouflaged. The bittern's habit of stretching up its neck and beak in one continuous line when alarmed, the dark streaking of the underparts blending with the upright reed-stems, assures it from observation from all but the sharpest eyes. The top of the head is black, the back streaked and mottled dark brown, the wings with broken bars of black and brown. A yellow eye, green legs and feet and a greenish-yellow powerful bill, completes the picture. It is 30 ins (76 cm) in length.

In flight the neck is drawn back and the broad wings are slowly flapped before the bird finally drops into a dense reed-bed which is its natural refuge. In its breeding area, which does not include Cyprus, the male bird betrays its presence in spring and summer by uttering a loud booming cry which carries a great distance but the characteristic note is not heard away from the marsh in which its mate is nesting.

To Cyprus the bittern is only an uncommon winter visitor and scarce passage migrant, though some may be overlooked for competent bird-recorders are naturally rare. Marsh birds in Europe are all forced to migrate when their homeland is made uninhabitable by frost, and the whole European bittern population has then to move to warmer quarters in Africa north of the Sahara, seeking the papyrus swamps of the Sudan and Abyssinia until the season comes

Bonelli's eagle

Red-rumped swallow

Crag martin

Plate 6

Imperial eagle

C.E.Talbot Kelly '70

round once more. No bitterns were recorded from Cyprus in 1967 or 1968 but it must not be inferred that none were present for *Botaurus stellaris* is a most secretive and (in winter) silent, bird.

Family CICONIIDAE

The two storks, the white stork and the black stork, are the European representatives of this mainly African family which visit Cyprus, and then only as passage migrants from Europe to their winter quarters. In our *Birds of Cyprus* we associated with the storks, the spoonbill and the ibises but these last groups have now been placed in a separate family.

In outward appearance storks resemble the larger herons in having long bare legs, longish necks and powerful bills which however, are not so spear-like as in the water-frequenting members of the heron family. They live on land and when in flight they carry their necks fully outstretched and not as the herons do retracted between the shoulders. Another peculiarity in storks is the lack of intrinsic muscles in the syrinx resulting in the birds having no voice. The white storks express their emotions in the breeding season by clappering their bills with necks upstretched making a noise which can be heard a long way off. Unfortunately, no stork has ever certainly bred in Cyprus, and the "com-

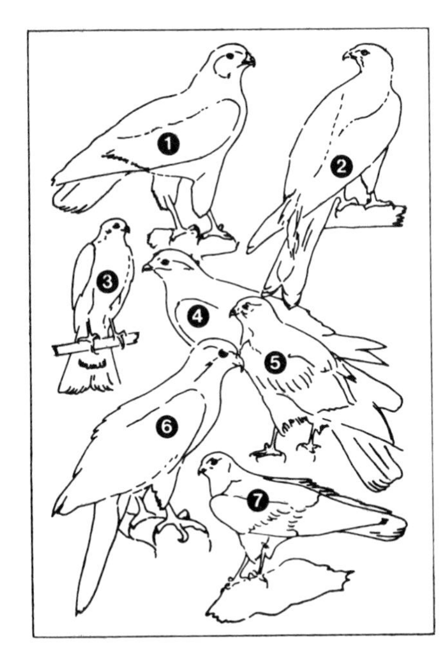

Plate 7

1. Steppe buzzard
2. Black kite
3. European sparrow hawk
4. Marsh harrier (immature)
5. Hen harrier (♂ adult)
6. Goshawk
7. Pallid harrier

mon" white stork of Europe and northern Africa will soon belie its name, so much scarcer has it become of recent years.

The white stork is more often recorded from Cyprus than the black stork (really brown with strong metallic gloss on the feathers) – which is rarely seen, its migration route lying normally to the east of the island. Both species winter in Africa and are more often observed migrating over land than sea. They are the only European representatives of a fairly wide-spread African family which are largely sedentary, especially in the Sudan.

WHITE STORK

Ciconia ciconia

The male and female are alike. The entire plumage is white with the exception of the black flight feathers. The bill, legs and feet are red. The long red bill, the legs, which are about 18 ins long, and the black and white plumage, make it a very easy bird to recognise. It stands about 2 ft 10 ins high and is 40 ins (102 cm) in length. In flight the long neck is fully extended and the legs outstretched. Storks fly in companies generally proceeding by soaring and drifting. On the ground the stork moves with gravity and deliberation.

The main flight passes along the coast of Asia Minor and the white stork's visits to Cyprus are in consequence few and irregular. We listed the records available prior to 1958 and these will be found in the *Birds of Cyprus*. Since the formation of the C.O.S. about that time, much more attention has been given by its members to migration, but no very clear pattern of the storks visits, other than irregular, emerges from their records. Small parties of eight to ten birds are recorded in the Spring of

some years from early March to the end of May, the Spring of 1957 being exceptional in this respect when parties of thirty and forty were seen to alight in April, perhaps due to the withdrawal of gun-licences and absence of firearms in that year. More recently storks have been observed – if at all – in the autumn from mid-August to mid-October. Not a single white stork was recorded in 1968; none in the spring of 1967 and only odd birds in August, September and October. The latest record is in mid-December. Those few that visit the island would appear to be odd stragglers rather than flocks. We are forced here to correct a statement in our *Birds of Cyprus* where we recorded, from information sent to us, a flight of "storks" on 21 August 1956 of unusual size and duration. Too late for correction we were informed that the flight was almost certainly of *cranes* and not white storks: one of the snags of accepting sight records from unproven observers.

When our book appeared in 1958, no white stork had ever been seen to *alight* during the Autumn passage, in Cyprus; we must now correct that as since that date ringed examples on their first flight from Germany and Poland have been captured in Cyprus in Autumn (cf. *Bull.* 6). When scanning the published records it must be borne in mind that throughout Europe the white stork is becoming more and more scarce as a breeding bird.

There has been one instance of a stork's nest being seen in Cyprus by a usually reliable observer; on 30 March 1877 at Nicosia. While quite possible there has been no confirmatory instance for nearly a hundred years.

White storks which breed in Europe east of the river Elbe migrate south via Asia Minor and the Nile valley to winter in East and Central Africa. Occasional birds alight on Cyprus and have recently been observed feeding at Kouklia and Akrotiri.

Black stork

BLACK STORK

Ciconia nigra

The black stork is almost the same size as the white stork. The sexes are alike. The plumage, which appears black at a distance, is brown with a strong metallic sheen. The underparts are white. The eye is brown, the bare skin round the eye deep crimson; the bill, feet and legs vermilion, the top of the feet dusky. It is a solitary bird and is not usually seen in flocks. It stands 2 ft 7 ins high and is 38 ins (97 cm) long.

This stork breeds mainly in eastern Europe from the Baltic to the Black Sea and small colonies have been found in the Iberian Peninsula. In winter the black storks repair to eastern Africa but few pass over Cyprus, the main passage lying further east. It has been reported seen in Cyprus on migration both in the spring and the autumn but seldom alights. We instanced a number of cases in our *Birds of Cyprus* (1958) when it had been reported in the Bulletins of the C.O.S., since when there have been a few records. A party of ten were on Akrotiri Salt Lake on 12 November, 1967 and a single bird the following year on 6 October. Odd records between August and November are instanced in our larger book and one from Larnaca on 5 April, the only spring record at that time. We seem to have been correct in describing its status as "occasionally, on migration". It is evidently very rarely seen before Autumn. To date there have been fifteen sightings from mid-September to late November.

[for illustration of Black stork see p. 19]

Family THRESKIORNITHIDAE

Dr. Wetmore in his classification (which we are following) includes in this family the ibises and the spoonbill which we had formerly included in the last mentioned family. Ibises are represented by only one species in Cyprus and the spoonbill has only one European representative in the family in any case. In appearance these birds are very dissimilar.

Ibises are comparatively short-legged birds with slender down-curved bills like a curlew but more curved, wings are rounded and bodies rather small. In the glossy ibis the plumage is dark and uniform and very highly glossed. They are highly gregarious and usually seen in large flocks performing complicated aerial evolutions.

The spoonbills are mainly renowned for the curious bill ending in a flattened spoon. In size they resemble the glossy ibis but stand more erect – about 2 ft 6 ins (76 cm) – and in colour are white, the head adorned with a few lengthened feathers which hang from the crown and wave in a breeze. They are much more solitary than the ibis and seldom encountered in more than very small numbers. In flight they are very erratic especially in the breeding season – but no attempt at nesting has been made in Cyprus either of this or the first named species. Like the stork family the spoonbill holds its neck fully extended when flying, with its black feet protruding beyond the tail.

GLOSSY IBIS [Plate 12, facing p. 64]

Plegadis falcinellus

In adult summer dress this is a very beautiful bird when close enough to observe the lovely metallic green, bronze and purple of the head, neck and mantle, and the chestnut-maroon underparts. This attractive dress is lost in winter when the metallic green on the crown disappears; the entire head and foreneck is then brown, darker on the crown, the feathers edged with white, giving these parts a streaky appearance. The rest of the neck and underparts are dull brown with traces showing of the summer plumage. Flight feathers are black glossed with green. Younger birds have the head and neck streaked like the adults in winter dress, and all trace of maroon on the underparts is lost. In appearance this is a strikingly slim bird with a long down-curved bill some 5½ ins (14 cm) in length and, like legs and feet, dark olive colour. In flight the metallic green, purple and bronze reflections on the wing-coverts can be clearly seen in the sunlight but at a distance when in flight the birds look to be quite black. They fly in considerable flocks bunched together and when indulging in aerial evolutions can fly very fast in a compact body. It is a frequent visitor to Cyprus in spring from late March to late May occasionally in June. Mainly late March and all April when it is often in large flocks on most of the larger inland waters. Small parties of eight to twenty are the rule on spring passage and odd birds, or two or three together, linger on the reservoirs. In some years – as in 1967 – over 100 birds have been counted in a flock, and once, on our first visit to Cyprus, we saw a huge flock at Dhekelia as we disembarked from a lighter on the open beach in a bad storm. They too could only have just arrived in late February – an early date. It passes the island again in the autumn when it is very much scarcer and usually in smaller numbers than earlier in the year. The passage lasts from early August to mid-September, exceptionally to mid-October. In late August and early September there have been occasions when considerable flocks have been seen flying along the north coast of Cyprus.

The glossy ibis is an occasional summer visitor in July.

The first recorded breeding record was reported in 1969 when a pair nested at the Akrotiri salt lake in the spring, but only one juvenile bird was later seen with the adults. We are indebted to the Secretary of the C.O.S. for this information. The glossy ibis makes its nest usually of reed-stems, usually among the reeds or sometimes on low bushes growing in the water, less frequently in larger areas. Three or four eggs are laid, distinguishable from those of the Heron family by their uniform colour of deep verditer-blue.

The nestling is black with a white patch at back of crown and white bands on throat. Bill pink, with three black bands, at base, mid-way and at tip. Juveniles resemble the adults in winter, but throat with white bands and the head and neck browner. Generally duller than adults overall and the under parts browner. All wing-coverts glossed green. [*Handbook of British Birds.*]

SPOONBILL [Plate 1, frontispiece]

Platalea leucorodia

Whole plumage white in both sexes, the feathers at the base of the neck yellowish-buff in summer only. A white crest of long feathers extends from the hinder part of the crown likewise tinged with yellowish-buff. The male's crest is longer than in the female. The long flattened bill is spatulate towards the tip, hence the colloquial name of this bird. Legs and feet are black but the bill is very variable in summer though black in winter with the tip yellow. Field characters are its large size, 34 ins (86 cm) in length and standing 2 ft 6 ins from the ground. Flight at first slow with regular beating of wings but often soars and glides. The neck is then held stretched out stiffly and the legs protrude beyond the tail. The evolutions indulged in when nesting are wonderful to observe, but there is no evidence the bird has ever attempted to nest in the island.

A rare and irregular passage migrant to Cyprus, sometimes remaining to summer on the reservoirs, the spoonbill is seen over a wide period at both migration seasons and has also been recorded in mid-winter. Kouklia reservoir has supplied most of the records, even one all summer in 1913 but the salt-lakes and occasionally the coast have supplied others mostly in April, May, September and October. There have been at least seventeen records up to 1970. It is a bird which stands out among the white herons as only *Egretta alba* compares with it in size, the spoonbill being a heavier looking bird and lacking the graceful carriage of the great white heron. The spoon-shaped bill is not very obvious – even if seen at all – when the bird is in the air.

Winter quarters of European colonies are largely in the Sudan and the Somalilands.

Family PHOENICOPTERIDAE

Flamingos are distributed over the temperate and tropical regions of both the Old and the New World and differ very little in general from one species to another. Their enormously long graceful neck and their long spindly legs give them an unmistakable appearance. Their adult plumage is white tinged in varying degrees with pink or carmine according to the various species. The only European-Asiatic representative, described hereafter, is familiar to most people as it thrives well in captivity and is to be seen in all the principal zoological gardens and on many pieces of privately-owned water. Being gregarious to a remarkable degree and strongly migratory, often shifting their breeding grounds when conditions are unsatisfactory, their numbers are continually fluctuating and their appearances in Cyprus and the length of their stay in winter, is governed by the state of the salt lakes.

A flight of hundreds of these birds, when the brilliant vermilion of the undersurface of the wing becomes visible to the eye, is a never-to-be-forgotten sight, especially if they are in flight against a setting sun. Although flamingos do not breed in Cyprus, their nesting habits are so remarkable as to once – in the far distant past – having been the occasion of a lawsuit, two distinguished naturalists of their time bursting with professional jealousy, each claiming to have discovered how the flamingo hatched its single egg and how it disposed of its legs in the process. It is reputed that one of the litigants obtained a farthing damage, and both a severe dressing down by the learned Judge for bringing such a frivolous case to court!

GREATER FLAMINGO

Phoenicopterus ruber roseus

[Plate 2, facing p. 4]

Perhaps surprisingly the general colour of the greater flamingo is white tinged both above and below with rose colour, the rose-pink deepest on rump and tail. The flight feathers are black the rest of the wings bright pinkish-vermilion; eye straw-colour; bill pink and black terminally; legs and feet bright pink. When seen at a distance the birds appear more white than pink. In flight the black pinions show in strong contrast to the vermilion wings. Young flamingos, often to be seen with their parents in Cyprus, arrive in grey-brown plumage with leaden-grey legs, some are surprisingly young to have made the journey.

This is undoubtedly the most striking bird which Cyprus has to offer, and as the birds are regular winter visitors in varying numbers, ranging from hundreds to thousands in very restricted areas, it is unlikely that any human visitor to Cyprus, with an interest in birds, will not see them to his heart's content between November and March, some appearing earlier and some later; non-breeding birds occasionally remain to early July. The migrations to Cyprus of the flamingo have been studied intensively by the members of the C.O.S. founded by National Service members of H.M. forces in 1957 and to that body which incorporates Greek nationals and local British residents we are indebted for a huge intake of knowledge since we published our *Birds of Cyprus* (1958) just after the Society began its operations. It is to their *Bulletins* and *Bird Reports* that specialists must refer for the key to the complicated migrations of the greater flamingo whose appearances and lengths of stay are so closely linked with the state of the Cyprus salt lakes, especially at Larnaca and Akrotiri, as well as to the conditions in the area where the young are reared. An analysis of the C.O.S. reports indicates that in some years the numbers may be very low, well into December remaining in tens. Normally in early December thousands are present, rapidly building up in late December or mid-January to peak numbers, i.e. 5,000 to 10,000 birds. Numbers decrease from late January or mid-February but in some years the numbers are supplemented in March after gales. Normally in March and April numbers do not exceed 300–400 – a small number, circa 100 or less remaining to June, usually immature birds. Just where these breeding grounds may be from which Cyprus receives its winter guests remains unsolved; perhaps as we have suggested they may be to the N.E. of the Caspian Sea or in the Persian Gulf.

Order ANSERIFORMES

Family ANATIDAE

Comprising the swans, geese and ducks, this is one of the largest families in the world and one which is very well represented in Cyprus by migratory species or winter visitors, but very few which remain to nest. Here again the state of the winter rains plays an important part, for all casual water dries up in the summer and the reservoirs and lakes where duck might be tempted to breed are few and far between. Moreover, it is only within recent years that a portion of these fresh water areas have been set aside as sanctuaries. Shooting is all too prevalent until May is well on the way, and until such a time as wardens are appointed to enforce the game laws, disturbance of suitable breeding places is sure to take place.

There are two species of swans, six species of geese and twenty-two species of ducks recorded on the Cyprus list today – a list which can claim as many ducks and even more geese than have been recorded from the mainland of Turkey, judging from published lists. In the two colour plates of the duck family which we include in this *Handbook*, many of the swans, geese and the better-known duck are cleverly illustrated.

In our larger work we gave a general description in some detail of the main characteristics of the three main groups of *Anatidae* into which the Cyprus representatives fall, stressing the broad depressed bills with highly developed lamellae which are common to all; the position of the legs far back on the trunk, the short heavy tarsus and webbed front toes. Despite the usually heavy body (the teals excepted) the members of this family can make immense journeys, in particular the northern European ducks in which their long pointed wings and powerful wing-muscles are conducive to swift and sustained flight. While swans are all much alike, and geese show little divergence so far as the Palaearctic species are concerned, the ducks vary tremendously one from another and used to occupy many genera. Modern taxonomists have now greatly reduced these placing many in the genus *Anas* following the lead of Dr. Hartert in his *Vögel der Palaarktischen Fauna.*

While the plumage of swans and geese is very similar in male and female, in the ducks there is a very great divergence in most species, the females being mottled often in brown and black; in fact the ducks of various species are much more difficult to distinguish from one another than from their own drakes, with which they have nothing in common, unless it be the wing-speculum. A point of interest is the varied colour-patterns exhibited by nestling ducks, while in both swans and geese their nestlings never show any strongly contrasted pattern.

Apart from the numbers of these birds which come to the Cyprus lakes in winter, *huge numbers* must use the island as a stepping stone from breeding grounds in Europe and Asia to winter quarters in Africa. The same geese and ducks which visit Cyprus are migratory all over the Middle East and even with the passage of time the variety of species which figure today on the Cyprus list cannot have their numbers much increased, but with the judicious shooting-laws properly enforced, the *individual numbers* could be doubled. The authors of this Handbook had practical knowledge of what happens in Cyprus if, for a period, firearms are called in. The island was then alive with duck of many species and the lakes black with water-birds of all kinds. Cyprus could be a paradise for Anatidae under such circumstances as we were permitted to witness with our own eyes. It lies on the natural highway from the

Delta of the Nile to Europe and western Asia, a great many species breeding in the far north.

MUTE SWAN [Plate 3, facing p. 5]

Cygnus olor

Entire plumage white, this huge bird measures at most 5 ft, the male being considerably larger than the female. A clear sight of the head and bill will enable this species to be distinguished at once from the equally large whooper swan which also visits Cyprus, for the mute swan has a large black knob at the base of the upper mandible, more prominent in the male than the female; the bill is pinkish red tinged with orange, the nail, lores and skin round the nostrils black.

In the whooper swan, which will be found listed in the appendix among the rarer birds on p. 213, there is no black knob in either sex and the bill is lemon-yellow which colour covers the basal half, the terminal portion being black. Another distinguishing feature is in the way these two swans carry the neck. The mute in a graceful curve with bill pointing downwards, the whooper with head and neck much more erect and bill horizontal. There is also a difference in the colour of legs and feet, slate colour in the mute, black in the whooper. The tail is carried tilted upwards at 40° in the mute, but horizontal in the whooper.

In flight the neck is carried stretched out in all swans, the great wings of the mute swan making much more swishing noise than those of the rarer species. To Cyprus the mute swan is an irregular and scarce winter visitor in small numbers. When recorded, usually noted in small flocks – sixteen is the largest flock seen – between the beginning of November and the end of January, but earlier and later dates are on record of smaller numbers. Dependent on fairly deep water the birds come to both the fresh water and salt water lakes when the conditions are suitable.

The huge increase in guns permitted in the island of recent years does not encourage the birds to remain. Severe wintry weather in the north is likely to be responsible for their visits as it is for their occasional appearance in Egypt on the Delta.

GREYLAG GOOSE

Anser anser

Of the five species of geese recorded from Cyprus, the greylag is the largest with heavy head and massive all-orange or yellow bill, with a white nail at tip. Its general plumage is grey-brown with ash-

Greylag goose

grey back and rump; the lack of contrast between the head and neck and the rest of the body should be noted, for in the bean goose the head and neck are much darker and in strong contrast. Again the bean goose has an orange and black, long tapering bill with a black nail at the tip. The legs of the greylag are pinkish flesh in colour and the forepart of the wing is pale grey. In the bean goose the legs are orange-yellow and there is no pale relieving area in the wing, the whole body and wings being brown.

The white-fronted goose to be described next, should never be confused with the greylag – for distinctions see under that species. Geese are very difficult to distinguish in flight and there are occasions when very big flocks have been observed without specific identity; see *Birds of Cyprus* p. 249. The present species has only been identified with certainty on a few occasions between November and 11 May on the reservoirs and salt lakes, as we recorded in our larger book. The largest number reported at the same time was twelve at Larnaca on 14 April 1957. In severe winters big flocks of "geese" may be recorded but years may pass with only a straggler being seen. Cyprus is as far south as the greylag is likely to occur. It does not seem to figure on the lists of winter visitors to either Egypt or Arabia unless it has done so since the standard works on those countries have appeared, though "grey geese" unidentified as to species have been reported.

WHITE-FRONTED GOOSE

Anser albifrons [Plate 3, facing p. 5]

This is the commonest goose to visit Cyprus in winter and is sure to be of the typical European subspecies. Comparatively small in relation to the greylag, greyish-brown in colour with a dark grey rump and extensive black markings (bars) on the whitish or buff underparts, the white-fronted goose is recognisable by the white forehead and by the pink bill, the nail of the adult being white. The feathers of the mantle have a broad light border. It weighs 4–5½ lbs, exceptionally 6 lbs. Feet and legs are yellow.

All observers in Cyprus agree as to the status of this goose in the island, which is reported in most winters in flocks of ten or more visiting the lakes and reservoirs. A flock of ninety has been recorded on Paralimni lake up to mid-February, and we have records in our major book from 20 December onwards.

It is a tremendous wanderer and goes further afield than the larger grey geese. We hear of them as the commonest goose to visit Egypt. Vast flocks are reported to visit Thrace, Macedonia and southern Greece and it is more than probable that the large flocks of unidentified geese which have been reported from Cyprus have been *Anser albifrons* than any of the other geese which figure on the Cyprus list. Since the publication of our larger book (1958), this goose has been observed to be most frequent in cold winters but its visits are irregular, sometimes fairly common in small numbers, in other years only a few or even none at all reported: the best time to look for it is mid-December to mid-February.

Its breeding range is wide. It is an inhabitant of the Polar regions and includes the Tundra zone of the U.S.S.R. and the islands of the Polar Sea. Large numbers winter south of the Caspian and more rarely in the Black Sea area, from which the visitors to Cyprus are likely to have come.

EGYPTIAN GOOSE

Alopochen aegyptiacus

This handsome but unsporting goose can only be considered a very rare and irregular winter visitor to Cyprus which has not been recorded lately, but which turns up occasionally for no apparent reason. Unlike all the other geese which have been recorded from the island, the Egyptian goose does not now breed north of the Mediterranean. It is the only goose which nests in Egypt and formerly bred in Palestine but was already becoming scarce in 1930. It is unique among the geese recorded from Cyprus as the only one coming from the south. It is not driven from its country by frost, and does not appear to have any particular reason to make a sea crossing in a northerly direction. We give its description taken from our larger book:

The forehead, crown, cheeks and throat are white, merging into brown at the back of the crown and neck. The feathers at the base of the bill and round the eye are chestnut. The mantle is grey, tinged with rust and very finely barred with black. The scapulars are brown with buff vermiculations; the back, rump and tail are blue-black. All the wing-coverts are pure white with a subterminal black bar on the greater coverts. The flight feathers are black glossed with purple and green, the innermost secondaries are chestnut. The breast, flanks and sides of the body are very pale buff with very fine brown bars. There is a large chestnut patch in the middle of the breast. The remainder of the underparts are white with faint grey vermiculations. The under tail-coverts are saffron, the under wing-coverts and axillaries white. The eye is golden-yellow, the bill, legs and feet flesh colour. The female resembles the male but is smaller and weighs about 1½ lbs less. When flying, in spite of the many colours mentioned above, this goose appears to be black and white. Its length is 24–26 ins (64–66 cm). The large white patch on the wing is very conspicuous.

There is an ancient mosaic in the ruins at Curium depicting this goose in colour, which visitors to the island will be interested to see. It has been suggested that single birds arriving in Cyprus may have come from the Tel Aviv Zoo, where there is a free-flying population which departs in winter. One exceptional arrival on 1 June is a very odd date for a visiting goose to appear, and supports that contention. In recent years the rare winter visitors which have turned up in Cyprus, late December to late February, may be traced to this source but failing ringed birds is so far only guesswork.

SHELD-DUCK [Plate 3, facing p. 5]

Tadorna tadorna

A very handsome large bird the male some 26 ins in length, should be easily recognised. Head and upper part of neck greenish black with amethyst reflections. A broad white collar below the neck; a bright chestnut band extends from the mantle to the breast, the rest of the underparts white, save for a band of black down the middle of the belly. Scapulars black glossed with green. Wing-coverts and upper parts white. Tail white tipped with black. The primaries are black, the inner secondaries with chestnut on the outer web, and a broad metallic green speculum. Bill carmine with dusky nail at tip, legs and feet pinkish-flesh.

The male is furnished in the breeding season with a fleshy knob of carmine colour. The much smaller female is duller and lacks the knob on the bill. In flight much white is visible in the expanded wing; the white rump and tail, the latter with black tip, are good identification marks.

This is a winter visitor in considerable numbers depending on the state of the continental weather. December to March are the chief months of its arrival in Cyprus in parties which vary from ten to 200 usually after S.W. gales. Early arrivals have been reported on 1 October and late records to 1 April exceptionally. Maximum numbers, often hundreds, are present from January until early March. A small flock in early June 1963 was very exceptional.

It is a duck which must be sought for on the sea coast or salt lagoons and does not favour fresh-water lakes. Its breeding range extends intermittently over much of Europe and Asia. The breeding places in Transcaspia may be the origin of the visiting parties in Cyprus in severe weather.

Neither this nor the next species are edible.

RUDDY SHELD-DUCK

Casarca ferruginea [Plate 3, facing p. 5]

Another very large duck, the male bird measuring about 26 ins (66 cm) in length. Head and neck are buff, the face whitish washed with cinnamon on the throat and fore-neck. Body plumage orange brown; a blackish collar is a variable feature. Mantle and undersurface yellowish cinnamon; rump, tail and upper tail coverts black, belly and under tail-coverts chestnut. Wing quills black, wing-coverts white. A speculum on the wing is metallic green. Eye dark brown; bill, legs and feet black.

The female resembles the male but lacks the black ring which usually adorns the lower throat of her consort. The head too is usually paler. The flight is strong if laboured and the bird recognisable on the wing by its orange-brown colouring, and curious wing pattern, the white wing-coverts being very noticeable. The wing lining is also white and the black tail a feature to observe. In the water this duck swims low at the front with head erect but the stern held high.

A breeding species in Palestine, Iraq, Asia Minor and southern Russia it is hardly surprising that it comes over to Cyprus from time to time, small parties, pairs or single individuals are seen more often than larger flocks – a flock of fifty in late November 1964 is exceptional, but in certain years it is reported to have been abundant, and in the emergency, when guns were prohibited, a flock of 150 was recorded. A winter visitor exclusively between early November and the end of March – more recently late November to late February it frequents the freshwater lakes and reservoirs, its habits being diametrically opposed to those of the common species. Of the two it is the more often seen in Cyprus and is a regular migrant to Egypt from November to early May. Its preference is for the estuaries of large rivers and sandbanks of which there are none in Cyprus.

MALLARD OR WILD DUCK

Anas platyrhynchos

This duck is so familiar to everyone that little description is necessary, the handsome drake with shining green head, white collar and brown mantle, and speckled brown underparts below the chestnut breast, should proclaim it. The wing is adorned with a metallic blue speculum banded with black and tipped with white. The female is light brown and mottled in appearance and shares the broad blue speculum, a feature which in addition to its exceptionally large size, separates this duck from the females of most other species which occur in Cyprus in winter. The bill is greenish yellow with a black nail, the legs and feet orange red.

Breeding throughout Europe and Asia south of the Arctic Circle this is quite the best known species to most people. Frost in the north of its range drives the birds south and it is then we can look for the large flocks which come to Cyprus in winter.

It was formerly considered the most numerous of the sporting duck to arrive, and great numbers were shot on the lakes. In addition to wintering there must be a big passage migration through Cyprus to the Nile valley in early autumn. Occasionally huge flocks turn up after severe gales. These may run to a thousand birds in January. After the end of January or mid-February the numbers gradually diminish. Small numbers may remain till mid-April and individuals may stay till late May.

Most of the European-Asiatic duck which come under the heading of edible birds are definitely on the wane, the countries through which they pass on their annual migrations taking a huge toll.

TEAL

Anas crecca

The teal is now believed to surpass the mallard and all other duck in numbers as a winter visitor to Cyprus. Its small size, 14 ins (36 cm) in length and tremendously swift flight is likely to distinguish it from all but the garganey. Members of the C.O.S. have kept statistics of the teal which visit Akrotiri salt lake and some of the island reservoirs; the numbers seen, running to thousands in December, January and February, are astonishing and are recorded annually in the annals of the Society.

The teal is another familiar bird to all sportsmen. The main points to remark are the metallic green patch on the side of the head bordered with white, a rich chestnut crown, cheeks and throat; and a creamy-buff patch on each side of the rump. The vermiculated black and white mantle and the heavily spotted white breast are other features to bear in mind. The brown and buff mottled female shares the green wing speculum with her consort.

Apart from the wintering numbers there is a strong migration through Cyprus when flocks may be seen passing over the northern and southern ranges and parties have been observed by competent observers in the Troödos mountains, flying low up the valleys and over the saddlebacks. We recorded this and the source of our information in our larger book but we have not seen it noted by more recent observers who, no doubt engaged in military duties near the coast, have less opportunity than forestry officers and Government officials to keep observations in these areas. It would be interesting to learn more about this movement and if it is restricted to the teal or shared by the garganey.

These duck may occur more often on autumn passage than records tend to show during late August and September. They rest by day out to sea both in Morphou and Polis Bays before flying up the larger valleys, as noted already; at dusk, when their passage is very inconspicuous and easily overlooked, they cross the dividing range.

MARBLED TEAL [Plate 4, facing p. 12]

Anas angustirostris

This is the only member of the genus *Anas* in which there is no mirror on the wing. The plumage is greyish-brown mottled with creamy-white; the crown, upper-parts and sides darker than the underside. Each feather has a pale middle and darker border, hence the mottled appearance. A large brown patch extends from the eye to the nape. The wing is grey and brown lacking the metallic feathers of blue and green which are such a feature of the common teal and many others. Bill long and blackish in colour; feet and legs olive-brown, the webs blackish.

Teal

The female resembles the male but has rather smaller dimensions.

The marbled teal at one time, circa 1888–1914 and probably later, figured on the list of breeding birds in Cyprus, having bred at Famagusta and Kouklia, though usually preferring small pools well overgrown with vegetation. It is a bird of freshwater lakes and marshland and would easily be induced to breed again in years of water plenty. We can imagine the Kouklia reservoir (as we once knew it) to be a much favoured haunt of this duck which today is a scarce though occasional visitor, coinciding with the spring and autumn passage, and in quite recent years not even figuring in the Cyprus Bird Reports.

It has a wide breeding area in Asia as well as an intermittent one in Europe and northern Africa, Asia Minor, western shores of the Caspian, mouth of the Volga, Transcaspia etc. It was reported at one time to be very numerous in the Sea of Galilee marshes. Its winter migrations are not well known but are mainly restricted to the warmer parts of its breeding range. Only sporadic appearances in Cyprus can be expected at this date, but now that more attention is being given to the forming of reserves where shooting is forbidden in the breeding season, we may hope for better results in the years to come.

GARGANEY [Plate 12, facing p. 64]

Anas querquedula

The garganey, slightly larger than the common teal, has a chocolate-coloured face and neck, with a fine white streaking visible at close quarters. There is a broad white line bordering the black crown and meeting in a V at the back of the neck. The speculum is green bordered by the double white wing-bar. The scapulars are long and drooping, black and white in colour. The back is grey, the breast chestnut-brown with black concentric markings, the belly white and the sides of the body barred with narrow black lines. The bill is black, the feet and webs dark grey and the eye dark brown. Its length is 20 ins (51 cm). The female is brown above and mottled below; she has dark-grey wing-coverts, a double white wing-bar and a pale speculum with no black.

In days long since vanished this teal bred occasionally when there was plenty of water in the lakes or reservoirs. We have old records from Famagusta and Morphou (1910–1911) and Kouklia, eggs taken 14 May, and from what we saw at Kouklia forty three years later in one spring, garganey would attempt to do so again on any piece of undisturbed water. In the last few years it has summered in 1967 and 1969. Both years with plenty of water. Of all the most favoured spots in Cyprus, Kouklia reservoir should most attract the garganey now that gunners are forbidden entry during the nesting season. It is a regular passage migrant from March to May and from August to October inclusive, occasionally in the spring months to be seen in hundreds. The garganey duck prefers to nest on dry ground within 30 yds of water in coarse grass or old reeds, lining the nest with dried grass, roots and stalks, adding the down as incubation proceeds. Ten to eleven eggs forms a normal clutch. Only one brood is reared.

GADWALL [Pate 4, facing p. 12]

Anas strepera

This is a fairly large duck some 20 ins (51 cm) in length but distinctly smaller and slighter than the mallard. The colour is warm brown on head and neck, the back greyish-brown; a pale mark above the eye, and the crescentic bands on the breast, are visible as the bird swims, but the best distinguishing character is the black upper and under tail-coverts which can easily be seen. At close quarters note the chestnut median wing-coverts contrasting with the velvety black greater coverts. In flight the white speculum is prominent and the wings will be seen to be more pointed than in the heavier species. Bill lead colour, legs and feet orange-yellow completes the males' description.

The female is easily confused with the mallard duck lacking the chestnut shoulder patch and black hindquarters of her consort; the best guide to her identity is the white speculum when it can be seen.

It can only be termed a scarce but regular winter-visitor to the lakes and reservoirs in singles or small parties, recorded from late November to the end of February. It is a very scarce migrant in the spring, usually late March to mid-April. In 1967 parties of twenty-eight and forty were recorded at Akrotiri Salt Lake on 31 July and 1 August but that was quite exceptional.

The gadwall is one of the true "Dabbling Ducks" which only dives when pressed and is more vegetarian than most in its feeding. It is more frequently seen on fresh than salt water.

WIGEON

Anas penelope

Another widely familiar duck, the wigeon drake is easily recognised by its golden forehead and crown, which is in strong contrast to the chestnut head and neck. The back is greyish, vermiculated with black. The speculum is metallic-green bordered with black and the shoulders are white. The underparts are white except for the pinkish breast and the black under tail-coverts. On the water the long black secondary feathers bordered with white are also a feature. It is 18 ins (46 cm) long. The female is a brown duck, rather redder-brown than the larger mallard; it has a rounder head and a shorter bill than that bird.

All gunners recognise the wigeon's call uttered in flight *whee-ou, whee-ou*, especially on a moonlight night.

To Cyprus it is an abundant winter visitor as well as a passage migrant, hundreds appearing on the lakes around Christmas time. In our former book we wrote of "thousands" coming to the freshwater lakes in a favourable year, one observer recording that he must have seen 5,000 in the air together. That was some sixty years ago and from examination of records kept since we wrote our book, it is obvious that such numbers do not occur today. In 1950 many duck were gathered in Akrotiri Bay, the majority being wigeon but their numbers have declined in recent years. Winter flocks start arriving late October to early November remaining to early or mid-March with maximum numbers 500 to 1,000. Small flocks and occasional individuals thereafter to late April.

Numbers fluctuate from year to year. It may occur more frequently on the autumn passage in September.

Wigeon are cited as passing over the mountain ranges in Cyprus as we have described for the teal, and flocks have been recorded flighting up the Troödos valleys. The report of large migrating flocks on the North coast of Cyprus is still under investigation.

PINTAIL

[Plate 3, facing p. 5]

Anas acuta

This graceful duck, nearly as large as a mallard, but much more slim in appearance, is distinguished by several prominent features: the white stripe on either side of the neck, the snowy white breast, the position when swimming in the water riding much higher than other duck and finally the narrow central tail-feathers protruding beyond the other rectrices and carried at an elegant angle. These long feathers are also plainly visible when the duck is in the air. For the rest the head and throat are chocolate brown, the mantle and sides vermiculated brown and white, and the grey scapulars heavily marked with black. The wing speculum is bronze green banded with black and broadly tipped with white. Bill lead colour, nail black, legs and feet slate.

The female is close in appearance to the mallard duck but noticeably darker, and the wing speculum instead of shining blue-green, is dull purplish-bronze.

When we wrote the *Birds of Cyprus* we remarked that the pintail appeared to be increasing as a wintering bird and that has evidently been borne out, the *Cyprus Bird Reports* for recent years containing sight records of flocks varying from 1000–3000 birds during January and February when the numbers should have reached their peak. The spring passage may run into thousands of birds, late February to mid-March, but the autumn passage from late September to end October is insignificant in comparison. The spring migrants continue to pass occasionally until the middle of May when small flocks have been seen off the coast.

A statement that it is "reported to have bred on reservoirs in mid-May" is best ignored until the authority for the record can be verified. We have failed to discover it among the older literature.

A marine duck outwith the breeding season, the pintail is regularly to be seen offshore, and in Cyprus frequents the Salt Lakes at Larnaca and especially Akrotiri in preference to the reservoirs. But it has also visited Kouklia when the water level is high.

SHOVELER [Plate 3, facing p. 5]

Anas clypeata

A common winter visitor and spring migrant which has bred in the distant past. Rather scarce on autumn passage.

A smaller bird than the wild duck, the shoveler is one of the most decorative of the Anatidae which we may hope to see on Cyprus waters both on passage and as a winter visitor. It is a duck which is easily identified; the head and upper part of neck glossy green, the crown and throat browner and the back very dark brown. Breast, lower part of neck and scapulars are white, the lower breast, belly and flanks chestnut. The wing speculum is metallic green and the lesser wing-coverts pale blue. The shape of the shoveler's bill, from which it gains its name, at once attracts attention for it is large and spatulate in shape, broad and spoonlike at the tip and black in colour. Legs and feet are orange. The male is 20 ins (51 cm) in length.

The female exhibits various shades of brown on the upperparts streaked on the head with sepia, the under-side brown washed with cinnamon. She shares the spoon-shaped bill of the male and also the pale blue shoulders. When flying the heavy bill is a noticeable character when clearly seen.

As a winter visitor it can be abundant from January to March, the numbers at times running to thousands. When guns were withdrawn in 1957 there were hundreds on Akrotiri salt-lake in January and all the lakes had numbers, even the flooded plain at Patriki had a few mingling with the mallard and teal. It is a species which has become more numerous instead of the reverse. The autumn passage is comparatively insignificant prior to October. There are some interesting ringing returns published by the C.O.S. in their Bulletins. One ringed in the Volga Delta was recovered in Cyprus fourteen years after.

A clutch of eight eggs was taken from a nest on Kouklia reservoir on the 14 May 1911, but details of its breeding numbers in those and earlier days have never been given.

RED-CRESTED POCHARD

Netta rufina [Plate 12, facing p. 64]

Distinguished from all other duck which visit Cyprus this species has a golden-chestnut head the soft paler feathers of the crown standing erect, giving a very distinctive profile when seen from a distance. The light brown back, glossy black neck and breast and white flanks form a striking pattern of contrasting colours. Very noticeable too when the bird takes wing is the broad white wing-patch extending over nearly all the quills. The bill is rose-red to vermilion; the legs and toes orange, webs duskier; the eye red.

The female is a dull uniform brown with pale greyish cheeks and a dark brown crown. The wing speculum is a drab white and legs and feet yellowish. In total length the red-breasted pochard is 22 ins (56 cm).

As a rare winter visitor to Cyprus the appearances of *Netta rufina* are evidently governed largely by the weather. There are not sufficient records to make out a regular pattern, and we considered ourselves lucky to meet with it once on 17 March 1954 on the Larnaca Salt Lake. Odd birds may only be expected if the continent is suffering from severe weather and after the very severe winter of 1910–1911 considerable numbers were reported in December at Famagusta and Larnaca on *freshwater* lakes where they remained till mid-February: an exceptional occurrence. Judging from the Bird-Reports, issued by the C.O.S., the visits of the red-crested pochard of recent years have been restricted to our personal observation in 1954.

Eleonora's falcon

Lesser peregrine

Plate 8

C. E. Talbot Kelly '69

COMMON POCHARD

Aythya ferina [Plate 3, facing p. 5]

A much smaller duck (measuring some 18 ins (46 cm)) than the last species, the common pochard's head is a darker chestnut-red and has the normal silhouette of a diving duck without any crest.

In sunlight the colour of the head appears much brighter and is a sure guide to identity, in strong contrast with the black breast and mantle. The rest of the back and the scapulars are pearl-grey vermiculated with black. The rump and tail are dark brown and there is a broad grey speculum on the wing which is otherwise dark. The underparts are greyish-white, bill black with a broad blue band across the middle. Legs and feet bluish-grey. Eye ruby-red.

The female has the head neck and breast brown; underparts grey mottled (not vermiculated) with brown. A grey wing-speculum, duller than in the drake, is the best guide to the female's identity.

More of a freshwater than a sea duck – and essentially a diving duck – the common pochard often frequents sea-water, when it may be seen in packs floating on the sea off shore. It is regularly observed in winter in varying numbers. No doubt the weather is responsible for the abnormally large visitations as that recorded in 1968 when some 3,000 were seen at Akrotiri 14–17 January after S.W. gales when only twenty remained till the end of February. This is a typical example of the fluctuations one may expect. Inland reservoirs are visited by flocks of fifty or more between early November and early April. In some years records of those reported are almost negligible as for instance in 1967 when never more than twenty were present at Akrotiri during January and February when they should have been at their peak.

WHITE-EYED POCHARD

Aythya nyroca [Plate 3, facing p. 5]

This pochard, often known as the Ferruginous duck is another duck with a chestnut head and neck but the colour is altogether darker and richer than in *A. ferina*, and the breast is the same colour

Plate 9

1. Hobby
2. Long-eared owl
3. Red-footed falcon ♂
4. Red-footed falcon ♀
5. Little owl
6. Saker falcon
7. Barn owl

as the head; the belly is shining white. There is a collar at the base of the neck and a white spot on the chin. The upperparts are dark brown, the mantle and scapulars dusted with chestnut.

The wing pattern is distinctive, the primaries white, tipped and bordered with brown. Eye in the drake is white, in the duck brown. Bill and feet greenish black. It is 16 ins (41 cm) in total length. The female shares the rich chestnut head of the male but is altogether browner and when swimming, unless its head can be seen, may easily be mistaken for a female tufted duck, the latter has a short crest, the Ferruginous duck no crest at all.

This duck was correctly described in our major work as a regular but scarce winter visitor, though not always noticed by local observers. Parties of six to twelve appear at intervals on fresh water in most winters and no doubt others come which avoid detection but it can never be considered as anything but uncommon in Cyprus. It occurs from late October to late March, occasionally till late April, and is scarce as a passage migrant. In 1970 a flock of twenty-five appeared on Akrotiri Salt Lake on 23 July, fifteen of these presumably from the same flock seen on 15 August.

It is reported to be a numerous winter visitor to Eygpt, Palestine and Sinai arriving in early October. It is known as one of the shyest duck preferring to remain hidden under vegetation than to venture on to open sheets of water. Entirely a vegetable feeder it has earned the reputation of being an exceptionally adept diver. Very young birds were reported to have been shot on Kouklia reservoir years ago on 1 September, perhaps pointing to it rarely breeding. Of recent years there have been odd summer sightings, and in 1969 one appeared in May on the Akrotiri salt lake.

TUFTED DUCK [Plate 4, facing p. 12]

Aythya fuligula

Of all the diving ducks this is perhaps the easiest identified owing to the distinctive crest-feathers carried by the drake, much smaller in the female and by the white sides of the male bird which are clearly seen above the water level when this duck is swimming. The purplish black head and neck, golden eye, and dark brown upperparts, together with the other characters mentioned make the tufted duck a conspicuous bird on the water.

In flight the white bar on the wing bordered with brown is a conspicuous feature and it is then that the white belly is seen clearly. Total length is 17 ins (43 cm). The bill is slate coloured with a black nail; legs and toes bluish, the webs black. The female is browner throughout and lacks the rich purplish reflections of the male, especially on the head.

A female scaup could be mistaken for a tufted if the broad white frontal-band of the scaup is not clearly seen. The white mantle of the male scaup and lack of crest on the black head separates these two diving ducks and great care should be taken before any scaup is recorded from Cyprus waters. See *Birds of Cyprus* p. 264. The scaup is mentioned in this *Handbook* in the Appendix of the rarer visitors on p. 214.

The tufted duck is a winter visitor, in small parties only, from mid-November to early April, most records from December to February. Passage migrants have been reported in April and October. The eight birds which appeared on the Akrotiri Salt Lake on 1 August 1967 were unusually early arrivals.

There is no reason whatever to throw doubt (Bulletin 15) on the breeding records mentioned in our major work on p. 264 at Famagusta, Morphou and Kouklia. Both recorders were distinguished ornithologists and one a well-known oologist incapable of making the silly mistake suggested.

WHITE-HEADED DUCK

Oxyura leucocephala

[Plate 4, facing p. 12]

This is an example of the stiff-tailed ducks and the only representative of this remarkable group to have occurred in Cyprus. They have very thick short necks and stiff rather long tails, often carried vertically.

The male in breeding plumage has the head white with a black patch on the crown and a mottled chin. Neck black, back grey vermiculated with dark brown. Tail blackish, upper tail-coverts chestnut. Breast chestnut, the rest of the underparts silvery-white mottled with grey. Wings grey, no wing speculum. Bill, which is swollen at the base, is blue-grey; iris dark brown; legs and feet dark grey. Total length 18 ins (46 cm).

The female is darker and lacks the white head of her consort. The crown is chestnut-brown as well as a band which extends from the gape to the nape enclosing a creamy-white area below the eye. The rest of the plumage resembles that of the male. We have purposely figured the male bird in colour, as one of the least known of the Cyprus Anatidae.

These ducks are said to prefer brackish to fresh water for breeding, with plenty of reed cover, but in winter and on migration they are met with on water of any type, usually on open lakes but sometimes on mountain streams. In Europe they are inhabitants of the Mediterranean Basin ranging eastwards to Turkey and Central Asia. Some populations move south in winter when they occur in Egypt, and it is then or on their return journey that a flock may turn up in Cyprus, as was the case in 1910 when a small party frequented the Kouklia reservoirs at the end of April, and presumably stayed a few days, as a duck of this species was shot that year on 4 May. There is also a single December record but of late years none had been recorded until 1967, when an adult female frequented Bishops Pool on the Akrotiri peninsula from the 3 to 23 December. This was followed in 1968 by a party of fourteen (eight definitely males) which were present at Akrotiri from 13 to 14 January.

RED-BREASTED MERGANSER

Mergus serrator [Plate 4 facing p. 12]

It is usual to compare the sea-loving merganser with the larger goosander, normally to be found on fresh water, which is listed in this book in the Appendix of rarer visitors on the strength of a single sight-record on the shore at Salamis in December 1957.

Both species have long narrow red bills adapted for the capture and holding of slippery fish. The male birds of both have dark bottle green heads but whereas the male merganser has a conspicuous crest of long disintegrated feathers, the goosander's is negligible. The merganser drake has a broad white collar which separates the dark green head from the chestnut brown breast and dark back, the sides of the body being grey and only the belly white. In the goosander the whole of the underparts are white suffused with salmon pink.

The two females are much alike and both are crested but whereas the merganser has a brown crown and crest that of the goosander is much more chestnut. A field character worth noting is the motion of the head in the Merganser when swimming, reminding one of the moorhen. It flies fast, close above the water, showing a great deal of white on the wing, across which are two diagonal black bands, the white half of the wing next to the body being then very noticeable.

This is a winter visitor occasionally to the coastal waters of Cyprus. We saw it ourselves for the first time in 1957 near Famagusta harbour when four were swimming off the rocky beach. Prior to December 1956, when one was seen at Dhekelia on 16 December, it had not figured on the Cyprus list. In all some thirty birds have been recorded between 1956 and 1964 during the months of November, December, January and March from Dhekelia, Larnaca and Famagusta, but mostly from the last named harbour, or the shore nearby. It is possibly more frequent off-shore than the scanty records imply.

Order FALCONIFORMES

Family AEGYPIIDAE

Contrary to the latest opinions, we place the vultures in a separate family from the Accipitridae comprising the hawks (other than falcons) and harriers; just as the ospreys are retained in a family alone. Vultures have many peculiarities which seem in our eyes to deserve family rank, not the least being their mode of life and dependence on carrion as a food supply.

Vultures are with few exceptions large or very large birds with large wing-span, remarkably keen eyesight and wings capable of sustaining them in soaring flight for hours on end. They have broad, rounded wings; with one exception, short tails, and very powerful short legs having equally short toes. Flying at great heights they range over a vast expanse of country in areas which they inhabit.

Mainly of dull plumage, brown or black relieved in some species with white, vultures, when on the ground, gathered round the carcase of some dead animal are ungainly creatures; their neck bare of feathers, and head but scantily clothed with down give them an almost repulsive appearance, while the heavy hooked bill, with which they tear the flesh of the carrion, detracts little from the view, more especially when squabbling over the best tit-bits, their heads stained red with gore. They will gorge themselves until they can barely stand and then fly heavily to a roost where they remain immobile digesting their disgusting meal which does not always stop at carrion.

The manner in which vultures will gather in the sky from nowhere when death or injury overtakes an animal on the ground is almost uncanny. Their eyesight is phenomenal.

Vultures are represented in Cyprus by two resident species the griffon and the black vulture and by two very scarce visitors – the Egyptian vulture and the majestic lämmergeier or bearded vulture, a vagrant on *very* rare occasions from the Taurus mountains. It should be recognised in the sky by its immense size, its wing-span being over 9 ft from tip to tip but more especially by the abnormally long graduated tail, more than one third of the bird's total length.

Vultures do not attack human beings or animals with the exception of the lämmergeir, and then only when seen to be in difficulties such as stranded on a precipice ledge.

As scavengers they are invaluable, ridding the land not only of rotting carcases but even of human excrement. For such services alone they are worthy of the strictest protection in any community, but in Cyprus this has not yet been accorded them and the numbers of breeding birds are sadly decreasing.

GRIFFON VULTURE

Gyps fulvus [Plate 5, facing p. 13]

This large vulture with its enormous wingspread of 8–9 ft is, except for the head, almost uniform brown colour. The sexes are alike. The creamy-white head is covered with down, and the ruff at the base of the naked-looking neck is creamy-white. The rest of the upperparts vary from sandy-brown to rufous-brown. The tail and wing primaries are black. The immature bird is pinker than the adult and the ruff is fawny-brown. It takes three years for the white down-covered nestling to reach maturity. Its length is 41 ins (104 cm) when the adult is full grown.

Crete and Cyprus are the only islands in the Mediterranean where colonies of the griffon breed. In Cyprus it is a very familiar bird and most useful in the community. It is resident in both mountain ranges and also on the sea cliffs in the south and west of the island. The best known colonies are at Episkopi on the south coast (twenty-four pairs at least), and at St. Hilarion, Buffavento and Pentadactylos in the Northern Range.

Formerly a very abundant bird in Cyprus, up to a hundred having been counted gathered at the carcase of a dead beast, we noticed a marked reduction in 1954 and never saw more than fifty-three birds at once. During our last visit we saw nothing like that number in one spot and learned the regrettable fact that flocks tended to be smaller during the last four or five years and that the island population is "decreasing in numbers, probably mainly due *to persecution* by man". Could any action be more ill-conceived. This outrage is *not* to be placed at the door of the Cypriot residents. There is some indication that the breeding population may receive additions to its numbers in winter from the north as passage migrants have been observed around Nicosia in February, March and April heading towards the Northern Range. Judging from the time of year probably immature, non-breeding birds. Griffons are worthy of full protection by any Government for helping to rid the land of garbage, they feed almost entirely on carrion and when a dead or dying animal is located by one or more of the birds, the fact is communicated to all the griffons within sight soaring high in the Heavens with the resultant gathering for the feast.

In our major volume we published an account of the griffon's nesting habits as seen near Koronia Forest Station from a most reliable source, since when excellent supplementary observations made by a group of young service men at Episkopi camp, throughout the nesting season of 1967, was published in *Cyprus Bird Report 14*. From these two valuable sources it appears the griffon has a lengthy breeding time extending in some instances to at least four months from egg laying till leaving the nest. Nest building may begin in the second week of January but in some cases not till 1 March. Nest sites on cliffs are usually inaccessible but open to the elements on cliff-ledges, the nests being built of dried sticks with fresh pine branches brought from a distance. It may be lined with dry grass and Palmetto. On this huge cup-like structure a single unmarked egg is laid. Eggs may be found from the end of January (an early date) to the end of February, rarely to the second week of March. The fledging period is a very lengthy business (see *Birds of Cyprus* p. 232.) It is usually but not invariably a colonial nester unlike the next species to be discussed whose preference is for trees and solitude.

BLACK VULTURE [Plate 5, facing p. 13]

Aegypius monachus

This is a slightly larger bird than the griffon vulture its total length about 41 ins (104 cm); in flight these two huge birds are very similar, the head a little larger and the black tail slightly longer in the bird we are discussing but these are minor characteristics not easy to note in flight. At close quarters the black vulture's beak will be seen to be more powerful and larger. The naked face is lead-blue, with some blackish down on the crown, whitish on the nape and round the eyes. The neck ruff varies from dirty white to pale brown, blackish in immature birds. The body is dark brown with the flight feathers black. The iris is light brown, the cere bluish-horn, the feet grey. Culmen strongly arched. Immature birds are even blacker in appearance than the adults which they otherwise resemble.

The chick is smoke-grey.

Of the two resident vultures this is the least often seen in Cyprus and is more solitary in its habits for except when paired or feeding the black vulture is usually seen alone. If sharing the feast with griffons and ravens these sometimes give way to it, it is then that its superior size and blacker plumage is most apparent.

A decade ago it was described as being common but for some reason it has decreased alarmingly in the Northern Range and today is very scarce or even rare. In the Southern Range it is locally more common, but still few in numbers, single birds being usually encountered. It wanders far from its breeding sites on occasions but uncommonly.

The black vulture formerly nested in both the Northern and Southern mountain ranges usually choosing a large pine-tree in which to build its huge nest of dead branches and other less savoury material in which it lays its single egg, the latter either white or white with reddish blotches. Only tree nests have so far been reported (without sufficient data being given by the finders) but in other parts of its range it has been seen on ledges on the face of cliffs and usually quite inaccessible. Trees are however its preference. What its breeding status is today in the respective ranges is uncertain. If it is lost to the Northern Range as a breeding bird which is our fear, it will be a tragedy. A black vulture sailing along the high ridges of the Cyprus ranges is a magnificent sight – for however clumsy it may appear on the ground, in the air it is superb. We shall not easily forget one close encounter when a magnificent specimen came gliding along the cliffs of St. Hilarion just as we reached the highest point. We never saw this vulture on the lower ground to our recollection except on one occasion but always in or above the foothills.

EGYPTIAN VULTURE

Neophron percnopterus

In comparison with the two vultures already dealt with the Egyptian vulture is a considerably smaller bird, but if in adult dress is very easy to recognise by reason of its

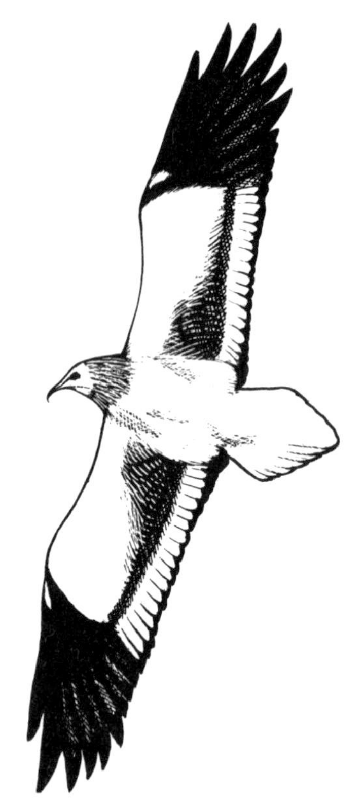

Egyptian vulture
(adult)
seen from below

entirely white body plumage and the black terminal part of the wings. Chin, throat, forecrown and sides of face are bare of feathers (as is a small patch on the breast) the skin of all these bare areas being bright yellow. At the nape and on the sides of the neck lanceolate-shaped, pinkish-buff feathers form a neck-ruff. The bill is yellow and slender with a black decurved tip, in marked contrast to the large vulture's heavy beaks; the feet are yellow and the iris orange. Its wing-span is about five feet. The tail in adults is white.

Young birds resemble parents in size but are dark brown for the first year, each feather tipped with fulvous or buff; from this stage the bird becomes brownish white and later with successive moults the brown feathers give way to white washed with pinkish-buff.

Both young and adults in flight exhibit a wedge-shaped tail and as the bird carries its head tucked in between the shoulders its silhouette is characteristic. White Egyptian vultures must be at least four years old. This bird is only a migrant to Cyprus first recorded over 100 years ago and then for lack of recorders not again till 1947 and 1954. Since the C.O.S. has come into being there have been a number of additional sightings – at least ten indisputable, pointing to the bird being an almost annual rare visitor at no very fixed season, though generally during migration time. In 1967 about 20 were seen together circling fairly low in the mountains on 26 September in the Southern Range, a most unusual experience, the observer being a visiting American ornithologist. September seems to be a usual month of appearance. Those seen in autumn would be migrating to winter in Africa south of the Sahara.

Family ACCIPITRIDAE

In our larger work *Birds of Cyprus* we followed the then accepted classification of the *Handbook of British Birds* (following Hartert) in which all the diurnal birds of prey were grouped under the family name, Falconidae, with the exception of the Aegypiidae (vultures) and the Pandionidae (ospreys). In this *Handbook* we recognise the Accipitridae and Falconidae as two distinct families, placing in the former the eagles, buzzards, sparrowhawks, kites and harriers, while retaining the true falcons in the Falconidae and the osprey in Pandionidae.

Both these two larger groups are well represented in Cyprus among the migratory birds, but to a much lesser extent among the residents. Apart from the imperial eagle and Bonelli's eagle, both of which breed sparingly in the island, the remaining representatives enumerated above are *all migratory species* visiting Cyprus either regularly or irregularly on their journeys to and from their winter quarters in Africa, from breeding grounds in Europe and Asia.

There is a vast migration of these raptorial birds every Autumn, mainly eagles and buzzards, in the eastern Mediterranean and recent investigations, well summarized in the *Ibis* 1967 pp. 489–501, have confirmed the view that "most of the larger soaring birds go round the Eastern Mediterranean rather than cross it anywhere (even via Cyprus)". Observations undertaken in the Lebanon and in southern Turkey by Mr. R. A. D. Cameron and his colleagues from Oxford University during the Autumns 1963–65 established many interesting facts which there is unfortunately not space here to recount. Even so Cyprus is by no means neglected entirely by these migrating hordes as the following list of species will confirm from the data accumulated over the last 10 years by the C.O.S.

In no group of birds is it more difficult to set out clearly the characteristics and distinctions* of the many individuals which not only vary greatly in size, between, for instance, an eagle and a sparrowhawk but they share one thing in common – a bewildering variety of plumage changes assumed with successive moults before the adult dress is achieved. In many species the sexes are alike, in some, e.g. the harriers totally different. In all the bill is short, with culmen strongly arched ending in a very short point with which their prey is torn to pieces; all have a cere, i.e. a soft membrane covering the basal portion of the upper mandible. Legs are generally powerful and the claws exceptionally sharp and decurved.

Both in this and the next family many of the species lay very handsome eggs spotted and blotched with reddish brown on a white ground, other eggs are as immaculate as the single egg of the griffon, but some of the eagles also lay white eggs though in both the eagles which breed in Cyprus their eggs are occasionally spotted. No harrier has ever bred in Cyprus and is not likely to do so, for these are ground nesting birds requiring extensive marshlands in which to rear their offspring. Among the other groups, nesting sites vary to an astonishing degree.

It is indeed sad that, with such a variety of raptorial birds on its list, Cyprus can induce so very few to breed, but as elsewhere in the world they are regularly and mercilessly persecuted by man – the worst predator of all.

---

*We wish to draw attention to a valuable publication by a Danish member of the Cyprus Ornithological Society Mr. Steen Christensen, on the field identification of eagles and buzzards which appeared, copiously illustrated, in a Danish periodical: *Dansk Orn. Forenings Tidsskrift* 1970 pp. 1–44, too late to enable us to make the use of its contents we should have wished.

IMPERIAL EAGLE

Aquila heliaca [Plate 6, facing p. 16]

In our major book (1958) we called this fine eagle the King of Cyprus birds, for it is truly a majestic bird which reminds us of our own golden eagle in the Highlands of Scotland and is much the same size. We described it as a large brownish-black eagle with the sides of the head, nape and hind neck pale yellowish-fawn colour. At the age of three some of the scapulars become white as our Artist has depicted in the accompanying plate. There is a small wedge-shaped white patch on the back, visible both when the bird is in flight or on the ground. The tail feathers are dark crossed by five or six grey bars, and in shape square. The underparts are uniform brown. Its total length is 30 ins (76 cm).

Immature birds are paler brown than the adults on the upperparts with darker streakings and some rufous on the crown. The underside is uniform as in the adult.

One of the older and best known ornithologists, resident in Cyprus between 1907 and 1912 described the imperial eagle at that time as a "not very rare resident", and sixty years later it is more correctly termed a rather *scarce* breeding resident. It could never have been numerous even in the southern range but eagles are never allowed to be, especially when they can be accused of "lifting" poultry. In one month in 1954 on our first visit to Cyprus we met with imperial eagles singly on five occasions and not entirely restricted to the northern or southern mountain ranges where they breed. At the present day 1970–71 they can be described as barely holding their own and more often to be seen in the vicinity of Mount Olympus than elsewhere, and much reduced in numbers – possibly no longer nesting anywhere in the northern range.

They breed in March and April, almost invariably making their large nest, described as a clumsy mass of branches, at the top of a tall pine tree. Eggs have been found, very slightly incubated, on 29 April. How many eggs this eagle lays in Cyprus has not been mentioned, but three is a normal clutch in the Lower Danube. The eggs may be white with scanty rufous markings, or they may be handsomely marked, spotted and blotched with reddish-brown and underlying lilac, or clouded with purple and spotted with rufous.

There is a possibility that the imperial eagle may also be an irregular but scarce winter visitor from the north. In February 1965 some immature birds of this species were seen on passage over Nicosia, heading north. It is a faint hope that on similar occasions a pair or two might break their journey and so rescue the resident population from the fate which seems otherwise to await it in the not distant future; i.e. extermination of yet another grand bird from the island fauna.

GREATER SPOTTED EAGLE

Aquila clanga

On the identification of this eagle I cannot improve on what I wrote in my fifth volume *Birds of the British Isles* (1956) when summing up the distinctions between it and *Aquila pomarina* in the following sentences: It is not possible to be sure of this eagle unless critically examined, for the similarity of the species to the lesser spotted eagle is such that only an expert is likely to be able to tell them apart . . . the very pale to white upper tail-coverts . . . have been shown to be an unreliable character for though birds showing well-marked white upper tail-coverts can be accepted as *A. clanga*, those having a little dingy white or none may be either. That applies only to the adult.

In general *A. clanga* is darker brown than *A. pomarina* and in both the plumage is uniform. Only in immature birds is it spotted; the younger the bird the more intense is the spotting of the upperparts, the juvenile in its first year having on the feathers of the back, rump and scapulars broad central spots or streaks of light buff.

Young of *A. clanga* differ from the young of *A. pomarina* in being of a darker colour and in having no rust patch on the nape; usually a well-marked area of white or whitish at the base of the tail and more conspicuous development of the white spots and streaks of the upperparts, especially on the mantle. A comparison for which I am indebted to several *Raptor* experts.

A greater spotted eagle has now been definitely identified by a specimen shot in immature plumage "hawking" over a Eucalyptus grove bordering Akrotiri Salt Lake on 27 September 1967. It had a large amount of white on the rump and no sign of the rust coloured nape feathers characteristic of the immature lesser spotted eagle. Further it had very heavy and extensive white spots on the mantle and wing-coverts, including the lesser wing-coverts. The ground colour was very dark brown with an almost blackish sheen on the feathers.

In flight, the specimen to which the above note refers, which was seen the day previous to being shot, had a rather bulky outline showing broad wings and a very short rounded or wedge-shaped tail. The head was comparatively small. Wing-beats were heavy and down-curved. This is the only acceptable record for Cyprus in the latest *Check-List* issued by the C.O.S. We must therefore consider the bird a very rare vagrant to the island.

LESSER SPOTTED EAGLE

Aquila pomarina

Both this and the greater spotted eagle figured in our book *The Birds of Cyprus* in 1958, the latter entry being enclosed within brackets, for at that date it was uncertain whether the bird known as *Aquila clanga* had a right to inclusion or not. These two eagles are so similar in appearance that even when handled care has to be taken not to confuse them. We described *Aquila pomarina* as "occasional in winter" and added "reported to have bred". Of that observation more later.

Describing the lesser spotted eagle's plumage we wrote "the adult eagle is dark brown, rather paler on the crown, wing-coverts and underparts. The male is 24 ins (61 cm) in length, the female 26 ins (66 cm). The sexes are alike.

"Spotted eagle" is a misnomer for only the immature are spotted, and even then only on the head, wings and underside, the adults are uniform. Immature specimens have a rusty buff patch on the nape which can be seen at close quarters only. A comparison between this and the greater-spotted eagle will be given under that species, see also *Birds of Cyprus* p. 207.

A record of *A. pomarina*, about which there can be no dispute, was of a male bird shot on 26 December 1912 at the Mogashia Marsh which was later identified at the British Museum. Since that initial identification a number of "spotted eagles" of one species or the other have been recorded in the annals of the C.O.S. but, upon reviewing the evidence on which these records were founded, only seven (up to the close of 1969) have been accepted as correctly identified and so listed in the latest Check-List compiled by the Secretary of the C.O.S. with the help of colleagues. They read as follows in the order in which the birds were shot (only one) or seen: one male shot, Mogashia Marsh, 26 December 1912; two near Limassol, 26 November 1956; one Cape Greco 29 November 1957; two near Kolossi 17 October 1957; one Famagusta 8 April 1965 (the only spring record); one Akrotiri 4 October 1968; one Akrotiri 10 October 1968.

As to the statement in our *Birds of Cyprus* 1958 p. 208 that nests of a spotted eagle had been reported from Cyprus in the past, it is agreed that no evidence or descriptions were supplied in support, and it is firmly believed that *no such eagles breed or have bred in Cyprus* despite rumours to the contrary.

BONELLI'S EAGLE [Plate 6, facing p. 16]

Hieraaëtus fasciatus

When it has attained adult dress Bonelli's eagle is not difficult to identify, its comparatively small size and wing expanse in comparison with the huge imperial eagle being very noticeable. The mostly white underparts from chin to vent, which contrast with the dark wings, afford an excellent field character for the eagle is more often viewed from below than above. The upperparts are dark brown, the head finely streaked. The ash-brown tail with five or six indistinct bars has a broad terminal band. The under wing-coverts are spotted black and white, the legs feathered to the feet. Length 26–29 ins (66–73 cm).

Immature birds are less easily recognised, one fully grown which we examined in Cyprus was entirely fulvous brown on the under side, darker above. Bonelli's eagle is fortunately often to be seen in the hills and mountains of Cyprus and in as much as any bird of prey can be described as a common species this eagle deserves the term. While usually met with on high ground at middle elevations (but occasionally up to Mount Olympus itself) birds have also been observed at Akrotiri and flying over the reservoirs in the low country, for they are bold hunters and no doubt find the duck and coot which frequent these waters in winter much to their taste. They will often hunt in pairs as recorded in the *Cyprus Bird Report* for 1964 when two were seen hunting along the river at Erimi one November day.

In Cyprus it has bred in both the Northern and Southern mountain ranges, making its nest in apertures on the side of precipices. One nest we examined was built in the cleft between a small tree and cliff-face made of fine twigs and copiously lined with fresh pine branches. Nests have also been found in ruins as at Buffavento Castle. The clutch is usually of two eggs, occasionally one, either pure white or marked with red and buff spots and streakings. It is an early breeder, eggs having been found on 3 February and others reported in January and March, but details are sadly lacking. Breeding dates confirm that nesting is spread over January, February and March in both mountain ranges. The Southern

Range contains the larger breeding population scattered over a much larger area. In the Kyrenia mountains (Northern Range) five or six pairs have been located. Some dispersal takes place in late autumn and early winter before the birds return to their breeding grounds. Sight records at Akrotiri in Autumn and at Kyrenia and Cape Andreas in Spring suggest that it may be a very scarce passage migrant or winter visitor in addition to being a resident species.

BOOTED EAGLE

Hieraaëtus pennatus

This little eagle has now been confirmed as a scarce but regular passage migrant to Cyprus mainly observed in September and October but exceptionally November and early December (once) and at least on one occasion in spring (March). It is the smallest of European eagles measuring 18–24 ins (46–61 cm) in length but "every inch an eagle" and can be recognised if in the pale phase of plumage, for the bird is dimorphic, by the almost white *or* tawny yellow underparts lightly streaked with brown, white wing-lining and dark flight feathers. The upperside is either dark brown or rufous brown with dark primaries and dark *unbanded* tail. The face is dark below the eyes but almost white on the forecrown, the rest of the head inclining to golden-brown on the sides of the neck and back.

In the other dark phase of plumage the underparts are uniformly dark brown. Juveniles are usually more rufous. The uniform tail is fairly long in adults and square tipped; the legs heavily feathered to the base of the bright yellow toes which are particularly strong for the size of the bird.

The booted eagle is renowned for its activity and rapacious character. Its swift flight in forested country in and out of the tree trunks is characteristic. In Spain its favourite food is reported to be rabbits, lizards and snakes and as the last are all too prevalent in Cyprus the bird would be a great benefactor if it could be persuaded to stay. It is interesting to learn that in S.W. Europe it crosses to Africa in September and returns in March, corresponding with dates when it is recorded in Cyprus. A great number are reported passing through Egypt to their breeding areas in the Balkan Peninsula, Asia Minor and southern Russia and it is strange that it has been so seldom recorded in Cyprus except at Akrotiri where regular observations on migratory movements are made.

WHITE-TAILED SEA-EAGLE

Haliaëtus albicilla

The general colour of an adult sea-eagle is ash-brown above and paler brown on the underparts, the head being strikingly pale in comparison. The tail feathers are white. The beak is yellow and the tarsus, which is bare of feathers on the lower half, is also yellow as is the iris.

When full grown this eagle measures 27–36 ins (68–91 cm) in length and has a wing-span varying from 7–9 ft. It is the largest of all European eagles.

A very important point to observe is the *shape* of the tail which is seen best in flight and is wedge-shaped. In flight this is the only certain way to distinguish it from the golden eagle which when young also has a white tail with a black band at the tip. A young sea-eagle has a brown tail without any dark bands across it; it also has a horn-coloured beak for the first few years of its life, finally turning yellow; the beak is nearly as long as the bird's head, the golden eagle's bill is considerably shorter.

Of the two eagles, both of which have been reported from Cyprus, the sea-eagle is the more sluggish bird. Owing to the similarity of the two species, past records require very careful scrutiny. The Cyprus Bird Reports for 1961, 1962, 1963 each contain accounts of eagles with white tails, believed to be *H. albicilla*, seen in the autumn months (September–November) inclusive at Episkopi. Akrotiri and Cape Greco. The older records 1912–1927 are more authoritative, especially an adult pair seen at a reservoir in 1912 and one obtained at Larnaca Salt Lake in January 1913 and now in the Royal Scottish Museum. There have been over a dozen birds recorded if we accept the identity of all as established. There are only three spring or early summer records: an adult pair in mid-April 1927 at Larnaca, one in May 1968 at Cape Andreas and the pair already mentioned in June 1912, at one of the reservoirs.

NOTE

The **Golden eagle**, *Aquila chrysaëtos*, has been mentioned on a number of occasions in the *Cyprus Bird Bulletins*. On the advice of the C.O.S. and those responsible for their new Check-List, we have *deleted* this eagle from the list of Cyprus birds none of the supposed sight-records being considered unquestionable.

BUZZARD, *Buteo buteo*

STEPPE BUZZARD, *Buteo vulpinus*

[Plate 7, facing p. 17]

There is an enormous migration of "buzzards" through Cyprus at both seasons, especially in the autumn when huge numbers, estimated between hundreds per day and reaching occasionally a thousand, have been reported. The spring return migration is much less in evidence and much smaller numbers are then observed at Akrotiri from late March to mid-April, occasionally to mid-May.

Common buzzards may be recognised by their broad wings, short barred tail and bare yellow feet. The underside of the wing shows much white in the lining with dark patches on each side. The colour of the upper-parts is dark brown, the steppe buzzard having the feathers edged with chestnut to a greater extent than in the common buzzard (*B. buteo*) of northern Europe. They are not easily distinguishable and certainly not in the field. On the underside there is considerable variation: usually the breast is pale to whitish, with the sides brown, and darker patches on a level with the carpal joint when the wing is closed. Immature buzzards are browner below; rusty buff with blobs and streaks of brown showing much variation.

Investigation in very recent years by the C.O.S. has gone to prove that the great majority of so-called "buzzards" migrating over Cyprus in Autumn *prior to mid-September* are all honey-buzzards (*apivorus*) and that the common and steppe buzzards are normally first seen (at Akrotiri) from mid-September to late October with peak migration in late September and early October, but further study is necessary to establish this with certainty.

Winter visitors which have been examined have proved to be of the typical race, and it is suggested in the latest *Check-List* that the Autumn flocks probably consist of mixed populations of *Buteo buteo* (the common buzzard of Europe) and *B. vulpinus*, the closely allied steppe buzzard.

The steppe buzzard breeds in S. E. Europe and western Asia; yet another subspecies named *menetriesi* (generally more chestnut than *vulpinus* and less barred on the underside) occurs in southern Russia and Turkey.

All these buzzards migrate to Africa in autumn and if a series could be collected in Cyprus during the passage, in all probability the races mentioned would be represented in smaller or greater numbers, in addition to the honey buzzards which, in our earlier volume we had considered separately.

EUROPEAN SPARROW-HAWK

Accipiter nisus [Plate 7, facing p. 17]

The male bird has the crown and upperparts slate grey, wings like the back but the tail greyish-brown crossed by four or five dark bars. Throat pale buff streaked with brown, rest of undersurface buff closely and heavily barred with reddish- and dark brown. Face and cheeks rufous. Eye orange, legs and feet yellow. The female is much larger and much browner than the male but shares the slate-coloured crown and has a browner tail and less rufous cheeks. The soft parts as in the male. Immature birds have rufous edges to the brown feathers, the under-parts white barred with reddish-brown.

Considerable variation is found in the plumage especially on the mantle and in the extent of the barring.

In Europe it is a widely distributed species ranging to the northern shores of the Mediterranean eastwards to Asia Minor and the area east of the Aral-Caspian seas. In winter the northern population moves south but the migration stops short at the Mediterranean and only a sprinkling of the whole reaches northern Africa.

To Cyprus the sparrow-hawk is a winter

visitor in small numbers and must be considered scarce, usually observed in the mountain ranges. It is described as fairly frequent in singles on spring passage and common in small numbers in Autumn mainly in late September and early October.

In spring it occurs from early March, most often in mid-April.

NOTE

Another species the **Levantine sparrow-hawk** (*Accipiter brevipes*) figures in the List of Rarer Visitors see p. 215. It has grey instead of rufous cheeks and much more heavily banded underparts. There are about eight definite records between 1957–1967 in April, September and October of birds on passage, at least one of which was caught on a lime stick at Paralimni.

GOSHAWK [Plate 7, facing p. 17]

Accipiter gentilis

A female goshawk is a powerful-looking bird, the male smaller as is normal in the birds of prey. Overhead its round-winged, long-tailed outline recalls the sparrow-hawk but it is considerably larger. Only by size can the sexes be distinguished. Both are greyish-brown above with whitish breasts closely and heavily barred, and with pale eye stripes. Seen from below the undertail-coverts are white. Adults have orange eyes. Immature goshawks are more richly coloured, the wings and mantle almost rufous and the buff breast spotted and streaked (*not* barred as in the mature bird) with drop-shaped brown markings.

To Cyprus it is an infrequent winter visitor, and scarce passage migrant, but seldom more than individual birds are recognised on any one day. We have seen it ourselves in the Troödos mountains, Stavros, Kykko and Halefka early in the year and passing individuals have been recorded from Cape Gata and Akrotiri.

There are many records of "migrants" between late September and late October but some confusion is believed to have occurred with the female sparrow-hawk as the goshawk is certainly not so common on passage as such records would imply. It is more likely to be a scarce winter visitor to the Mountain ranges from late October but mainly in mid-winter, as the latest Cyprus Check-List suggests.

As recorded in literature a few European-Asiatic goshawks wander south in winter and have been recorded from northern Africa but goshawks are not regular migrants. Trans-Mediterranean passage barely exists. It is a scarce wanderer to Egypt, but to describe it as a "frequent passage migrant" (Cyprus Bulletin 15 p. 23) is we suggest, misleading and probably based on misidentifications. The goshawk is mainly sedentary but is given to wandering. A number of racial forms have been described, that from Asia Minor and the Caucasus bearing the specific name *A.g. marginalis*.

BLACK KITE [Plate 7, facing p. 17]

Milvus migrans

This is a large uniformly-coloured hawk which in a favourable light, such as one might expect to find in Cyprus, shows a contrast between the dark brown mantle and tail, the chestnut breast and the greyish head. Young birds show pale markings on their underwings, though not so noticeable on the wing as in the red kite. The forked tail of the black kite, though marked, is less forked than in *Milvus milvus*. The wings are angled. The European black kite when adult has a black bill with yellow cere; legs and feet are yellow, the tarsus unfeathered. Total length about 22 ins (56 cm).

The European population has a breeding range from Spain through central and southern Europe to Asia Minor and south Russia. A few also breed in north Africa from Morocco to Tunisia north of the Atlas Range. There is a movement south in the autumn on a wide front, but Cyprus does not lie in the main path of this passage, which lies farther to the east via Sinai and Palestine. Even so in early August 1966 about 50 were counted over Akrotiri Salt Lake and in 1968 a party of 30 were seen on 29 August but thereafter only six additional birds on four other dates, pointing to rather an uneven passage. Most records are in mid-September, occasionally recorded in November. Away from the south coast birds on passage are scarce.

In spring from late March to mid-May it is

rather scarce, sometimes occurring in small flocks.

HONEY BUZZARD

Pernis apivorus

The honey-buzzard differs in silhouette from the common buzzard by its narrower wings and longer tail. In addition to passing through the normal plumage changes before attaining fully adult dress, it has two quite distinct colour phases which it may retain throughout its life: these we may define as (a) a white phase and (b) a dark phase. In the normal dress the upperparts are dark brown with the forehead, lores and cheeks strongly washed with grey, which in old males extends over the crown. The light brown tail has two distinct bands near the base, then an area of very indistinct narrow bars and a broad terminal band, the bands and bars being a purplish-sepia. The underparts in the normal honey-buzzard are heavily spotted or barred with brown or blackish on a white ground. In the white phase the head is often entirely white; the underparts are also white with a few brown bars, or sometimes streaks on the side. In the dark phase the entire plumage is brown which varies from amber to sepia in different birds. It is found breeding from southern Norway to the Urals, though its distribution is erratic. The winter quarters are in Africa.

Honey buzzard

To Cyprus it is a regular passage migrant in large numbers, most of the records being of autumn birds. It is rarely recorded in spring: early March and April. In the past there has undoubtedly been considerable confusion between this bird and the common and steppe buzzards. Recent observations by the members of the C.O.S. in Cyprus, and in the Lebanon, go to prove that buzzard migration in late August to mid-September is monopolised by the honey buzzard, often in hundreds, sometimes in thousands, and the passage may be continued to late October. Up to, and during mid-September, honey-buzzards *alone* are passing, but after mid-September the passage of common and steppe buzzards joins in, as mentioned under *Buteo buteo*.

The above resumé is what the present pattern *appears* to be, but it is emphasized by the compilers of the latest Check-List that further investigations must take place before this can be established. The difficulty of separating the three buzzards in flight has caused erroneous conclusions to be drawn, and more observations are needed to clarify the picture.

The account of an individual bird ringed in the Soviet Republic some 220 miles S.E. of Tomsk, Siberia, and recovered in Cyprus is given in our larger work.

MARSH HARRIER [Plate 7, facing p. 17]

Circus aeruginosus

This is the largest of the four harriers recorded from Cyprus as passage migrants and winter visitors in varying numbers. Its body plumage when adult is dark rust-brown; crown and chin creamy-buff, streaked dark brown. Underparts chestnut with dark centres to the feathers. No white (or very exceptionally) at base of tail. Tail silver-grey. Wing-coverts and inner secondaries mostly brown, remainder blue-grey making a broad oblique band across the wing contrasting with black terminal portion of primaries. Legs bright yellow, tarsus entirely bare, thigh feathers rufous.

The female is like the male, only slightly larger, 22 ins (56 cm), but wings and tail brown, no pale band on the wing. Underparts dark brown.

The bird goes through a variety of plumage changes before reaching those above. When hunting it flies low and pounces on its prey. Normally it roosts on the ground. It is commonly seen on marshes and lakes in Cyprus but never numerous, usually in winter or periods of migration mainly between early September and late October, but birds are recorded a month earlier and later on occasions. On 1 October 1968, thirteen marsh harriers were seen, but that is an unusually large number for one day; single birds or up to five at once is more normal in autumn, with long intervals in between when none are observed.

The spring passage lasts from early March to mid-May mainly in April when birds are fairly common.

HEN HARRIER [Plate 7, facing p. 17]

Circus cyaneus

Very like Montagu's in appearance, head, wings and tail uniform slate-grey; tips only of primaries are black. Rump white. Throat and breast bluish-grey; rest of underparts and under wing-coverts pure white. Cere, legs and feet yellow, tarsus bare; bill black; iris orange. The larger female is 22 ins in length (56 cm), mainly brown in colour, the crown paler than the mantle and streaked with dark brown; wings dark brown, tail light brown, crossed with five dark bands. Upper tail-coverts white which show in flight; underparts buffish-brown streaked with light brown. Immature very similar to adult female. For comparison between females of Hen and Montagu's harriers see under Montagu's (p. 47).

To Cyprus it is a not uncommon winter visitor from early October to late April and a scarce passage migrant from late August to November, mainly seen during September and October, and in spring from early March to May, mainly in the month of April when we have seen odd birds crossing the Northern Range. There have been a number of observations since our major work appeared, by members of the C.O.S. within these dates.

In winter the birds may be seen anywhere in twos or threes where there is any marshland over the whole island and when on passage some birds cross the mountains while others skirt the coast. The records in Autumn from the Akrotiri Salt Lake are scanty and never more than two on one day between 26 August and 27 September. In some winters hen harriers are very scarce.

MONTAGU'S HARRIER

Circus pygargus

Smaller in size and more elegant in form than the hen harrier which it closely resembles, it has the upper-parts slate-grey palest on the crown and wing-coverts; the primaries are black. A narrow black bar crosses the grey wing and the whole area at the base of the tail is much narrower than in the hen-harrier and less pure white. Breast grey, belly and thighs white streaked with rufous-chestnut.

The female closely resembles female hen harrier but as in the male the white at base of tail in Montagu's is generally narrower. Compared with the female of the pallid harrier (*C. macrourus*) the plumages are very similar and only when handled can they be definitely recognised by the wing-formula. Unless seen with their consorts the females of these three harriers are better left unidentified when not handled. It is all too easy to confuse one with another.

In habits it differs from the marsh and hen harrier in quartering dry grasslands and being less addicted to marshes and swamps in its winter quarters.

Its status is still somewhat obscure. It has been reported a number of times between August and late November. Spring records are scarcer from late March to early May. It can only be regarded as a scarce migrant especially in spring. It is certainly not as common as the pallid harrier.

PALLID HARRIER [Plate 7, facing p. 17]

Circus macrourus

From the male harriers already described, this – the most frequent passage migrant of the four – is distinctive by reason of its entirely white underparts without any grey on the throat or breast. It is entirely pale silver-grey above, except for the black terminal part of the primaries. Its wings are long and tapering, a true harrier in form with fairly long yellow legs and feet tucked under the tail. A white patch at the base of the tail is caused by the grey and white upper tail-coverts. The middle pair of tail-feathers in the male are grey like the back, but the remaining rectrices are white irregularly barred with grey. The absence of a black bar on the wings at once separates it from Montagu's harrier, perhaps the nearest to it in shape and effortless flight, as the bird skims the ground. The female can easily be confused with both *C. pygargus* and *C. cyaneus*. In all plumages it can be distinguished by its wing-formula but that is a useless field character.

This is a bird of dry open steppe country. It does not frequent marshes. It is a passage migrant at both seasons in fair numbers, rarely seen in winter but very common on the spring passage. It may be occasionally seen in summer; an immature bird remained all through the summer at Kouklia in 1969. First seen in June; on what grounds it was said possibly to remain to nest has never been established. If any of the four species did breed in Cyprus this is the most likely of the four to do so. It is evidently much more numerous on passage than we assumed in 1954–58. Autumn records range from mid-August to late October rarely into November; there are only three certain winter sightings. Spring passage lasts from mid-March to late April, rarely a few in May.

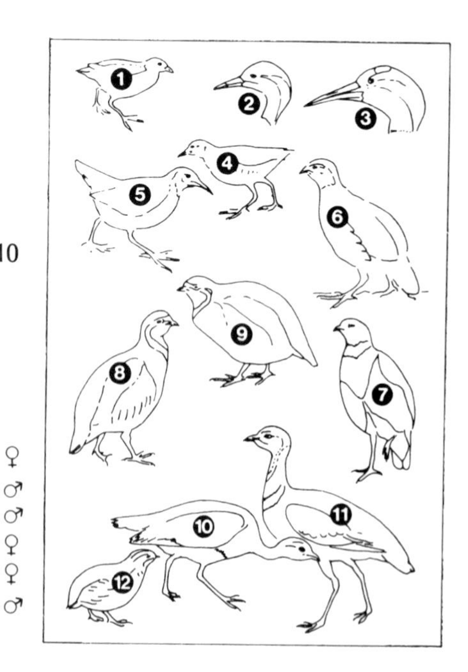

Plate 10

1. Little crake
2. Demoiselle crane
3. Common crane
4. Spotted crake
5. Water rail
6. Common francolin ♀
7. Common francolin ♂
8. Cyprian chukor ♂
9. Cyprian chukor ♀
10. Little bustard ♀
11. Little bustard ♂
12. European quail

C.E. Talbot Kelly '70

C E Talbot Ke

Family PANDIONIDAE

Ospreys, of which there are a number of geographical races, are all contained in the genus *Pandion* which is monotypic, none of the races having evolved sufficiently to be worthy of specific rank other than *Pandion haliaëtus*. They are of World-wide distribution but only the typical subspecies occurs in the Palaearctic Region. Ospreys are entirely fish-eating and their anatomy is directed to that end.

At first sight an osprey might be mistaken for one of the smaller eagles, but closer inspection shows characters which are not shared by that group. Most noticeable are the scaled feet and tarsi; the scales are often spiny, particularly so along the anterior part of the tarsus; the toes are covered with smaller scales which give way to horny scutes; the claws are very long and immensely powerful, sharply curved and ending in needle-like points. The soles of the feet are spiny with large prickly bosses, which enable the bird to maintain its hold on slippery fish. Most remarkable of all, the outer toe is reversible, a character unique among the diurnal birds of prey, but shared to some extent by the owls. In the Pandionidae the whole of the tibia is feathered beyond the tibio-tarsal joint. In other features the ospreys conform more closely to the Falconidae. The powerful bill is strongly arched, the upper mandible protruding far beyond the tip of the lower. Of medium size, they are easily

Plate 11

1. Marsh sandpiper
2. Dotterel (winter)
3. Geoffroy's sand-plover (winter)
4. Avocet
5. Spur-winged plover
6. Black-tailed godwit (winter)
7. Reeve
8. Ruff
9. Common pratincole
10. Stone curlew

identified by their habits which will be discussed under the species.

So far as we know the birds have no nesting place in Cyprus and while they breed on islets further west in the Mediterranean, it is very unlikely they would ever be allowed to establish an eyrie, either on Cyprus itself, or on one of the offshire islands such as the Klidhes.

OSPREY

Pandion haliaëtus

Roughly the size of a buzzard it is conspicuous by reason of its white head and underparts. The crown is streaked and a band of dark brown passes from behind the eye to the nape separating the white crown from the white cheeks. Feathers on hind crown tinged with russet and lengthened to form a short crest. Upperparts and tail dark brown. The white underparts are relieved by an area of light brown on the crop. Eye bright yellow, bill hooked and black; legs and feet immensely powerful, greenish yellow in colour, the soles of the feet furnished with prickly spines. Total length 23 ins (58 cm), wing expanse 19–20 ins.

Immature birds are lighter coloured, the feathers with white borders on the upperparts.

The osprey's habits and mode of fishing, plunging feet foremost after fish betray it from afar. To Cyprus it is but an uncommon passage migrant which can be encountered at both seasons but its appearances, singly or at most two or three at a time, are erratic.

It is recorded for every month from July to November inclusive but is uncommon in the summer when lakes have dried up; mainly seen during the Autumn from mid-September to mid-October.

In Spring it occurs chiefly in April, a few into late May. In years when there is plenty of water in the reservoirs and lakes it often stays for many days. The osprey does *not* nest in Cyprus or on any of the off-shore islands (so far as is known at present) as it does on so many of the islands further west, when it prefers off-shore isolated islets upon which to build its huge stick nest, sometimes choosing an inaccessible headland for the purpose. It fishes for its prey both in fresh and salt water.

Family FALCONIDAE

The true falcons are all included in a single genus *Falco* and provide in Cyprus a very attractive assemblage of ten species, ranging in size from the little merlin, rather less than 12 ins (30 cm) in length to the lanner and saker whose females measure 18 and 20 ins respectively from bill to tail-tip. Typical of the family is the peregrine, which is the only one of those so far mentioned which (in the lesser peregrine) is a resident bird, with eyries round the coastal cliffs.

Cyprus is famed as being the most easterly breeding place known of Eleonora's falcon, a bird with a very restricted range in the nesting season and one which by reason of its world scarcity is afforded full protection. As its main colonies are close to the R.A.F. station in the Sovereign Base, it has a good chance of increasing in numbers. Its life history is given fuller notice in this *Handbook*. The common kestrel is the only other resident species, the colonies of the lesser kestrel which in the past has bred in Cyprus having apparently ceased to exist. Only one other species requires special mention – the red-footed falcon, the sexes of which are so dissimilar that they are usually mistaken for two species. They are regular and numerous visitors en route to their breeding places where they appropriate the forsaken nests of rooks etc. Wintering in the Sudan they are among the most attractive migrants to Cyprus on both spring and autumn passage, living largely on insects.

The chief characters of this family have been mentioned under the last family heading and need not be repeated here.

HOBBY [Plate 9, facing p. 33]

Falco subbuteo

Whole upperparts wings and tail slate-grey, darker on the head, the area round eye and the moustacheal streak, being nearly black. Cheeks and throat white. Rest of undersurface white heavily streaked with black. Thighs and under tail-coverts rust-red. Cere and skin round eye bright yellow. Bill horn, legs and feet bright yellow. Legs unfeathered below the joint. Wings comparatively long and pointed but tail short. Total length 12–14 ins (30–36 cm) according to sex. Its small size and exceedingly swift direct flight is noticeable in the field. At times it will soar to great heights.

The hobby is a summer visitor to Cyprus, a normally woodland hawk, it shuns close forest, preferring open woodland where it can hunt for its prey – small birds and all kinds of insects – with more freedom of movement. It is also a passage migrant in considerable numbers from Europe, where its range extends to the Ural Mountains. The main autumn passage through Cyprus of birds on their way to Africa occurs from late September to mid-October; in some years the numbers may run to forty in a single day for several days on end, in other years the numbers are much reduced, governed perhaps by climatic conditions in Europe or the Middle East. The spring passage from mid-April to late May is much less noticeable. In Cyprus birds may be seen from coastal districts to the Troödos mountains but paired birds are scarce and widely scattered.

The hobby invariably utilises the nests of other species, never building for itself. Deserted nests of crows and magpies, and (in Cyprus) *possibly* jay's nests, are appropriated. Three eggs are usually laid, they are densely spotted and mottled with rufous of various shades. It is not known to what extent, if at all, the hobby breeds in Cyprus today – in any case it can only be a very scarce breeding species. Eggs are said to have been found at Larnaca 25 July 1913. Its status as a nesting bird requires serious investigation.

PEREGRINE [Plate 8, facing p. 32]

Falco peregrinus

The peregrine which breeds and is presumably resident in Cyprus all the year round is known as the lesser peregrine *Falco peregrinus brookei*.

The upperparts from the crown to the rump are grey, rather darker on the crown. The white cheek patch and the black moustachial streak are both conspicuous features. The wings are dark grey, the tail blue-grey with dark slate bars. The chin and throat are white, the upper breast shading from white to pinkish-buff, with dark shaft-streaks broadening to drop-shaped markings; the rest of the underparts are pinkish-buff, heavily barred and spotted with black. The flanks, axillaries and under wing-coverts are all barred. Half the tarsus is feathered, the yellow feet with black claws are free of feathers. In flight the body looks torpedo-shaped, the wings narrow, long and pointed, the tail slightly tapering. When hunting, the stoop is almost vertical and extremely fast, with the wings almost closed. The male measures 14 ins (36 cm) in length, the female 16 ins (41 cm).

The local race was determined when a bird was collected at Famagusta and the skin preserved. It frequents the cliffs of the Cyprus coast and has also nested in the Klidhes islands. Localities on the main island from which pairs have been located include Cape Andreas, Cape Greco, Cape Gata, Episkopi, Cape Astro, Cape Arnauti, the Paphos forest and – a decade ago – St. Hilarion. It is not known if the peregrine breeds in all these places today. Quite possibly it will be found to nest in other places mainly on the sea-cliffs in the southern and western part of the island and along the Karpas Peninsula. It breeds in March and April.

A female was disturbed from a clutch of four eggs in an old raven's nest on a south-facing ledge of rock-stack on 15 March 1959. (*Ool. Record* 1961 p. 4) at which date the eggs contained medium to small embryos. Eggs were normal in size but rather pale, the ground colour completely hidden by light red-brown with smears and spots of darker red and brown.

NON-BREEDING PEREGRINES RECORDED FROM CYPRUS

Two other non-breeding peregrines have been identified on the island, the typical European subspecies *F. p. peregrinus*, and the Siberian peregrine *F. p. leucogenys* (*calidus* of former authors) during the migration periods. The last is reported "commonest on passage". In the autumn raptor movements over Akrotiri Salt Lake reported in 1967 and 1968, between one and four individuals were recorded passing on specified dates between 1 August and 13 October, but never more than four on one day. Peregrines have been encountered in the mountains in the winter months which are presumed to be winter visitors and others are reported to "winter around open waters till April". The Siberian form is known to be a great wanderer from its northern homeland and is certainly the most likely of the migratory peregrines to occur in Cyprus outwith the breeding season. Few spring records have been reported of birds on passage.

SAKER FALCON

Falco cherrug [Plate 9, facing p. 33]

The adult male saker has the head creamy-white, streaked brown on crown, rest of upperparts grey-brown, often with bluish wash, every feather fringed buff; chin white; rest of underparts white, heavily blotched and streaked brown. Inner webs of primaries with irregular barring scarcely reaching to inner fringe; first primary slightly shorter than the third. The adult female is larger than the male.

To Cyprus the saker is a fairly common and regular autumn passage migrant and a scarce winter visitor but it is not a bird that a visiting ornithologist can rely on seeing! We considered ourselves very fortunate when coming to Cyprus to investigate the bird-life of the island between 1954 and 1958 to have seen both saker and lanner falcons on separate occasions *inland*, close enough to distinguish the species. In our major work we have referred to a passage of saker falcons – as they were *reported* to have been – in early October 1957, when up to 15 a day were said to have been observed passing Akrotiri.

It may be seen in that locality from early September to late October or even late November on passage. Single birds frequent the lakes and reservoirs between December and February.

There have been only a few spring records in March and rather more in April to the end of the month. The numbers seen may vary annually or the variation may be partly due to observers not being in the right place when the birds are passing. In 1968, for instance, the sakers and lanners identified at Akrotiri between 26 September and the end of October amounted to six in all, and even fewer in 1967. In 1969 when particular attention was paid to the raptor migration, large falcons of either this species or lanners proved to be fairly common.

The difficulty of distinguishing these two large falcons in the field has accounted for some confusion. The principal points of distinction were given in table form in *Birds of Cyprus* (1958), p. 194, and will be repeated under the next species.

LANNER FALCON

Falco biarmicus feldeggii

The lanner is evidently a scarcer migrant to Cyprus than the saker judging by the *Cyprus Bird Reports* of the last ten years when more attention has been paid to the movement of raptors through the island than in former days. It may however be expected to occur sporadically at the same seasons, and occasionally to winter. The first record refers to one shot and preserved on 1 February, 1913, near Famagusta thus establishing the species. We have only seen one, by Patriki Village on 13 February 1958, of whose identity we were satisfied. We may be equally certain of the one seen on 24 September 1968, by a highly competent observer, and a March record has also been accepted in the latest check-list but a number of earlier records are clearly suspect as the result of inexperienced recorders or of too hasty identification in the field.

Describing the bird in our larger work we wrote "The top of the head is cinnamon-rufous to deep creamy-buff; the upperparts are brown with a bluish tinge. There are black streaks behind and below the eye. Underparts whitish lightly spotted with black. The female resembles the male in plumage but is larger, 18 ins (46 cm) against 15 ins (38 cm) in total length".

The main points of difference are as follows:

	Lanner	*Saker*
Crown	Cinnamon-rufous	White, streaked dark brown
Cheeks	Black moustachial streak prominent	Moustachial streak pale, not heavy black line
Mantle, back, wings	Brown, rather dark throughout	Greyish or rusty-brown with blue wash, definitely paler than Lanner on upperside
Chin	White, unmarked	White, unmarked
Underparts	White, sparsely spotted with black	White, heavily blotched and streaked with brown
1st primary of wing	White mirrors on underside of feather coalesce to show almost continuous white area along border, see ref. to fig. opposite.	White mirrors prominently defined on black web; each white mirror separately displayed, *Vög. Pal. Fauna*, II, text fig. 177, p. 1059.
Total length	male about 15 ins (38 cm) Female about 18 ins (46 cm)	Male about 16 ins (41 cm) Female about 20 ins (51 cm)

The Lanner should perhaps have been dealt with under the heading "Birds least often recorded," but because of its similarity to the Saker it is best included in our main section to stress the distinction between the two species.

ELEONORA'S FALCON

Falco eleonorae [Plate 8, facing p. 32]

The sexes of this falcon are alike but it has two very distinct phases of plumage. In one the plumage is dark slate grey – nearly black, in the other the upperparts only are slate, the chin and throat white with a black patch below the eye, the breast whitish slightly streaked with black, the lower breast and abdomen rufous, heavily streaked with black. Tail nearly uniform. Immature birds closely resemble immature of the hobby.

Since we published our large volume in 1958 a great deal has been learned by the members of the C.O.S. about the falcon and thanks to their efforts and to the Mountain Rescue Service of the R.A.F. their eyries on otherwise inaccessible cliffs have been visited and many young birds ringed at the nest.

This is a summer visitor to breed in Cyprus, mainly on the sea-cliffs of which there are well-known colonies at Akrotiri, Episkopi and Cape Gata, and perhaps occasionally on ledges on inland precipices where we personally identified a pair of the light-breasted phase which seemingly intended to nest (see *Birds of Cyprus* 1958 pp. 196–197).

It is good news that Eleonora's falcon is reliably reported (in 1969) to be "very much on the increase despite odd birds being shot." The species is now on the list of protected birds. Evidence from ringing has shown that these falcons return to the same nesting areas the following year. Where they go in the non-breeding season is still a mystery but of great interest was the capture of a bird in Madagascar which had been ringed in Cyprus showing the trend of the migration down the East African coast. The accounts in the archives of the C.O.S. of ringing operations at the Cape Gata and Akrotiri colonies by the R.A.F. Mountain Rescue Team, when many fledgling birds were ringed, make absorbing reading. These operations took place either in the 3rd or the last week of September, when on an average nine birds were successfully ringed by the intrepid climbers at Cape Gata. At the Akrotiri colony ringing took place (in 1969) on 15 September when twelve young birds were ringed, the smallest was estimated to be three weeks old, the eldest seven.

The Eleonora falcons breed on ledges from 12–150 ft above the sea on crumbling cliffs; two to four eggs are laid. The eggs have a close resemblance to those of *Falco subbuteo* from which they differ in being somewhat larger and on the whole paler. Typical specimens have an ochreous ground, uniformerly marked with speckles and spots of pale rufous.

Another type, described as "elongated pale pinkish eggs" was seen in the sandy depression of a ledge, 20 ft below the clifftop on the cliffs south of Akrotiri on 8/9 August. Without ropes the nests are mostly invisible from the top but on the dates mentioned in the year 1959 "eight pairs of mixed light and dark phase were counted on a 500 yds stretch of cliffs" (*Oological Record* XXXV p. 4.) We have recently been informed that dark and light phase birds have been found paired together in the Akrotiri and Episkopi colonies, a dark male with a light female. At least eighteen pairs were located in 1969.

August and September must be reckoned the height of the nesting season. This late nesting is believed to synchronise with the autumn migration of passèrine birds from Europe, supplying the parents with an abundance of food for their young and their own consumption. Examination of food-remains at the nest sites has shown what a great variety of bird-species are included in their diet, the falcons even catching sandmartins and swifts, birds as large as the oriole and even the roller while the favourite species attacked appears to be the hoopoe. Insects are a regular item of food; one nest contained a locust, and crab claws and shells have been found in others.

MERLIN

Falco columbarius

The merlin is the smallest of the birds of prey to visit Cyprus, the male being only 10½ ins (26 cm) in total length while the female is some 2½ ins larger. Its low dashing flight when in pursuit of its prey has gained it a high reputation among falconers and is wonderful to see. The male has a bluish-slate back, the wing-coverts coloured like the mantle, the primaries brown and the secondaries with bluish outer webs. The wings are narrow and pointed. The broad nuchal collar is rufous-buff; also breast and flanks which are broadly and heavily streaked with blackish-brown. In some birds the ground colour of the underside is more creamy-buff than rufous. Tail bluish-slate broadly banded and tipped blackish. Bill bluish-horn, yellow at base of lower mandible; legs and feet yellow, eye dark brown.

The female has the upperparts brown with pale edges to the feathers; tail brown with narrow bands of buffish-white. Underparts of body creamy-white with broad rufous-brown streaking. Soft parts as in the male.

In one race or another the merlins' breeding range extends from N.W. Europe to Kamchatka and the European population is a partial migrant in winter to the Mediterranean Basin. There is only a small passage of these little falcons through Cyprus in comparison with those which reach Asia Minor and the countries further east. In some years it is a fairly common autumn migrant in singles, occasionally in small parties, while in some seasons only a very few are recorded. A few appear to winter in Cyprus usually in the vicinity of lakes and reservoirs, but are difficult to distinguish from the passage migrants. The spring passage is more noticeable than the autumn, birds having been recorded from mid-March to April. None remain to breed.

RED-FOOTED FALCON

Falco vespertinus [Plate 9, facing p. 33]

One of the most attractive bird-visitors to Cyprus the red-footed falcon cannot escape ones notice when the migration is in full swing, for Cyprus lies right in its path. The sexes are so different that anyone seeing these falcons for the first time would be forgiven if he thought two species were involved. The male is almost completely leaden blue-grey, almost blackish-slate on head and rump, only the centre of the abdomen, thighs, ventral region and under tail-coverts being reddish-chestnut. The tail is black. Bill reddish-orange with bluish tip; cere and legs bright orange-red; iris dark brown. It is 12 ins (30 cm) in length.

The female has crown and nape bright chestnut, mantle, scapulars and back slate-grey closely barred with black, wings blackish, tail pale blue-grey narrowly barred dark brown with broad subterminal blackish band, the tip rufous. Face and throat pale buff, moustachial streak chestnut; rest of underparts dull chestnut. Soft parts as in male, the bright orange-red legs and feet being a notable character to observe, as are the long narrow wings. The flight is characteristic.

Young birds are liable to confusion with young hobbies. The young falcon's tail is closely barred, in the hobby it is uniform slate on the upper side only.

An entirely beneficial bird which lives very largely on insects, it is to be welcomed in both its summer and winter quarters but to Cyprus it is but a passage migrant at both seasons though in autumn to be seen in favourable years in some numbers from late August to late October. Main winter quarters are in the Sudan, birds passing south through Egypt in October and returning north again in April subject to the usual fluctuations. The Spring passage from N.E. Africa to Asia Minor is mainly observed in Cyprus from mid-April to the beginning of May. We gave an account (*Birds of Cyprus* 1958 p. 200) of witnessing an arrival of red-footed falcons on the Patriki plain on 26 April. A colonial nester which appropriates the nests of other colonial breeding species such as rooks, this falcon has never certainly bred in Cyprus and is never likely to do so. Recent observations in 1968–69 show that this species often migrates at a great altitude, more or less beyond human vision. It is possible that a large passage occurs regularly over Cyprus as recorded in 1957 and again in 1968.

LESSER KESTREL

Falco naumanni

We cannot add to our own description of this small falcon as published in our larger work from which we take the following: This bird is slightly smaller and more delicate in build than the normal kestrel. The lesser kestrel's crown is a clear blue-grey. The back and mantle are a uniform chestnut-red, the throat is creamy and the rest of the underparts pinkish-buff with drop-shaped spots on the sides of the breast and flanks. The tail is pure blue-grey with a broad black sub-terminal band and white tip, more conspicuous than the white tip of the kestrel's tail. The female closely resembles the female of the common kestrel. The lesser kestrel is a more gregarious bird than the kestrel and is much noisier; there is a chattering call kik-kik-kik-kik. Its length is 12½ ins (31 cm).

The lesser kestrel was formerly considered a summer resident and a passage migrant to Cyprus, much more generally seen *on passage* than during the hot summer months when only a few are reported. In spring we have encountered them singly from the earliest days of March and later in the month in small parties resting on telegraph wires. Paphos was a favourite place in which we watched them in April, evidently just arrived. Early forerunners have been reported a month earlier but by May most of them have passed on their way.

A notable spring movement was reported in 1961 when flocks each numbering up to one hundred birds passed through many places between the 30 March and 15 May. The return journey takes place mainly in mid-, or late September and in early October, sometimes considerable numbers are involved. It appears to be fairly common in flocks of up to fifty birds.

In former days, circa 1909, breeding was reported by reliable observers and fresh eggs were secured on 5 May among other dates, the birds nesting in crevices of rocks. This was not an isolated instance. Today, 1970, the lesser kestrel seems to have become only a passage migrant for no-one has reported a nesting bird or a nesting colony for many years. There are hundreds of suitable sites but kestrels of any species have been relentlessly shot, and the birds may have given up the uneven battle in an island where there are more gunners than kestrels. In Europe the lesser kestrel is recognised as an extremely beneficial bird to the agriculturist.

European eggs show great variation in marking, but in series are paler and smaller than those of the common kestrel.

KESTREL

Falco tinnunculus

The adult male and female differ considerably in plumage, the former having the crown, nape and sides of neck and also the rump and tail bluish-grey, the tail having a black terminal band tipped with white. The rest of the upper-parts are reddish-chestnut closely spotted with black. A black moustachial streak is a prominent feature; cere and eye rim are lemon yellow. The white chin merges into buff underparts, boldly streaked and spotted with black. Eye brown, bill bluish-horn, legs and feet yellow. The female has the head pale chestnut streaked with dark brown, rest of upper-parts reddish-chestnut barred regularly with blackish-brown, the pale chestnut tail washed with grey is closely barred and has a terminal blackish band. Underparts are buff streaked with brownish-black. We have seen very pale aberrant specimens in Cyprus which have kept apart from normally coloured examples.

Immature birds closely resemble the female adult. Common kestrels when hovering in the wind are recognisable at a distance but the lesser kestrel also hovers to a much lesser extent.

Resident in Cyprus its numbers are being sadly reduced by shooters; it is also a common migrant at both seasons. Nesting begins in early April, eggs having being found on fifth near Nicosia and up to twenty-third. We have found a full clutch on 5 May. Nesting sites are varied, often in sea-cliffs, in ruined buildings, earth cliffs, river banks or even in abandoned crows' nests. It breeds in both mountain ranges and on the Southern coast.

Eggs are blunt ovals and vary much in the intensity of their markings, as well as in their measurements.

The spring passage of European migrants seldom begins before March and the return migration takes place from early September to late October. In the winter it is common both on the plains and in the mountains when unfortunately it is a favourite target of Cypriot shooting parties that swarm on the plains.

Order GALLIFORMES

Family PHASIANIDAE

The only representatives of this large family in Cyprus are the chukor, francolin and the quail and all are firmly established, the former as breeding species covered by the game laws with reserves set aside for their protection (if the law could be properly implemented) and the quail mainly as a passage migrant though some are believed to nest.

Fairly comprehensive accounts of Cyprus's two game birds are given both in our former volume and – more up-to-date – in this *Handbook* and need not be enlarged upon here, other than to beg Cyprian sportsmen *not* to kill the goose that lays the golden egg, however that can be expressed as neatly in Greek! The black francolin in particular needs all the protection that can be afforded it, if it is not to be wiped out. Only strict obedience of the Cyprus Game Laws can save it from total extinction in the island.

In this great cosmopolitan family are grouped what are commonly termed "game birds", characterised by the impervious nostrils, singular uniformity in the arrangement of the feather tracts, scanty amount of down in the adults, certain anatomical and muscular modifications, and feet adapted for scratching in the soil. All the true game birds are to be found in the Sub-Order Galli, a leading character, which can be readily observed, being the position of the hind toe (hallux) which is raised above the level of the front toes. The *Phasianidae* agree in having strong unfeathered tarsi, the male in most of the francolins being furnished with one or more strong spurs on each leg. The bill is short, the upper mandible somewhat arched and overhanging the lower; the nostrils are exposed, never hidden by feathers. The wing is rounded, of ten primaries, and comparatively short; notwithstanding this many of the francolins and partridges – and not least the Cyprian chukor – are renowned for their powerful direct flight. The tail is short in the francolins, partridges and the quails. Spending most of their life on the ground the members of this family are all good runners and often adopt that manner of avoiding their enemies rather than taking to flight. They lay for the most part uniformly coloured eggs, though in some, as in the Cyprian chukor, the shell is freckled. The chicks of all game birds are very attractive little creatures, closely covered with down which in some species supports a pretty pattern.

An attempt has been made on several occasions to introduce the pheasant, and see-see partridge into the island but all such introductions have ended in failure.

The pheasant *Phasianus colchicus* was introduced in 1910–1911 and again in 1952 at Troödos, Paphos, Aghirda, Athalassa, Kouklia and Larnaca among other places.

The See-see or sand partridge *Amnoperdix heyi nicolli* was let loose in 1937, ten pairs in all, at Ayios Napa and Pyroi. The Napa birds disappeared but at first the Pyroi birds did well and spread according to Mr. G. F. Wilson, a noted sportsman, naturalist and Financial Secretary with over forty years Government Service in the island.

Both the above were bad choices, having been uprooted from their normal environment. We should have thought that if any more such introductions are attempted the helmeted Guinea fowl, *Numida meleagris*, would have a far better chance to establish itself in the scrub-covered foothills and rocky mountain gorges. It would be an excellent source of valuable food and though more apt to take refuge in running than flying, is not to be despised as a sporting bird.

COMMON FRANCOLIN

Francolinus francolinus

[Plate 10, facing p. 48]

The black patridge as this bird is named in some parts of its range is of more than passing interest to the ornithologist for it is a species, as we mentioned in our larger work (1958) which was originally described and named by Linnaeus, who based his description on the painting by Edwards of a bird depicting a Cyprus specimen; Cyprus is consequently the type-locality. It is a bird which is easily recognised and which figures in the accounts of Cyprus travellers in 1738 and 1760. The male, some 13 ins (33 cm) in length, has the throat and breast black, the crown blackish-brown; a large patch behind the eye is snow-white. It has a chestnut collar and rich brown mantle the feathers of which are fringed with buff; rump and tail black with narrow white bars. Sides of breast and flanks are spotted with white and the abdomen pale chestnut. Eye brown, bill black, legs and feet brownish red to orange: a very striking bird. The female mainly dark brown above, a dull chestnut patch on nape; sides of head buff, the ear-coverts brown. Throat white and underparts buff barred irregularly with brown.

Originally an inhabitant of southern Europe it has now been exterminated there; the same fate could have befallen it in Cyprus. Between 1930 and 1940 it was only reported from the Karpas and the Paphos district at opposite ends of the island, but perhaps occurred elsewhere. By 1950 it was on the verge of extinction; a few pairs were known to remain in its two principal strongholds and odd pairs were reported from Akamas, Akrotiri and the Polis area. The francolin had its chance to recover during the Eoka emergency when the British administration withdrew fire-arms from the population and forbade their use – an act which undoubtedly saved this species from total eclipse in the island. By 1958 it had made a good recovery and has since continued to increase despite poaching, thanks to the Government protection now afforded it and the new reserves where it is forbidden to be hunted. It favours scrub-covered land, especially the brush-covered river-bottoms, but also comes on arable land.

Its call note is loud and grating, of several syllables.

Breeding takes place from early April onwards. The nest is a hollow on the ground lined with dry grass; eggs number six to eight sometimes more, sometimes less; ground-colour greyish to olive-brown occasionally tinged with green, unmarked.

Today it owes its more prosperous outlook to the efforts of the C.O.S. and especially to its recent Cypriot President: George Savvides O.B.E. It is increasing only with strict protection near the British base at Episkopi, where it is well established and is now fairly common. It is still found at the end of the Karpas Peninsula and may still occur at Akamas and perhaps in the Paphos area, but whether it breeds in the last two is not known.

A much fuller account of this bird and its Cyprus history was published in our *Birds of Cyprus* (1958) pp. 366–370 with a half-tone plate from a colour painting in the Zoological Society of London by Major Henry Jones. Besides being resident in Cyprus *F. francolinus* is represented in Asia Minor, Syria, Iraq and Persia, ranging eastwards to northern India but is everywhere sedentary. Several races have been described.

CYPRIAN CHUKOR

Alectoris chukar cypriotes*

[Plate 10, facing p. 48]

In our larger volume (p. 364) we allied this bird with the Greek rock-partridge (*greaca*), but it has now been shown that two species are involved and the Cyprus bird must bear the name as given above, a geographical race of the chukor of Nepal. It is predominantly *the* game bird of the island and despite intensive shooting has managed to survive, for it is a prolific bird and is not restricted to the low ground and cultivated areas where it is generally sought by local sportsmen.

In summer and early autumn it is to be seen in good coveys but these are later heavily reduced during the late autumn and the whole winter, when shooting game is permitted.

The sexes of this bird are alike, the white cheeks and throat enclosed by a black band, the crown and breast pure grey as is also the rump; the rest of the upper-parts greyish brown. A white superciliary extends over the eye. Very striking are the flank feathers barred with black and chestnut on a white ground, the belly is buff. The tail is more cinnamon than chestnut in Cyprian specimens. Bill and legs are red. The total length is 13½ ins (34 cm).

There is much rocky uncultivated ground in Cyprus, densely covered with scrub and in this type of rough country the bird has a better chance to persist than in the olive and carob orchards at coast level. The game reserves also help it to survive although the game laws are often abused.

The nesting period lasts from early April to mid-May. Very little nest material is found in the scrapes and these may be either well-concealed under a cistus or other bush or much more exposed. Eggs number eight to (rarely) sixteen, average twelve to fourteen. Many fall prey to the ravens and crows. The shell is pale stone colour, freckled with pale brown and is typical for the species. The Cyprus chukor will need all its resources to withstand the licensing of 26,000 people to carry firearms in this comparatively small island in the winter months.

EUROPEAN QUAIL

Coturnix coturnix

[Plate 10, facing p. 48]

The quail is both resident in, and migratory to, Cyprus but to what extent it can be termed a nesting species does not appear to have been determined by naturalists resident themselves in the island. As a spring and autumn visitor there is much more evidence, for it appears on the plains in increasing numbers in late March and April, while calling becomes more general in May, when the island is already very dry in the arable country and on the inland plains, the lakes drying up.

The quail is too well-known to anyone interested in birds, be he naturalist or gourmet, to require detailed description such as we have given in our larger work. It is a very small bird measuring only 6 ins (15 cm) from bill to tail, and is far the smallest of the game-birds in Cyprus where button quail do not exist. It resembles a miniature partridge in colour pattern. It can only be considered an uncommon breeding species else surely there would have accumulated more breeding notes about it, whether double-brooded and so forth. It is reported to be commonest as a nesting species in the

*For reason why this chukor is considered a race of *Alectoris chukar* in place of *A. graeca* (the specific name employed in *Birds of Cyprus* 1958) see *Ibis* 1962 p. 366.

Morphou district. It nests entirely in grass or growing crops, the nest a depression in the ground lined scantily with grass. Eggs number six to twelve, yellowish-buff freckled with brown.

The majority of the spring migrants must move on or pass right over the island, for Cyprus is in the path of a regular route to and from Egypt where quail in the past (if not still) were netted in tens of thousands when on autumn passage.

The autumn migration through Cyprus probably coincides with that through Egypt which is at its height in the second week of September and peters out at the end of October. One report from Cyprus refers to "a small increase in numbers" in October and November! There is no doubt that a number remain to over-winter for hunters may be seen frequently with quail dangling on their belts in the winter months, and recently (1968) fourteen were seen caged on 20 November in Limassol Market: a very late date to have been on passage.

Family GRUIDAE

Cranes, of which two figure on the Cyprus list are very well known throughout the whole of the Middle East by reason of their punctual migrations – the passing of the cranes over Cyprus being an event in the lives of all residents especially those who reside on the north coast when the common cranes which have bred in northern Europe, the Balkans, Asia Minor and Turkestan migrate in flocks in autumn to winter in the Sudan and Abyssinia among other places in Africa. As they fly they utter their loud trumpetting note. Normally they fly high but if for any reason they are flying low the noise a large flock can make has been described as "quite deafening". Cyprus is used to a small extent only as a resting place.

Cranes are large grey birds about 4 ft in height with long necks and very long legs, they have a short stout bill and broad rounded wings, the secondaries almost as long as the primaries. Being naturally gregarious they are seldom seen singly unless it be an ailing or injured bird. August is the month when they may be expected. Both species which visit Cyprus are graceful birds on the ground but especially the Demoiselle which is noted for its stately carriage. Like the common crane it loves marshlands – it too winters in the Sudan from October to March and Cyprus is in the main line of its flight from where its breeding places are found in Asia Minor, the Dobruja and southern Russia.

Unless within easy hearing distance of its calls it is impossible to distinguish high-flying cranes from one another. We have seen cranes flying over the sea off the Cyprus coast at a very low elevation in a long gyrating line but more often they are high overhead, the flocks in V-formation like wild geese. They migrate both by day and by night when only their calling betrays them.

COMMON CRANE

Megalornis grus [Plate 10, facing p. 48]

Standing about 4 ft in height and mainly grey in colour the crane can only be confused (when distance is too great to make out details) with the Demoiselle crane, the next bird to be described. Both have distinctive markings on the head and neck and as the heads of both species are figured here in colour they need not be described here in more detail. The peculiar shape of the adult crane's posterior when walking is caused by the very long secondaries which droop over the tail and are tipped with black, forming a kind of "bustle" as they have been described. The flight feathers (primaries) are black. The white *stripe* down the black neck is a feature of this bird which is not shared by the Demoiselle. The eye is red, the long legs and feet are black and the bill greenish horn tinged red at the base.

Cranes fly in line or in V-formation with neck and legs fully extended.

Migration through Cyprus is very regular. In Autumn the passage falls roughly into two periods, the first during the first two weeks of August to early September but sometimes continuing all through September, and the second from mid-October to November, mainly mid-October. The numbers then are much smaller than in August. Occasionally small flocks have been seen into December but only occasionally staying all winter. Many fly at night.

The spring passage north occurs from early March to late April, the main body in the latter half of March, some passing in May. Some birds undoubtedly come down to rest awhile, and we have been told by residents that they will then feed on grapes which are not on their normal menu, though they are known to relish acorns and olives, as well as insects, locusts and small birds and mammals. The call note is a loud trumpetting metallic cry which they utter in flight announcing their passing.

Common crane

DEMOISELLE CRANE

Anthropoides virgo

[Plate 10, facing p. 48]

Points to observe when identifying this crane are (1) the long white ear-tufts which curl backwards and (2) the elongated black breast feathers. The crown and nape are ash-grey, forehead mottled grey and black; sides of head, throat and underside of neck black. Rest of body plumage pale grey. Primaries blackish, the secondaries are so long that when the bird is standing, they completely cover the short grey tail. Eye red, legs and feet black, bill olive tipped with red. Total length 38 ins (97 cm).

The call is higher-pitched than in the common crane and is constantly uttered during the bird's flight. Migrating flocks fly high often during the night, calling as they go. The Demoiselle is reported to descend during passage more often than its larger relative and to be less numerous. Its food is the same as for *Megalornis grus*.

To Cyprus it is a regular passage migrant from early March to late April. Some flocks are considerable, a party of 250 was seen circling Akrotiri lake on 4 April 1967. A flock will sometimes stay for two or three weeks if not harried. A flock of ninety birds was seen resting on Akrotiri Salt Lake on 17 August 1963. Autumn passage has been observed from early August to early September, most in latter half of August. The arrival of over 770 demoiselle cranes in August 1970 to the Akrotiri Salt Lake which were positively identified, is of very great interest. No common cranes were present at that time. This record has been accepted by the authors' of the new *Check List of Cyprus Birds* to be issued in 1971, who kindly advised us of this unusual occurrence.

Family RALLIDAE

The rail family is represented in Cyprus by five true rails or crakes which may be distinguished by the absence of a horny shield on the forehead (as for instance is exhibited in the coot) and the absence of lobate webs on the toes. They include the well-known landrail or corncrake and water rail and three smaller crakes; these last are noted for their small size, sombre plumage and very retiring ways, making observation of their habits very difficult for the ordinary observer. The other four on the Cyprus list, all larger birds, possessed of bony ornamental frontal-shields, include the moorhen, two gallinules and the coot, the last named with broad lobes to the toes somewhat resembling the feet of the grebes. The gallinules are both very gaudily plumaged in purple and green but as they have only recently occurred as rare vagrants the ornithologist visiting Cyprus can dismiss them from his mind.

Of this assemblage only one of the smaller crakes has once bred, and that only discovered of recent years. Few birds are more difficult to find breeding and there is more than a possibility that nesting in this group still remains to be discovered while it is certain that we have still much to learn about them from patient watchers.

The moorhen and the coot are the only other members of this migratory family which have bred sparingly, with better protection they would surely do so regularly. All the others are migrants from Europe which it is reasonable to suppose occur much more numerously in Asia Minor – all figure on the Turkish list except Allen's gallinule which is a known wanderer and likely to turn up anywhere.

WATER RAIL [Plate 10, facing p. 48]

Rallus aquaticus

This is a small dark bird with fairly long, slightly decurved red bill and with barred black and white flank feathers; the rest of the plumage of upperparts is brown streaked with black. The sides of the head, throat and breast are blue-grey; abdomen buff and under tail-coverts nearly white. The tail is very short. The eye is red, legs and feet brown. Total length 11 ins (28 cm).

Cyprus is too dry an island to normally attract the water rail except as a passage migrant and not uncommon winter visitor. The unusual number of thirty four birds seen at Akrotiri on 12 January 1962, contrasts with the numerous instances when only single birds are recorded in the winter months. It is probable that little groups migrate over the sea together and on arrival disperse to selected habitats. In autumn they have been reported to occur from mid-September onwards. They are most commonly reported in late autumn and during the winter, November to February. When numbers are variable due probably to continental weather conditions. The spring passage is barely noticeable in March but from early or mid-April many pass through the island and are recorded occasionally up to mid-May.

Two records, 17 July and 20 August, both in 1963, point to it occasionally remaining in the summer. A nest has only been discovered once by an exceptionally gifted field-naturalist. It contained a broken egg typical of the species. This was at Akrotiri Salt Lake on 19 April 1958, where birds had been heard close by and during the previous winter. The nest was deserted; it was built of dead *juncus* stems, some 12 ins above waterlevel, in a large patch of *juncus* at the base of a clump of tamarisk.

SPOTTED CRAKE

Porzana porzana [Plate 10, facing p. 48]

A small bird of 9 ins (23 cm) in length reminding one of a miniature dark-coloured corncrake, olive-brown above with the feathers spotted and streaked with white including the wings but spotting smaller. Crown, throat, stripe above eye and breast grey, with indistinct speckling on breast. Abdomen whitish; under tail-coverts buff. Flanks barred olive-brown and white. Bill greenish-yellow, legs olive-green.

Very skulking in its habits and very difficult to flush when it will fly only a few yards before plunging into cover with legs dangling. It sometimes cocks its tail in the manner of a waterhen and then the uniform under tail-coverts are exposed. It swims easily, moving its head to and fro as it does so; flight *appears* weak, but this is illusory else how does it cross the sea.

It is a spring and autumn migrant to Cyprus and has occurred in winter (*late* November) on several occasions. Early passage migration has been recorded in March and continues until early May, once in June, most records occur in April of single birds. No breeding record. Reverse migration observed throughout October and remains found mid-September in nest of Eleonora falcon. Widely-spread in Europe it crosses to Africa on a wide front in autumn and is recorded from light-houses. It does not traverse the Sahara. It was at one time thought to be a winter visitor to Cyprus but recent observations have not confirmed this.

BAILLON'S CRAKE

Porzana pusilla

The smallest of all the crakes, 7 ins (18 cm) in total length, with a blue-grey face, the European race bears the name *intermedia* and is the one which passes through Cyprus on migration both in spring and Autumn. In appearance it closely resembles the little crake, *P. parva*, but has a white outer web to the first primary and is rather more rufous on the upperparts which are boldly streaked with white on back and wing-coverts. Another prominent feature to observe is the black and white barring on the flanks and under tail-coverts. The legs vary in colour to some extent from dull flesh-colour to brown; bill green, no red at the basal end.

Spring is the period when this very minute bird is seen more regularly than during autumn but it can only be considered scarce at the best of times. Records date from late March to the end of April. The bird reported in *Birds of Cyprus* by us to have been collected in "February" near Larnaca was in fact shot in *April*; we have now been able to examine the skin.

There are fewer records than for the other small crakes to Cyprus but it must be borne in mind how difficult these small birds are to see in the environment they select. The European population pass over the Mediterranean to winter in Africa, but autumn Cyprus records are notably few and range from 11 October to 4 November *since* our larger volume was published in 1958, perhaps even the same bird!

Plate 12 (below)

Glossy ibis Garganey

Black-winged stilt Red-crested pochard

Mediterranean shag

Plate 13 Audouin's gull Slender-billed gull

LITTLE CRAKE [Plate 10, facing p. 48]

Porzana parva

The only crake with which this bird can reasonably be confused is the even smaller Baillon's crake neither of which are much larger than a sparrow, but whereas Baillon's crake has white-streaked wing-coverts, those of the little crake are *without spotting*. The upperparts are olive-brown with large black centres to feathers of back and scapulars, the crown olive-brown unmarked. Lores, face, throat, breast and belly slate-grey. The flanks are uniform grey, but the under tail-coverts are barred black and white. Bill green with reddish base, legs and feet green. Total length 7½ ins (19 cm).

The female differs slightly having a white throat and the remaining underparts buff. This important point was overlooked in our larger work.

Mainly observed singly in the spring months March and April (the earliest record 26 February, the latest in mid-May), the little crake has occasionally turned up, as at Akrotiri and Larnaca on 31 March, 1957, in little parties before the birds disperse or continue their journey north. They are more in evidence in spring than in autumn when a few only have been recorded in October and early November.

The calls of the crakes are nearly impossible to differentiate. This one is said to utter a high-pitched *Kick-Kick*, or *pok pok pok – pur-r-r* which conveys very little to the writer!

The little crake breeds locally in Europe and winters in the Mediterranean area and northern Africa but its travels do not bring many to the Eastern Mediterranean judging from Cyprus records.

CORNCRAKE or LANDRAIL

Crex crex

The plumage colours of the corncrake are rather complicated: upperparts and scapulars light brown, the middles of the feathers black giving a spotted appearance. Crown streaked with black, cheeks ash-grey. Wing-coverts bright chestnut; flight-feathers brown with chestnut fringes. Chin white, throat and breast yellowish-buff, belly white. Flanks and under tail-coverts streaked with cinnamon-brown. Inner wing lining pale chestnut. A broad white band along inner margin of wing. Bill horn-brown, short and stumpy, eye reddish-brown, legs and feet greenish. The corncrake is larger than the crakes with which we have already dealt and measures 10½ ins (27 cm) from bill to tail with a wing spread of 18 ins. Only the long-billed water-rail compares with it in size.

Known to most bird students from its peculiar notes in the early summer months, visitors to Cyprus must rely on other characters to identify it, as it does not normally utter the curious rasping cry when on passage and only then does it pass through Cyprus in spring and autumn. Calling has been recorded (15 February, a very odd date) and 6 March. In spring it passes from early March to early May, mainly the latter half of April. In Autumn from mid-August to mid-November, mainly in late September and during the whole of October.

An occasional bird may appear out of the migratory season. The bright chestnut patch on the wing and sluggish flight with legs dangling may then betray it. It is often (in Europe) a victim of telephone wires, and in Cyprus is taken by the *Falco eleonorae*.

Breeding everywhere in Europe and western Asia, the birds cross on a wide front to winter in Africa when some even reach Cape Colony.

Corncrake or landrail

MOORHEN

Gallinula chloropus

Probably the best-known member of the rail family the European waterhen, as it is sometime termed, is easily recognised by the red shield on its forehead, red bill with yellow tip and the red garter on its green legs. The body plumage is almost uniform, olive-brown above, dark slate-colour below with white oblong streaks on the flanks. Under tail-coverts are white with a black central stripe, a conspicuous feature as the moorhen flirts its tail continuously when walking. With every step it bobs its head and this characteristic is most marked when the bird is swimming the head being jerked to and fro. Though its wings are rounded and it rises sluggishly from cover, it can fly fast and direct when occasion demands. When on the ground or treading on waterlily leaves for which its long toes are adapted, it lifts its feet deliberately.

The moorhen was formerly a common migrant to Cyprus especially in the spring from the end of March to the end of May, but it is now less often encountered at that time of year, and being an easy target has small chance of surviving the endless onslaught upon the water-birds in this island of guns. It has bred at Limassol in 1910 and juveniles were noted again in May 1957 and August 1962. Eggs have a buffish or greenish-white ground and are speckled with reddish-brown. Breeding has been confirmed in recent years: at Akrotiri in 1959, and in 1967 one adult and seven young in down were seen near Asomatos. The chicks are covered with black down, sparsely on the head.

Return migrants are reported to arrive from 1st September, and to occur all through the autumn on passage. In 1967 and 1968 Moorhens were seen on lakes and reservoirs throughout the winter but its numbers fluctuate and in some years it is scarce.

COOT

Fulica atra

Another equally familiar member of the Rallidae, the European coot is a highly migratory species which on the onset of winter in northern latitudes move south in their thousands to a more equable climate. Easily recognised by the white frontal shield on the forecrown and white bill, the whole adult plumage is slate-black. There is a narrow white edge to the secondaries only visible when the wing is open. Legs and feet are greenish, the latter lobed. It is a larger bird than the moorhen, 15 ins (38 cm) long, and is much sought after by Cypriot gunners. It is a wary bird and prefers to keep to the middle of open water well out of gunshot.

As a visitor to Cyprus in winter the coot arrives in considerable numbers when a cold spell envelopes central Europe and Asia and may then be seen on the lakes and reservoirs in hundreds from mid-November to late February. The main influxes occur in January. It is also a passage migrant at both seasons in variable numbers. In olden days – early in the 20th century, coots came "in thousands" but this is no longer the case and their visiting numbers are definitely decreasing.

Coot

Once a common breeding bird in Cyprus, nesting is now quite an event. April and May were the months when eggs were taken when there had been late winter rains, but usually the coots have departed by mid-April and the open waters are dried up in May. The large nest is made of aquatic vegetation, the eggs are stone-colour with fine speckles and spots of dark brown. The chicks are covered in black down, the tips of which on neck and throat are reddish-orange, on the mantle and wings yellow and on the rest of the body whitish. Broken egg-shells were found in nests at Kouklia reservoir in August 1967, and in 1969 at least two pairs bred at Kouklia and what has been described as "large numbers" at Akrotiri, a very unusual occurence at the present day.

It is not certain to what extent through-migration takes place in Cyprus or for that matter in Autumn either.

Family OTIDIDAE

The bustards form an assembly of magnificent sporting birds which are confined to the Old World; they form a composite group which have well-marked characteristics both in their structure and in their habits. The chief external characters to note are the lack of a hallux or hind toe, a stout tarsus covered with scales, a three-toed foot with each toe short and broad, well adapted for swift and silent running, and the broad flattened crown but a blunt straight bill in which the nostrils are conspicuously placed. In size bustards are for the most part large to medium birds, the largest of all being the great bustard which is not unknown in Cyprus, the smallest, the little bustard, which is also dealt with in the pages which follow. A medium-sized bustard – Macqueen's – is likewise discussed; it is indisputable that all bustards are becoming really scarce even in the great deserts where, before the advent of the motor, they had a fair chance of life.

The two largest of those, which on the rarest occasions have visited Cyprus as migrants, are inhabitants of much wider spaces than over-populated Cyprus can offer, roaming far and wide in the deserts of West central Asia, Iraq, Syria, Sinai and Arabia. It is a sad fact that wary as they are these fine birds can be approached within shooting distance by a party in a motor car with the inevitable result that, like the rarer gazelles, they are now becoming very scarce. Macqueen's bustard is a favourite quarry of Arab falconers, for the Houbara, the group to which it belongs, is just about as large a bird as the saker falcon can tackle, but it does so regularly in Iraq. Females of Macqueen's bustard scale 4½–5½ lbs according to the season of the year and males up to 7 lbs. The most likely member of the family to occur in Cyprus is the Eastern form of the little bustard (see Plate 27 *Birds of Cyprus*) – a bird which would be a great asset to the sporting fraternity in Cyprus for it is one which, given a chance at first, might well establish itself. It is reported to be present "in thousands" on the trans-Caucasian plains. Could it be induced to settle in the Mesaoria? How attractive it would be! Water again may be the problem.

LITTLE BUSTARD [Plate 10, facing p. 48]

Otis tetrax orientalis

In winter plumage there is little distinction between the sexes. The mantle, scapulars and back are sandy-brown finely vermiculated with black. The crown and nape yellowish-buff, with black streaking continued down the neck. Breast inclines to rufous-buff, rest of underparts pure white. When the wing is opened the amount of white exhibited is startling. Legs dull yellow. In summer the male bird has a very distinctive dress and is then unmistakable, the neck black, bordered with a broad V-shaped white band separating the bluish-grey sides of head and upper part of the throat, and with a second white band across the black of the lower throat.

This race of the little bustard breeds in eastern Europe and western Asia, and is given much to wandering to the west where it then overlaps the range of the typical subspecies. It used to be an occasional visitor to Cyprus sixty years ago, and we read of twelve having been shot in December/January 1909/10, during an exceptionally hard winter. Almost the last record was in 1926 since when only one pair has been recorded, on 29 September 1967, but the scarcity of ornithologists in Cyprus, for the thirty intervening years, may easily account for none having been brought to notice. It is given prominence in this book as the bird is still reported to be a winter visitor to Iraq and Persia and some flocks or individuals may wander further south-west in exceptional weather conditions. It is now said to be very scarce in eastern Europe but still numerous on the Steppes of Western Siberia and Kazakhstan.

The great bustard and the Houbara have also been seen in Cyprus for which records see pages 215–16 in the List of Rare Visitors.

Order CHARADRIIFORMES

Family HAEMATOPODIDAE

The oystercatchers which are the first family of the huge Order Charadriiformes to be considered are widely distributed on the coasts of the New and Old Worlds, but they do not breed in tropical Africa or southern Asia or in very high latitudes. It is a small family and all the species – either pied or all black in colour – are contained in the genus *Haematopus*. Only one species in various geographical races occurs in Europe, *H. ostralegus* which is black and white with bright orange-red bill. Fairly large birds 16–21 ins (41–53 cm) long. The bill is long and laterally compressed; the legs stout, the three toes slightly webbed. Wings are long and pointed, the tail short. On the shores which they frequent – both rocky or muddy, they stand out among the other waders by reason of their pied plumage and large size as they run about searching the pools left by the receding tide, or probe for mussels and other shellfish. Very gregarious, they fly rapidly, piping as they go, from one feeding ground to another in small flocks and outwith the breeding season sometimes join up into very large companies of several hundred birds.

In Cyprus its appearances are irregular as shown below and never in great numbers as on our tidal estuaries at home.

OYSTERCATCHER

Haematopus ostralegus

Entire head, breast and back black, rump white, tail black and white, entire underparts white. Bill orange-vermilion, legs and feet coral pink, eye crimson. Such is the adult summer dress. In winter the long bill is reddish-horn, the legs flesh-colour, and the front and sides of the neck are white. When in flight the black and white pattern of the wings is striking and the white tail, with broad black terminal band, very noticeable. In length the oystercatcher measures 17 ins (43 cm).

As a migrant to Cyprus the bird has appeared on a number of occasions but it is not a regular visitor at any season, and has been recorded always during the passage of other wading birds either in March and April or again in August and September during the movement south.

The oystercatcher has a vast breeding distribution in Europe and Asia, nesting as far south as Asia Minor and east to the river Ob. where an eastern subspecies occurs. Many remain to overwinter in Europe, but others cross to Africa and are found in various localities so far south as Mozambique. It would be surprising if some of these overseas migrants did not find their way to Cyprus, but records are by no means numerous. Years may pass without one being seen and then perhaps only single birds come to our notice.

Family CHARADRIIDAE

A large family which can be conveniently split into two sub-families had we, as we have not in this *Handbook*, recoursed to smaller or larger groupings. The two groups would then have been named Charadriinae for the shore plovers and Vanellinae for the lapwing-like birds, the latter very different in appearance and in habits from the former sub-family.

Of the shore-plovers Cyprus can claim only one species as a breeding bird – the Kentish plover – but seven others in the genus *Charadrius* which includes such well-known cosmopolitan species as the two ringed plovers and the golden plover; the grey plover, an equally familiar bird to British observers is placed in the genus *Squatarola* for anatomical reasons. The dotterel which formerly was considered worthy of generic separation by earlier taxonomists under *Eudromias* and which is renowned for its amazing tameness in the breeding season allowing itself to be stroked on the nest, is another all too rare visitor to the island which here only finds mention in the Appendix. It is included in the same genus *Charadrius* as those already mentioned.

These are all more or less familiar shore birds which with the exception of the greater and lesser sand-plovers can all be seen in the British Isles.

The lapwing group of which our British lapwing is a typical example is poorly represented in Cyprus, only two species of *Vanellus* being present. The common lapwing of Europe which arrives in numbers to winter and the attractive spur-wing which is reliably reported to have bred but rarely does so today and would find it impossible to survive if it attempted to do so outwith a Reserve. The spur-wing is the best known plover throughout the Middle East being a familiar bird in Asia Minor, Syria, Israel and Egypt and would be a great asset in Cyprus from every point of view. It is unfortunately very irregular.

SPUR-WINGED PLOVER

Hoplopterus spinosus

[Plate 11, facing p. 49]

Were it not constantly and ruthlessly shot at sight this beautiful plover could be among the regular breeding birds of Cyprus, and before the island became an armoury of shot-guns it was probable that it nested more often than would be supposed from the meagre breeding records handed down to us.

The spur-wing is a handsome bird which does nothing but good on the land and if it could be protected as our lapwings are protected at home, the Cyprian farmers would have cause to be grateful to it. It is a bird easily recognised, the black head, crest and throat, white face and neck, black breast and belly, and ash-coloured back and wings are features which proclaim its identity from afar. A typical plover in flight when the area of white on the wings, as seen from below, contrasts with the black pinions, it again reminds the observer of *Vanellus vanellus*, but this spur-wing has the bill, legs and feet black and the eye red. The sharp spur at the wing joint is too short to be seen in life except at very close quarters.

Apart from the usual records in the migratory season, birds have been secured in June and November and January. It is certainly more often encountered in the spring from early March to late May from all accounts, than in the autumn mid-September to late October. Some pairs have nested in the past or attempted to do so at Famagusta and Kouklia.

It cannot be considered a regular breeding species at the present day, and is both rare and irregular as a summer visitor. The nest is a depression in the earth with scanty lining of grass in which four eggs are usually laid, with amber, olive or cream ground, thickly spotted with black or sepia and pale-lilac secondary markings. It is a splendid bird to encourage from all viewpoints.

LAPWING or GREEN PLOVER

Vanellus vanellus

Too well-known the world over to need detailed description the lapwing is a most handsome bird at any season but quite lovely in the spring. The crown and crest greenish-black; upperparts dark green, glossed purple and bronze. Upper breast bluish-black, belly and axillaries white. Tail white, with a broad black tip and both the upper and under tail-coverts bright fawn-colour. Legs and feet brownish flesh-colour, bill black, eye brown. In flight the bird is unmistakable, the wings are rounded and the flight erratic especially in the breeding season. It can however fly purposefully and direct when on migration.

The lapwing visits Cyprus in very large numbers in some winters, but numbers must largely depend on the weather in central eastern Europe and western Asia for whereas in some years it can be counted in hundreds, we have known years when it was by no means abundant. 1954 was such a year, a reminder of olden days. Normally it puts in appearance about mid-October occasionally late September and remains until the middle of March, rarely to the end of the month. The main departure takes place in February. On one December day in 1967 2,000 lapwings were counted between Nicosia and Famagusta, pointing to the increase which has taken place in these welcome visitors within recent years. The largest flocks are to be seen on the Mesaoria plain. As a passage-migrant flocks of 20 to 150 can be counted passing over Akrotiri and other vantage points. It winters from western Europe to Palestine and many flocks cross to northern Africa. There is no Cyprus breeding record.

NOTE

The first example of a **white-tailed plover**, *Vanellus leucurus* was shot in the spring of 1970 and the skin preserved, see Appendix p. 216.

RINGED PLOVER

Charadrius hiaticula

A small rather plump bird about 7½ ins (19 cm) long, light brown above with white collar and underparts and a black band across the breast; cheeks are brown like the crown with a white superciliary streak. A white forehead, bordered with black, is a conspicuous mark. The bill is bright yellow with a black tip. The wings are brown and in flight a prominent white wing-bar is exhibited and the black and white pattern of the tail. The legs and feet are bright yellow. For differences of the lesser ringed plover see next species.

The ringed plover has now been found to be present in small numbers all the year, but is mainly a passage migrant at both seasons. Two races, one breeding in Europe, the other (*tundrae*) in Siberia are likely to occur annually on passage.

The first spring migrants may be expected in mid-March and are present in small numbers till end of May when most have passed on; the return passage begins in August and continues till mid-October. A few wintering birds are reported from all over the island; there are very few midsummer records, but at that time of year Cyprus is very hot for bird-watching as well as for the birds themselves. It is probable that the conspicuous flocks seen passing in May are the birds named *tundrae* from the Far North.

LITTLE RINGED PLOVER

Charadrius dubius curonicus

Apart from relatively smaller size and less robust appearance, there are two or three minor distinctions between this and the last species which can be noted at close quarters. The blacker bill of *curonicus* has no yellow on the upper mandible. The wing-bar of the ringed plover is *absent* in this species, and if by chance the bird can be handled, it will be seen that the shafts of the primaries are brown except for the white outer one. The leg colours too are different, in *curonicus* pale flesh-colour to yellowish, in *hiaticula* bright orange yellow. Viewed through field-glasses the yellow eye-rim is a characteristic mark. Both the black frontal band and breast band are narrower in *curonicus* than in *hiaticula*.

Unlike its larger relative which it resembles in general appearance it has bred in Cyprus on a few occasions and may do oftener than its eggs have been found. It is a common passage migrant from mid-March to the end of May and again from August to mid-October. Some must overwinter as thirty were present at Larnaca Salt Lake on 17 December 1967 for example. Most of the year they can be seen by the margins of lakes and reservoirs.

Up to 1958 there was only one recorded breeding, in early May 1911 by Famagusta freshwater lake, when eggs were said to have been taken. More recently a pair were reported to have bred at Akrotiri in April 1963 and in the same year a freshly fledged young was found in a gravel pit at Akrotiri on 3 June. In 1969 two pairs were seen at Akrotiri and nests were found. These records do not amount to much but only in the Sovereign Base have observations been made of recent years, and there are miles of coast and inland territory where birds may occur and never be reported, or even seen, by persons capable of putting a name to them!

Nests of the little ringed plover are mere scrapes without any lining, placed in various situations, seldom more than 100 yards from fresh water. The eggs have a buff or greenish-buff ground densely marked with specks, spots, streaks and lines of dark amber-brown or (and) black. The chicks are even more difficult to locate than the eggs.

KENTISH PLOVER

Charadrius alexandrinus

Wherever one's travels take one in the wide world, the Kentish plover seems certain to be the first wader encountered and is familiar to most bird-lovers, for it is a cosmopolitan species. The male has a white frontal band separated from the rest of the crown by a black band. Nape and upperparts ash-brown. Collar and underparts white. A blackish patch on each side of the breast is level with the carpal joint. Tail dark, bordered with white. Bill black, legs and feet lead-colour. Total length 6½ ins (17 cm). The female lacks the black band on the crown and has ashy patches instead of black on the breast. Both sexes have a black line running from bill to eye and a narrow white wing-bar.

Although nesting in Cyprus, near lakes and reservoirs, the Kentish plover cannot be termed a common breeding species. It is more numerous at the time of the spring passage, lasting in this species, from February until May, and in still greater numbers, if reports are reliable, in September and October. There is an influx of winter visitors in December and January when flocks of 500 have been seen.

In most of its habitats the Kentish plover rears two broods, and presumably does so in Cyprus, although detailed notes are lacking. April, May and June are the months when eggs have been found in this island up to date. Extraordinarily difficult to find, the eggs assimilate so closely to the colour of the ground, that many may be overlooked. Three eggs are the normal clutch placed in a hollow of sand or dried mud or shingle. They are yellowish-buff spotted and scrolled with blackish. When on its nest the female will sit until nearly trodden upon. After the young are full fledged, the families gather into flocks when upwards of 100 birds may be observed in late summer. It is not known if the breeding birds stay permanently in Cyprus, but it is assumed that they do so.

GEOFFROY'S SAND-PLOVER

Charadrius leschenaultii

[Plate 11, facing p. 49]

This is a larger bird than the ringed plover, 8 ins (20 cm) in length, with a heavier all black bill and olive legs. Sandy-brown above and white below with the rufous (not black) breast band narrowly edged with black in the breeding season. Forehead white. A few black feathers at base of bill, and a narrow black line extending across the forehead from eye to eye; forecrown cinnamon, hind crown hair brown; the breast fulvous-cinnamon, belly white. Entire upperparts hair-brown. The adult female has no black on the forehead and the breast paler than in the male.

An Asiatic species breeding from the Kirghiz Steppes to Korea and wintering in Africa, southern Asia and Australia. Only in 1913 was this large sand-plover recognised as a migrant to Cyprus in flocks in non-breeding plumage and no more was heard of it until members of the C. O. S., formed about 1957, became active. The plover was then found in spring migrating through the island in March and April. In 1961, up to 30 were seen in various localities between 18 January and 23 April – an exceptional number for Cyprus. Others have been recorded June to October but in 1967 "not one single record of this species was obtained during the year". Its visits must consequently be erratic. The writers have seen it once in Cyprus and all the records of recent years must be attributed to British Service personnel, mainly from Akrotiri, but on one occasion nine at Boghaz. The latest record as this book goes to press is of a flock of eight birds first seen in 1970 on the Akrotiri Salt Lake on 17 June and then frequently observed until early August.

NOTE

For record of a *Charadrius mongolus*, the **lesser sand-plover**, see Appendix p. 216.

GOLDEN PLOVER

Charadrius apricarius

This well-known European bird, which breeds from the British Isles to Siberia and winters in the Mediterranean Basin, is a winter visitor to Cyprus and regular passage migrant. It is too familiar a species to need detailed plumage description, and should not be confused with any other visiting plover to Cyprus. In winter it is mottled brown above speckled with dull golden-yellow, a whitish face and underparts, the breast buff. There is no white bar on the wing which is coloured like the upperside, but the axillaries and underside of the wing are white. Tail and rump are dark. Eye brown, bill black, legs and feet greenish-grey. Total length 11 ins (28 cm).

As the spring advances the golden plover assumes a handsome appearance, the lores, throat, ear-coverts, middle of breast and the belly become jet black, bordered with white. The upperparts including the crown are spangled black and bright golden. Immature birds resemble closely the winter dress, and intermediates, between winter and summer plumage, may be encountered when on passage. Golden plover are highly gregarious, they migrate in bands of varying numbers and remain in flocks or small parties on the plains after arrival. Their preference is for lowland ground between the shore and the mountain foothills, such as for instance the Nicosia air-field and surroundings, or the Patriki Pools, where flocks of up to 100 have been counted in February, rather than the shoreline as preferred by the grey plover. Golden plover are usually to be seen in Cyprus from October and November – sometimes in late September – till March, occasionally in hundreds from late December to early February. There is a record from Akrotiri Salt Lake on 14 July 1960, when two were seen, but summer records are most unusual, the 20 September being an early date to see them in the island on their way south to Africa and beyond.

GREY PLOVER

Charadrius squatarola

In its winter dress, in which most birds occur in Cyprus, this plover is a plain-looking bird some 12 ins (20 cm) in length. Ash-brown on the upperparts mottled with white and whitish rump; a streaked crown and white area above the bill reaching to beyond the eye. The underparts are white mottled with brown. The axillaries are black, very noticeable if the bird raises its wing.

As we stated in *Birds of Cyprus* (1958) the grey plover is a winter visitor and passage migrant to the island and while there are also summer records, e.g. 26 June and 27 July, specimens in summer plumage are rarely seen.

The summer dress is usually present by June and quite transforms the bird, the upperparts boldly spotted black and white, forehead white and over the eye, hind crown black and white. Underparts jet-black from chin to vent. In flight the whitish rump and tail and black axillaries show prominently. Bill black, legs ash-grey, the dark eye is strikingly large.

The spring passage is the most marked from the end of March to mid-May, birds seen in the latter month usually in intermediate dress. The autumn passage throughout October is small in comparison; only exceptionally, as in 1924–25, is it present in large numbers in winter.

This is one of the most widespread birds in the world, breeding in the Tundra Zone of the Arctic and migrating to reach South Africa, China, Ceylon, the Malay, Australia and New Zealand, when it is an inhabitant of the coastal areas seeking its food, mainly crustacea and molluscs, along the shoreline.

[for illustration of grey plover see overleaf]

Grey plover, breeding plumage (left); winter plumage, (right)

Family SCOLOPACIDAE

Snipe and sandpipers is given in the *New Dictionary of Birds* as the general name for the family which includes a very diverse assembly of "wading birds", which we, in Britain, name the sub-order Charadrii. Just as the last family discussed is conveniently divided into two sub-families, so with the Scolopacidae, some taxonomists separate it into at least three (or four) minor divisions. The turnstones have for instance been banded about between the Scolopacidae and the Charadriidae in a sub-family Arenariinae comprising the two turnstones of the Old and New World in the genus *Arenaria* and the surfbird (*Aphriza*) of the New World.

Foremost in the family Scolopacidae, or rather those which first come to mind when the family is mentioned, are the woodcocks and snipe, grouped in a sub-family Scolopacinae. All are winter visitors, capable of making long flights. They have long and quite straight bills, the distal end flexible, the tips of the mandibles capable of being opened below ground to abstract food located by feeling for it. Snipe and woodcock have their eyes situated far back on the head. All are noted for their camouflaged colour-pattern simulating the ground to an amazing extent. When danger threatens they take refuge in complete immobility and can almost be trodden upon before they rise. The common snipe is then noted for its zig-zag flight.

The next two sub-families, the Tringinae and the Calidritinae of modern usage are less easily defined. The Tringinae, including the curlews, whimbrel and godwits (whose correct position is still in abeyance), the Tringine sandpipers in the genus *Tringa* and the Shanks retained here in the time-honoured genus *Totanus*, which include in our list the two redshanks, greenshank and the marsh sandpiper.

Finally the true Sandpipers in a division named the Calidritinae (or Eroliinae of some authors) in which we find assembled such well-known shore birds as the dunlin, knot, stints and the curlew sandpiper placed in the genus *Calidris*. Three other birds are more happily established in Monotypic genera: the sanderling (*Crocethia*), the broad-billed sandpiper (Limicola) and the ruff (Philomachus) whose female is known as the reeve. All the above figure in the following pages. In such a widely differing assembly is it surprising that differences of opinion exist among taxonomists as to their affinities and correct position in the family tree? – the latest "opinions" are not necessarily of course the correct one, though often followed blindly by those wishing to be thought up-to-date.

Most of the Scolopacidae are imbued with very strong migratory tendencies, breeding in the far north and travelling immense distances, to be found as non-breeding species in many far-away corners of the earth. The sanderling for instance breeds in the highest latitudes of the Holarctic, visiting in the "off season" the coasts of every continent. Many birds show great differences of plumage in the breeding season, typified by the unique ruff and reeve, the males of which develop ornamental "ruffs" of varied and mixed colours to an extravagant extent.

One and all of these birds, in both the Charadriidae and Scolopacidae, cross the eastern Mediterranean on their migrations, at dates varying little anywhere in the Middle East from those given in such detail for Cyprus in the pages which follow.

TURNSTONE

Arenaria interpres

Perhaps a more regular visitor in autumn than formerly realised, the bird is generally seen in the duller winter plumage of varied brown and black upperparts, with white rump prominently displayed in flight. The tail is tipped with white, above which there is a dark band formed by the shorter tail-coverts. The throat is white, the breast blackish-brown continued in a half collar round the neck, the rest of the underparts white. A prominent feature is the orange legs and feet. The bill is blackish.

As spring approaches the breeding plumage is assumed and the upperside is then a far brighter pattern of white, black and bright chestnut. There is much white on the head which is marked with black, a black breast and white belly. The legs appear still brighter orange, and the whole effect is of a bright tortoiseshell bird with stumpy bill and short stout legs, exhibiting a great deal of white when it flies, including a stripe across the wing.

It must still be reckoned only an uncommon migrant to Cyprus, but there have now been enough records to include it as a regular, if scarce, visitor. Autumn birds have been seen between the 3 August and mid-October (once 2 November). Most in September, within the last dozen years. These dates are close to those mentioned in our *Birds of Cyprus* where we also recorded two in May.

Breeding in the far north of Europe and Asia it travels as far as Cape Province and Australia and is then almost cosmopolitan in its winter distribution – one of the World's greatest Globe-spanners.

GREAT SNIPE

Gallinago media

Very similar in colour to the common snipe, but body looks larger, 11 ins (28 cm) against 10½, with a comparatively shorter and stouter bill; the great snipe has other points of difference which should clearly distinguish the two species. The crown is less distinctly marked, the wing-coverts are more heavily bordered with white and the flanks more boldly barred, as are the entire underparts. There is more white in the tail which is composed of sixteen feathers in place of the normal fourteen in *G. gallinago*. Eye brown, bill blackish, the culmen and base of lower mandible olive. Legs and feet olive.

On the wing the great snipe is very different from the sporting bird, almost sluggish; it seldom flies far when flushed – it rises with a whirring noise but seldom calls, when it does so its note is louder and deeper than the other bird's familiar *"scarp"* and the white tail feathers are then prominent.

Formerly believed to be only a spring visitor to Cyprus occurring between mid or late March and the last week of May, odd birds have now been seen early in September and early in December, pointing to an insignificant return journey.

Migration takes it to tropical Africa. It is a scarce visitor to Egypt and is considered an uncommon bird in the Mediterranean Basin. It is not surprising that few have been noted in Cyprus, the main flight route being farther east via Persia, Iraq and the Red Sea to Abyssinia and Somaliland but also to west tropical Africa. As a sporting bird it simply does not count.

COMMON SNIPE

Gallinago gallinago

A richly-patterned brownish bird with upperparts varied with black, rufous and buff. Crown blackish-brown with a central and two lateral pale buff stripes. Two pale stripes extend down each side of the back. Neck, throat and upper breast buff, varied with dark brown markings, flanks barred with dark brown. Tail patterned but very little white on outer edge. The long delicate bill is dark brown, reddish at base; legs and feet greenish, eye dark brown. Total length (including bill) 10½ ins (27 cm).

A winter visitor and passage migrant to the island, exceptionally numerous after bad weather on Continent. Early arrivals appear in August, some even in late July, the wintering birds leaving again in March. Some passage migrants can be observed from late February until mid-May but only in the winter months can the snipe be considered fairly plentiful – and then not regularly. Judging from old reports of snipe-bags the birds must have been much more numerous in olden days, the huge increase in guns and the spraying of marshland against mosquitoes being the main cause of the decline in the winter population. Now a few may be seen in suitable places where formerly many could be flushed. Odd birds have been seen now and again in the summer (none recently) but in some years none are recorded between late March and early September. Continental weather has considerable bearing on the numbers seen from year to year.

When flushed the common snipe utters a loud *"scarp"* and follows a swift zigzag course until out of gunshot range.

JACK SNIPE

Lymnocryptes minimus

Considerably smaller than the last species discaused the Jack, with only twelve feathers in its wedge-shaped tail against fourteen in the larger bird, can usually be distinguished by its flight, for if suddenly flushed, while still following a tortuous course, its turns are much less abrupt than those of the common snipe. Moreover it seldom utters a sound when disturbed. Like the other snipe, it has pale stripes lengthways on its dark head. The upperparts are dark brown with a lateral ochreous-buff stripe on each side. The rump is dark brown; the tail, in which there is no white at all, is dark and is margined and mottled with rufous. The brown throat, breast and flanks are greyish-buff tinged with reddish and marked with dark brown. The remainder of the underparts are pure white.

Most records of this snipe have been of single birds, rarely more than two, and at much the same periods as the common snipe between early September and April. It is reported to be commoner as a passage migrant, mainly late March to early April and again late October to late November, than as a wintering species. It is certainly far scarcer than the common species, though frequenting the same places. The rainfall in winter must affect its stay in the island. As a sporting bird its value is negligible.

WOODCOCK

Scolopax rusticola

Just as the three snipe which visit Cyprus are well nigh impossible to detect on the ground, so to an even greater extent does the plumage of the woodcock harmonise with the surroundings upon which it lives. Colour protection to the highest possible degree is here exhibited. Its feathers: barred, crossed and vermiculated, of grey, cinnamon, rufous, black and yellowish-buff offer a complete camouflage, and as the bird will remain motionless until almost trodden upon, its disguise is perfect.

A glance at the text figure will enable the enquirer to visualise this bird – about the size of a rock-pigeon – better than any complicated description of the plumage pattern. The dark brown eye is very large for the size of the head, the forehead slopes backwards, the crown

Woodcock

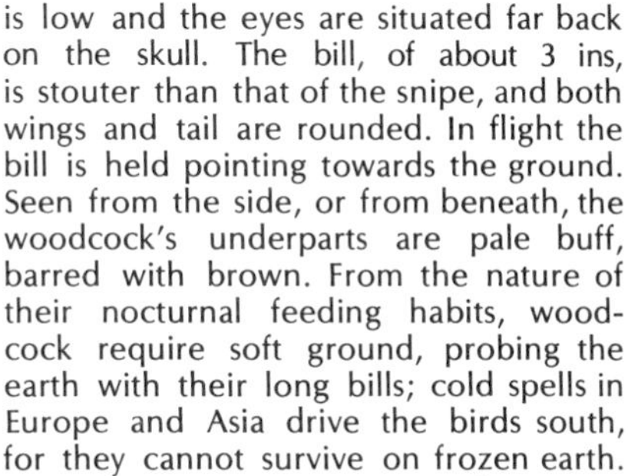

is low and the eyes are situated far back on the skull. The bill, of about 3 ins, is stouter than that of the snipe, and both wings and tail are rounded. In flight the bill is held pointing towards the ground. Seen from the side, or from beneath, the woodcock's underparts are pale buff, barred with brown. From the nature of their nocturnal feeding habits, woodcock require soft ground, probing the earth with their long bills; cold spells in Europe and Asia drive the birds south, for they cannot survive on frozen earth.

To Cyprus many come in the winter months, crossing from Asia Minor, but to a much less extent than in former days. It arrives usually in November and leaves in February. Some turn up earlier, in October, some stay later till the second week of March, rarely into April. Fifty years ago a heavy influx from overseas was reported after severe Continental weather, but there have been no such influxes in recent years. Probably most numerous from late November till late January.

Wooded areas, where the ground remains soft in the gulleys, are favourite habitats, but it occurs too in the lowland pine-woods (as near Akrotiri) and in Juniper scrub. The Karpas is another favourite haunt in which to flush them, but the Southern Range, where shooting is difficult and streams never dry up, provide the safest refuge of all, though not safe from dogs, for these winter guests.

COMMON CURLEW

Numenius arquatus

A large wandering bird of shore and moorlands, 22–23 ins (56–58 cm) in length including its very long (about 6 ins) decurved bill. Its plumage is pale brown regularly streaked with dark brown, very conspicuous is the white rump, streaked with brown, when the bird takes wing. The neck and breast are pale brown regularly streaked with dark brown as is the crown of the head. The belly is white streaked and spotted with sepia. The underside of wing and axillaries are white barred with dark brown. Bill dark horn-colour, eye brown, legs and feet greenish-grey.

The male curlew is smaller than the female and has a shorter bill by as much as an inch. Best known by its call-note *curlee curlee.*

To Cyprus the curlew is a winter visitor and passage migrant in small numbers, though on occasions flocks of 20–80 have been counted. Usually from one to six are met with on the coast. There are a few early records at the end of August and from then on single birds or small parties can be seen until the end of April.

The possibility of other species of curlew occurring in Cyprus on occasion must be born in mind especially the paler Siberian curlew. *N. a. orientalis* with pure white rump and unspotted white axilliaries and narrow streaks on the undersurface. This bird has not yet been recognised, though very likely to occur on passage.

The slender-billed curlew, *Numenius tenuirostris*, has twice again been reported to have occurred, see Appendix p. 216.

WHIMBREL

Numenius phaeopus

Closely resembles the common curlew in its plumage though it is a smaller bird 16–18 ins (41–46 cm) in length with a much shorter bill (under 3½ ins). It is darker on the uppersurface and wings and readily distinguished from the curlew by the markings on its crown which is dark brown divided down the centre by a pale cream streak. Like the curlew it has a white rump. Eye dark brown; bill dark horn, pinkish at base of lower mandible; legs and feet greenish-grey. The Whimbrel's call in spring, rendered weddy-tetty-tetty-tetty-tet, is characteristic and it also has a bubbling trill, not easily translated to paper.

The older naturalists do not appear to have noticed the whimbrel in Cyprus and it was not until 1957 that its presence was recognised at Larnaca – a party of five on 4 April. It has since been recorded in May, June, August and September, as an uncommon visitor during the periods of migration. In the latest assessment, where twenty-three only are recorded, it is reported to be irregular and very scarce, but it may have been overlooked, and may occur more often than recordings suggest. The last record received (accepted by the C.O.S.) is of a single bird seen on 5 and 6 July on Akrotiri Salt Lake.

BLACK-TAILED GODWIT

Limosa limosa [Plate 11, facing p. 49]

A graceful rather tall wading bird about 16 ins (41 cm) in length, including the long straight bill which is flesh-pink on the basal half and brown towards the tip. Ashbrown above in winter dress and with neck and breast the same colour, it is white on the belly. The tail is mainly black with a brown tip, the basal part and upper tail-coverts white; in flight the black terminal portion of the tail is very noticeable in contrast to the white area at the base. There is also a conspicuous white diagonal wing-bar when the wing is opened. As spring approaches the godwit assumes a brighter dress, the whole upperparts are darker interspersed with russet; the entire neck becomes russet as well as the breast, merging into black barring on the abdomen and the under tail-coverts. Eye dark brown, bill brownish, yellowish towards base; legs and feet lead-grey or blackish-green. When flying the long legs extend beyond the tail.

The black-tailed godwit is generally to be seen in Cyprus in autumn in September and October, but then rarely in flocks. In spring mainly in March and April when it is relatively common in small numbers. Occasionally also recorded in May. It can only be accounted abundant in exceptionally cold spells sometimes experienced in Europe in the early months of the year.

The **Bar-tailed godwit** (*L. lapponica*) has also been recorded on occasions since our larger book was published, but it is a very rare visitor. Slightly smaller than the one described here, it stands lower and only the feet stretch beyond the tail in flight. In the bar-tail the long bill is distinctly upturned. The tail is barred black and white and it has no contrasting white bar on the wing; like the black-tailed godwit it is a bird of the foreshore but the Cyprus coastline is lacking in the terrain to which these long-billed work-eating birds are most suited and it is not surprising *Limosa lapponica* is so seldom seen. Ash-brown and white in winter, the bar-tail assumes a rich chestnut dress on head, neck and underparts in summer. See Appendix p. 216.

GREEN SANDPIPER

Tringa ochropus

Of the various sandpipers which have occurred in Cyprus the so-called green sandpiper stands out for its black and white appearance rather than any pretensions to being green. It is darker on the mantle and back and has more white in the tail-pattern and on the rump than any species with which it could be confused. The contrast between dark upperparts and broad white area above the tail is very striking, added to which the four heavy black bands across the tail should clinch its identity. Moreover if the bird lifts its wing, the underside will appear blackish barred white – a diagnostic character. The underparts of the body are mostly white, the breast and flanks faintly streaked. The bill is black, the legs olive; from bill to tail the bird is about 9 ins (23 cm) in all.

The legs are comparatively short, thus distinguishing it from the marsh sandpiper; the almost entirely white outer-tail feathers distinguishes it from the wood sandpiper, in addition to the bird's larger size. It has a ringing call *tweet weet weet*, pleasant to the ear.

To Cyprus the green sandpiper is a visitor at all seasons but principally in spring from the latter days of March to the beginning of May, most common up to mid-April. Usually numbers are small: two or three at a time, but flocks of 20–30 birds may be encountered in both spring and autumn. After stormy weather larger numbers have been noted at Akrotiri and a record gathering of 100 was reported at Kouklia reservoir on 26 April 1967. It is seen in fair numbers from June to September after which it is irregular.

There is no inland country away from the lakes or reservoirs to attract this sandpiper far from the coastal belt.

Wood Sandpiper — Green Sandpiper — Marsh Sandpiper

WOOD SANDPIPER

Tringa glareola [see text-fig on p. 79]

The colour of this sandpiper in winter dress, in which it is usually seen in Cyprus is bronze brown, the white spotting of the upperparts – a good guide to identification in *summer* plumage – being then much reduced. It has a white rump but much less conspicuous than in the green sandpiper. The underside is mainly white with barring on the flanks. The tail is white barred black, less heavily than in *ochropus* except for the central pair of feathers which are heavily barred on an offwhite ground. Bill very fine and pointed; legs and feet sage-green. The feet protrude well beyond the tail when in flight, a character which distinguishes it from the green sandpiper. The call-note, uttered in flight, is syllabled *giff-giff-giff*. It gains its English name from its fondness for perching on trees, mainly noticeable in the breeding season, so not of much use as a field character in Cyprus.

The wood sandpiper visits Cyprus in spring and autumn when many pass through the island on both journeys. A few remain exceptionally to summer, but after the end of October the autumn passage is over and no more are seen again before March. In normal years they are very numerous throughout March, April and May and again in August and September with stragglers into October, rarely to November. It does not remain to winter as once believed, but passes on to its winter quarters in Africa which extend to Cape Province. Its powers of flight are very great.

COMMON SANDPIPER

Tringa hypoleucos [see text-fig. on p. 79]

Of all the sandpipers which we deal with in this book this is perhaps the best known of all to European ornithologists, but it has no very distinctive marks of recognition. More slenderly built than the others we have discussed, it is more likely to be encountered along the margins of reservoirs and inland fresh-water than the other passage migrants, for it is to be seen here and there all the year round and is very faithful to particular haunts to which it returns. Its colouring is olive-brown on the upper-parts, the wings with a bronze sheen,

Plate 14

1. Caspian tern
2. Little gull
3. Gull-billed tern
4. Mediterranean black-headed gull
5. Collared dove
6. Black-bellied sandgrouse ♀
7. Black-bellied sandgrouse ♂
8. Rock pigeon
9. Wood pigeon

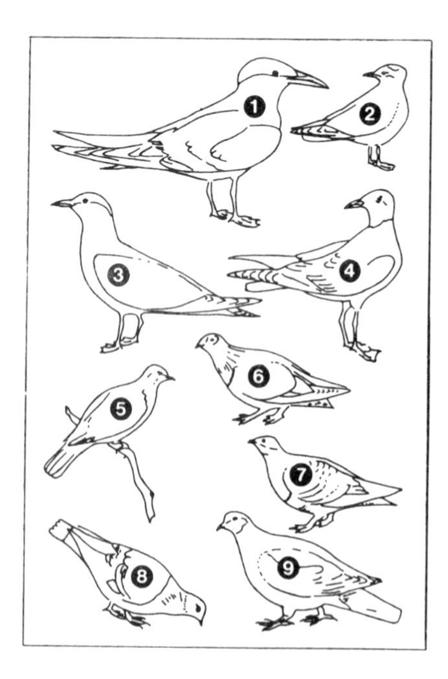

C.E.Talbot Kelly '70

C.E. Talbot Kelly

and the underparts white, though in summer dress the breast is more spotted than in winter. In flight a white wing-bar is noticeable. When standing it constantly flirts its tail, showing the white under tail-coverts, and bobs its head. When flying the wings are rapidly beaten followed by an occasional glide as it skims low over water. Its note is a shrill *twee-twee-twee* invariably uttered when the bird takes wing. The rump is dark brown, distinguishing it at a glance from the other members of this family. Total length about 7¾ ins (20 cm).

Mainly in spring and autumn but particularly numerous in April, May and September in some years, this sandpiper is to be seen all through the winter in a few particular haunts. In other years it is markedly less numerous on passage for which falling off in numbers it is difficult to account.

Spring passage lasts from mid-March to late May mainly April; autumn from July to late October, mainly up to mid-September.

There is little in Cyprus after May to attract this fresh-water loving bird in the summer months, but there are reports by many observers of them being seen round the salt lakes in July and August.

REDSHANK

Totanus totanus

There are likely to be at least two races of this widespread species passing through Cyprus; but the Continental typical race is so far the only one recorded and that is subject to variation in plumage. Anyone who frequents the sea-shore must be familiar with this bird – of medium size, an olive-brown back streaked with black and grey; a white rump and tail, the latter closely barred with sepia. Underparts mainly white the chest and flanks spotted with olive-brown. The medium long legs are diagnostic, bright orange red in adults, yellowish in immature; bill slate colour, red at base.

In flight the redshank shows a barred grey and white tail, pure white rump, and white posterior half of the wings. It has a loud whistling alarm call if disturbed and then, when settled, bobs its head in the manner of a common sandpiper. It never calls when in a flock. The bill is long and thin. The sexes are alike.

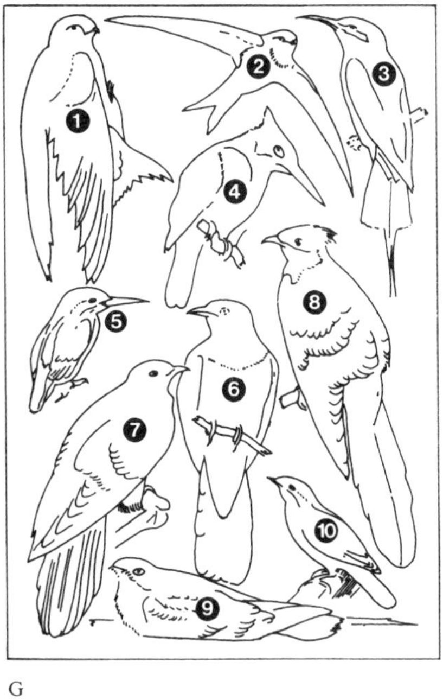

Plate 15

1. Alpine swift
2. Pallid swift
3. Blue-cheeked bee-eater
4. Pied kingfisher
5. European kingfisher
6. European cuckoo ♂
7. European cuckoo ♀ (hepatic)
8. Great spotted cuckoo
9. European nightjar
10. Wryneck

In breeding dress the upperparts are olive-brown, barred and flecked with very dark brown, almost black. Birds recorded as late as 10 July must surely have shown signs of this plumage.

To Cyprus it is a very abundant winter visitor and passage migrant at both seasons in flocks of up to one hundred individuals both in autumn and spring. Occasionally seen in summer.

The spring passage is at its height in the last half of March with small numbers sometimes present in mid-April, occasionally to late May. In autumn it occurs from late July, its numbers increasing after late October, the winter visitors merging into the spring passage migrants. All birds have usually gone on their way after mid-April.

DUSKY OR SPOTTED REDSHANK

Totanus erythropus

Very like the last bird described, from which it may be distinguished in winter plumage, which is then grey, only with care; the breast is then closely striated and a white eyelid can be clearly seen with the use of binoculars. A dark line passes from the base of the bill through the eye. Innermost secondaries barred sepia and white (not pure white); bill noticeably longer and general appearance larger. In summer dress the dusky redshank is more easily recognised for then the upperparts are sooty black, the mantle and scapulars being *covered with white spots.* Legs in winter orange-red but in summer the legs are very dark like the plumage.

When the dusky redshank rises, uttering a sharp *tu-wee, tu-wee,* it exhibits a white lower back and rump, and white upper tail-coverts, but these tail-coverts are closely barred with black. As it spreads its wings much less white is visible than in the common redshank, a characteristic clearly seen if the bird is overhead. This is because the secondaries – pure white in the common redshank – are barred in *T. erythropus.*

We had listed this bird in our earlier book as an occasional passage migrant in the spring (February to May), but since 1958 further research has proved that single birds and small parties may occur throughout the year; there have been infrequent records in mid-winter. Autumn passage is mainly from mid-August to early September, rarely in numbers, usually singles or a few together. The Spring passage is now believed to occur mainly from late March to mid-April, and birds are rare from May till the start of the autumn movement. The latest record to hand however is of a bird at the Akrotiri Salt Lake on 1 July 1970.

GREENSHANK

Totanus nebularius

Rather a larger bird than the redshank, 13 ins (33 cm) in length, standing higher on its very thin olive-green long legs, it may be recognised by its grey winter plumage, brilliant white rump-patch and long, fine, slightly upturned, bill. The underparts are white. The central tail feathers are barred, the remainder pure white. There is no bar on the dark wings.

As summer approaches the greenshank's plumage undergoes a change, the upperparts become browner and heavily streaked. Throat and breast are likewise streaked and the flanks barred with sepia. We have never heard its note in Cyprus, described elsewhere as a sweet *tew-tew-tew.*

It is a passage migrant to Cyprus on both spring and autumn migrations and is seen occasionally in summer. In spring from early March to mid-May, rarely later; main passage late March to late April. It is usually

Greenshank

scarce in autumn but can be seen from early July to mid-October, most often in July (females), and late August and September (males).

MARSH SANDPIPER

Totanus stagnatilis

[Plate 11, facing p. 49 and text-fig. on p. 79]

This sandpiper reminds one of a miniature greenshank in its winter plumage but is a smaller bird in all its dimensions, some 9½ ins (24 cm) in total length. The forehead and eye-stripe are white; crown, mantle and scapulars ash-brown; the back, rump and upper tail-coverts white. The tail is mostly white, the central rectrices with ashy margins. Whole undersurface white. Bill dark brown, green at base; legs and feet olive. The absence of any white on the wing should be noted.

A passage migrant to Cyprus chiefly in spring when flocks of twenty-five birds have been recorded; usually arrives from early March to late May, largest numbers in late March to late April; it has also been observed in summer with records in July and August, when its appearance is very different, the upperparts are then paler than the winter dress, with a reddish-buff tinge, the whole spotted and barred with black. The sides are also barred. Recorders have usually omitted to describe the plumage of these midsummer birds.

With such numbers regularly seen between March and May, the autumn passage in comparison is very slight and is reported to be nearly restricted to the end of August and the first ten days of September, rarely into October. The marsh sandpipers returning from Africa, where they are widespread migrants, to their breeding grounds in the Steppe zones of the U.S.S.R., must surely pass over by night without stopping, for we hear of the huge numbers formerly seen in Egypt, and yet in Cyprus they are then decidedly rare.

LITTLE STINT

Calidris minuta

The diminutive size of the little stint, and its near relative Temminck's stint, identify these two birds at once when they are compared, as is so often the case, with the other familiar shore birds like dunlin, sanderling and Kentish plover with whom they mingle so frequently. In length they measure only 5½ ins (14 cm) from bill to tail, dunlin for instance being nearly two inches more.

In winter the little stint is mainly ash-brown on the upper-parts with only traces of darker colour; the tail feathers brown, the central pair darkest. The breast is pure white with only faint streaking towards the wings. Bill *and* legs are black. Young of the year are more warmly coloured the feathers of the mantle and scapulars edged with buff and cream, and the throat and breast tinted with buff. In summer the feathers of the upperparts are broadly fringed with bright rufous and the spots on the breast, of same colour, contrast with the white belly. Temminck's stint at this season is dingy in comparison.

For other distinctions between this and the next bird described see under *Calidris temminckii.*

The little stint is a common visitor to Cyprus in spring and autumn more so perhaps in the early months of the year from mid-March to late May, rarely to early June. In autumn mid-July (seldom earlier) to mid-November, mainly mid-August to early October. It is also a winter visitor in variable numbers in small flocks.

TEMMINCK'S STINT

Calidris temminckii

In certain stages of plumage this and the little stint are not easily distinguished both being very small. A sure guide when in the hand is to examine the shafts of the wing-feathers for in Temminck's all but the outermost are brown, the *outermost* white.

In winter the forehead is greyish-white; the crown, mantle and scapulars olive-brown; the rest of the upperparts sepia and the greater wing-coverts tipped with white. Central tail-feathers are blackish-brown, the outer pair pure white and the others ashy. Throat white, breast ashy-grey, rest of underparts and the axillaries white.

In summer plumage Temminck's is more

mottled above than in winter, the feathers with dark centers and the fringes tinged with rufous – never so bright as in the little stint in the same dress. Bill black, legs and feet olive or brownish. As it rises the white outer tail-feathers are a feature to note in Temminck's stint, whereas in the little stint they are ash-brown.

On the whole Temminck's has a greyer appearance in winter than *Calidris minuta*.

In immature plumage the more uniform dress of Temmincks' is distinctive. The two have very distinctive songs and habits on their breeding grounds but this is of little help in Cyprus! One point is worth remembering though, Temminck's stint shows a preference for inland waters when on migration, which trait is not shared by the more shore-loving little stint.

To Cyprus Temminck's stint comes on both the spring and autumn passage, normally late April to mid-May, but the season lasts from mid-February to late May. Then again in July to the end of October occasionally into the first half of November.

DUNLIN

Calidris alpina

How many geographical forms of the dunlin pass through Cyprus on their migrations has never been established. In our larger work we recognised *schinzii* the so-called southern dunlin, but for the purpose of this Handbook binomial nomenclature is enough. Mixed flocks of three races, *alpina*, *schinzii* and *centralis* have been recognised (through ringed specimens) passing through Hungary on passage, so what one may discover by collecting specimens in Cyprus is anyone's guess, where the Asiatic races have to be considered as well.

In size dunlin measure 6¾ ins (17 cm) in length and are so numerous in Europe that few visitors to Cyprus, who are bird-minded, will fail to recognise their friends from the tidal estuaries at home with which they may be familiar: brownish-grey above, with a streaked greyish breast, a white wing-bar, and white at the sides of the dark rump and tail, are not very distinctive markings; the black bill is long, in comparison with some shore waders; the legs and feet olive. In summer there is a dark blackish patch in the centre of the breast, and the upperparts are chestnut, streaked with black. This plumage is often encountered in birds migrating south and traces of the summer dress linger for a long time.

It may be looked for along the shore in Cyprus and by the margin of the salt lakes, both as a numerous passage migrant and winter visitor.

In spring on its journey north from late April to mid-May, numbers vary considerably, the migration being very light in some years and heavy in others when flocks of 100 may be seen, mainly in early May. In autumn the main passage is in mid-August and throughout September but the migrants may be seen any time between mid-July and late October. During bad weather an influx from the north may be expected; winter visitors are present from November to February in variable numbers.

CURLEW-SANDPIPER

Calidris testacea

Rather larger than the dunlin, quite 8 ins (20 cm) in length, this sandpiper has more easily distinguishable characters by which it can be identified, best of which, as the bird takes wing or a flock flies past, is the white rump-patch. At rest on the ground this character is lost and then concentration must be centred on the shape of the bill which is distinctly down-curved, though not strikingly so as in curlew or whimbrel. It is longer than the dunlin's (which accounts in some measure for the difference in length between the two

Curlew-sandpiper

species) and tapers to a point. In winter the upperparts are ashy-brown mottled with darker centres to the feathers, the tail is fringed with white and the rump white as mentioned already. The underparts are white, with dusky lines on the foreneck and lower throat. The eye-stripe is better defined in the curlew-sandpiper than in the dunlin and the former has rather longger legs. Bill black tinged with olive; legs and feet olivaceous tinged with brown. In autumn many first year birds seen on passage have buff margins to the feathers of the back.

The summer dress is very different, the upperparts cinnamon-rufous mottled with black and white edges to the feathers; the sides of the face, breast and belly rich vinous-chestnut. Under wing-coverts, under tail-coverts and axillaries are pure white. Bill, legs and feet are all nearly black.

Breeding in the Arctic regions of Asia, a large part of the population winters south of the Mediterranean, passing through Cyprus on both journeys to and fro. Usually to be noted on the coast. Late spring arrivals have been seen already in full breeding dress. It occurs from early March to early June, mainly late April to mid-May. The autumn birds pass from mid-July to mid-October only odd stragglers in the early winter months.

SANDERLING

Crocethia alba

In its light grey winter dress, with pure white underparts, the feathers of back and mantle with dark centres to the feathers, the sanderling is quickly recognised from among the other small shore-frequenting waders. In size, 8 ins (20 cm) in length, there is little to choose between it and the dunlin, though in reality rather larger. In flight a distinct wing-bar is noticeable, and the white rump is then set off by the dark upper tail-coverts. In early autumn many birds are in mottled plumage of black and white.

In summer the sanderling is almost unrecognisable as the same bird, so drastic are the plumage changes. The upperparts show a mixture of cinnamon-rufous, black and white, the breast has turned from pure white to pale chestnut. At all seasons the bill and legs are black.

The sanderling is one of the farthest-travelled migrants from the Arctic lands and islands where it passes the short summer months, reaching on its winter journey "the uttermost parts of the earth" reaching the southernmost limits of Africa, Australia and South America.

Only a few of these charming little birds reach Cyprus and do not tarry for long, for always they have far to go. Numbers are not very variable. Spring migrants from mid-April to early June, most frequently from early May. In autumn from mid-August to October, mainly in the last half of September. As a winter visitor it is reported to be scarce, especially in mid-winter but occasionally quite common in November with occasional flocks in December. Few records exist from December to March.

RUFF AND REEVE [Plate 11, facing p. 49]

Philomachus pugnax

Almost unique for the reason that different English names have been given to the male and female. The great distinction between them, the donning of an ornamental ruff in the breeding season is restricted to the male alone, moreover he is strikingly smaller than his mate – or

Ruff, (winter plumage)

mates – for the ruff has a strong tendency to mate with more than one female, and shows an entire lack of parental care. The male is famed for his pugnacity in the mating season, indulging in formal contests which have earned for it – in France – the appropriate colloquial "combattant". Like other lek birds they are grossly promiscuous and have an almost unlimited sexual capacity. It is clearly a very successful species for its world numbers must be immense.

In winter dress, in which it normally appears in Cyprus, both ruff and reeve are ashy-brown above, often with some black mottling on the mantle; their breasts are dusky, their underparts white. In flight a bird of either sex displays a narrow white wing-bar, and a white oval patch on each side of the tail.

Birds of the year, in autumn, have the dark feathers of the upperparts fringed with buff or rufous-brown, while the breast is warm pinkish-buff; the crown rufous, streaked with black.

In summer the reeve resembles the immature described above but is greyer and is marked with black on the sides of the breast. At this time the male is strikingly different and assumes the ruff, in many colour varieties, and ornamental ear-tufts. The feathers of the mantle also vary in colour and the sides of the breast show black or purple gloss.

While the ruffs on passage through Cyprus are generally in the unromantic dull plumage, males with their ornamental feathers fully developed have been recorded by the writer as early as 27 March; by the middle or end of that month hundreds of both sexes have arrived on their way to their European breeding grounds and flocks of large size – 500 birds or more – are recorded arriving from the latter part of March onwards, the numbers dwindling until early May when the fresh-water lakes are drying up.

By the end of May practically all have passed on their way. They are absent in summer until the main return passage sets in from mid or late August but usually in September and October, followed by lesser parties until December.

The spring migration is on a much greater scale through Cyprus than the autumn passage.

Ruffs winter in Africa in tens of thousands, congregating in the Sudan and the Inundation Zone of the Niger in millions, their flocks darkening the sky.

Family RECURVIROSTRIDAE

The two genera *Recurvirostra* and *Himantopus* now included in this family each represent very highly specialised birds, the avocet placed in the former, the stilt in the latter. Both birds are well known by reason of their bills and legs and their black and white – though dissimilar – colour-patterns. The bill in *Recurvirostra* is, as its generic name indicates, up-turned, long and slender, drawn out into an extremely fine point, whereas in *Himantopus* that appendage is quite straight, very fine and ends in a needle-like point. In both genera the legs are long, exceptionally so in *Himantopus*. The avocet's feeding actions are remarkable, the bird sweeping its bill from side to side with lowered head on the surface of the water, the stilt on the other hand spears its prey with its very fine bill.

As Professor Voous has pointed out in his remarkable work *Atlas of European Birds* – incidentally one of the most informative books of the century – the habitats of the stilt and avocet only overlap in regions of brackish water. It is on the Salt Lakes of Cyprus that this is emphasised, but whereas the avocet can only be included in the Cyprian avifauna as a winter visitor and passage migrant, irregular at other times, the stilt is a breeding bird whose successful nesting is governed more by suitable water conditions in the lakes and reservoirs, than by any other factor.

AVOCET [Plate 11, facing p. 49]

Recurvirostra avosetta

A striking black and white bird about 17 ins (43 cm) in length with a long black fine bill which is upturned; its legs are stout, of medium length and blue-grey in colour. The pattern of the bird's plumage is best seen in the illustration. The bird has a black cap and red eye clearly noticeable at close quarters. In flight the black median wing-coverts and primaries contrast with the rest of the white wing.

Avocets visit Cyprus in varying numbers when they can be seen by both salt and fresh-water lakes, but only rarely do large flocks arrive. Mainly a winter visitor between January and April, others appear at intervals throughout the year but their arrivals, as well as their numbers, vary considerably. The year 1961 for instance was exceptional in that eight autumn records were scheduled between 12 August and 3 December when twenty-three birds were seen in all, the largest party being of six.

The spring movement, when very few are normally recorded, lasts from the end of March to mid-April, a few during May. Single birds are more often reported than parties up to ten individuals, but sometimes in March up to a 100 have been seen. Very occasionally it appears in summer.

BLACK-WINGED STILT

Himantopus himantopus

[Plate 12, facing p. 64]

Another conspicuous black and white bird, which it is quite impossible to confuse with anything else owing to its exceptionally long and very slender legs, 8–9 ins in length, which vary seasonally in colour from rose-pink to vermilion. It is furnished with a straight fine, sharp-pointed bill. The adult male is pure white on head, neck and underparts; the mantle and wings jet-black. The adult female resembles her consort except that her mantle, scapulars and wing feathers are brown instead of black. The tail is grey, only the outer feathers inclining to white. The eye is red and very conspicuous against the white face.

Young males have head and neck grey, the mantle brown, and buff edges to the scapular feathers. In total length from bill to tail the stilt is about 15 ins (38 cm), and in flight the legs protrude some 7 ins beyond the tail. The all black (brown in female) wings are very pointed and show no trace of white in them as does the avocet.

Compared with the last mentioned bird, the stilt is very much commoner in Cyprus. Mainly a passage migrant in spring in varying numbers, generally in March and April, occasionally lasting into May, it has bred on various occasions, both now and in the past as related in more detail in our larger work. As regards autumn passage there are only a few records between early August and late October.

In the spring of 1957, between 3 April and 11 May, forty three birds were seen at one time. In 1968 flocks of up to fourteen were present at Akrotiri, Larnaca and Kouklia until 22 April. Plentiful water conditions in the lakes and reservoirs are a major requirement in persuading the stilt to breed, but it has suffered more than any bird by having its eggs robbed. Nesting has increased recently. In 1969 at least seven pairs built nests in May and June on islets in Akrotiri lake and without doubt chicks were reared that year but how many was uncertain. In some cases at any rate breeding was successful – and that within easy reach of a village.

The stilt usually lays three to four eggs in a nest comprised of grass, rush or reed fragments forming a pad resting on half-flooded tussocks; others found on dryer ground are merely hollows in the mud lined with withered grass or *salicornia*.

Nesting in Cyprus takes place rather late as already indicated, so that a wet spring is essential for successful breeding. Normally a tame bird, easily approached, they become very excitable in the breeding season, uttering a yelping cry *Kyik-kyik-kyik* as they perform astonishing aerobatics overhead on being disturbed, or feign fatal injury on the ground or in the water. The well-known egg is pyriform in shape, the ground colour ranging from pale clay or stone to brownish buff with well-defined markings of dark brown, umber or black. Some eggs are spotted, others boldly blotched.

Family PHALAROPODIDAE

The phalaropes, of which there are but three species in the World, are certainly among the most interesting. They are the most aquatic of all the Order to which they belong, two at anyrate spending their lives at sea except during the breeding season when they return to the Arctic and sub-Polar regions where they first saw the light of day. Very small birds; the toes are lobed. All are gregarious to a very high degree and subject to tremendous migrations in the off season. They swim with ease, riding high in the water, having very dense plumage on their underparts. In their remarkable life histories the normal sex relationship is reversed, the female being the larger and in nuptial plumage more gaudily dressed, taking the lead in courtship. The male exclusively incubates the eggs. So different are the three pharalopes from one another that they are placed by most systematists in three different genera, only one of which, *Lobipes*, is represented in Cyprus by the accidental occurrence (see Appendix p. 216) of the red-necked phalarope, the same bird that has its southernmost breeding place in the British Isles. It is this species which has been reported as abundant at certain times in winter off the South Arabian coast. How they reach this destination is unknown for "no example of migrating [red-necked] phalarope can be traced" according to Meinertzhagen, who suggests they may accomplish the passage "in one bound". Phalarope are very rarely recorded in the Mediterranean. We have observed grey phalarope migrating off the Pacific coast of South America in thousands and a wonderful sight it is.

Family BURHINIDAE

The stone curlews or thick-knees as the birds in this family are named are inhabitants of dry stony places, either plains of foothills, covered to some extent with scrub, in the shelter of which the birds can escape their enemies by running in preference to taking flight. They are noted for their shy disposition, for their large golden eyes and for the thickness of the tibio-tarsal joint from which one of their trivial names is derived. They are coloured to match the ground on which they spend their lives and if they stay perfectly still with their heads and neck on a level with the ground, they are exceedingly difficult to see.

In Cyprus there is one species (or sub-species) which breeds sparingly but the bird is also migratory for which see under the species heading. The most conspicuous mark is the white throat which is usually kept hidden, and when on the wing a white wing-band is noticeable. Often in pairs, they gather into small flocks when on passage, and outwith the breeding season.

STONE CURLEW or THICK-KNEE

Burhinus oedicnemus

[Plate 11, facing p. 49]

There are almost certainly two races of the thick-knee in Cyprus, the typical subspecies as the passage migrant, and *saharae* as the breeding race (as reported). It is notable for its fairly large size, 16 ins (41 cm) from bill to tail, its round head, large yellow eyes and long yellow legs. In colour it varies from sandy-brown to pale grey, sand-colour or sometimes rufous clay-colour, the migratory birds being darker and less sandy than the residents. Its streaky upperparts and breast blend exactly with the earth it lives upon. The bill is black terminally, pale yellow basally. Its belly is white and only shows in flight when a double white wing-bar on the basal half of the wing attracts ones eye. Its greenish-yellow legs are notable for having only three toes like the bustards. It can run incredibly fast, but will also rely on its protective colouring to avoid detection by lying flat against the ground with neck and head stretched out before it. It is then impossible to see unless it moves. Being crepuscular its golden eyes are very large.

Its eggs are as difficult to see as the bird itself, laid on the bare earth with no nest material. Two is the full clutch harmonising with the colour of the ground. Few have been discovered but fresh eggs have been taken in late April and early May. A great many fall to local gunners in April when the overseas migrants are on passage, widely spread over the plains or the Karpas peninsula; they are a favourite game of the Cypriot sportsman and may often be seen dangling from their belts. Flocks of some sixty-seven birds have been reported in February in some years. An exceptionally large migration was reported from many places in Cyprus in 1959 when hundreds of thick-knees on passage were seen migrating out to sea between 18 and 21 September, many passing over at dusk and during the night. An influx of migrants is reported to occur in September and October when a distinct passage takes place.

Its numbers as a breeding species require to be investigated as also its local breeding distribution which is imperfectly known.

Family GLAREOLIDAE

In this family are grouped the pratincole (*Glareola*) and the courser (*Cursorius*) which are very different in appearance. The former contain two species the common pratincole and the black-winged pratincole, for we are not among those systematists who consider the latter to be a locally dominant colour variant of the other, see *Birds of Cyprus* (1958) p. 326 where our views are explained.

Pratincoles are long-winged, long-tailed birds about 9 ins (23 cm) in length, the tail deeply forked. Both have occurred in Cyprus but are better known in those countries of the Middle East in which locusts are still a plague. The pratincoles are their greatest enemy and destroy thousands of these pests when they appear. They have very short legs and in flight have some resemblance to large swallows.

Very different are the birds in the genus *Cursorius* for whereas the pratincoles mainly feed in the air, the coursers are birds of *terra firma*, and as their name implies are capable of exceptional speed on the ground. Instead of being brown in colour as are the pratincoles the coursers are "protectively" garbed in creamy sand-colour, much shorter wings and tail, and fairly long fine whitish legs upon which they depend to escape from danger. Coursers are only vagrants to Cyprus but are very common birds in all the desert areas of the Middle East countries: Sinai, Syria, Turkey, Iraq, Persia and Egypt, as well as Arabia and the Sudan, all are within the coursers range and breeding area.

COMMON PRATINCOLE

Glareola pratincola

[Plate 11, facing p. 49]

This is the pratincole which has its axillaries and a patch on the under wing-coverts deep chestnut, a major point of distinction between it and the next bird discussed. It is a very distinctive species, nearly 11 ins (28 cm) in length, olive-brown on the upperparts except the upper tail-coverts and basal half of the tail which are white. Chin and throat are cream to yellowish-buff completely encircled by a narrow black band. Breast light brown, belly and under tail-coverts white. Bill black, red at the base; legs, which are very short, reddish brown; iris brown. A point to remark is the strongly contrasting wing-pattern when compared with the more uniform upperparts of *Glareola nordmanni*. The very long wings are very noticeable especially in flight, the wing span being nearly 22 ins fully outstretched. Anyone who is familiar

with its flight will never confuse it in the air with any other bird.

It is a gregarious species which in Africa can be seen in huge swarms in places which it frequents; tame and fearless, birds permit close approach. The pratincole is a passage migrant to Cyprus, fairly common in spring, scarce in autumn and rare in summer. Kouklia is a favourite locality in which to see it, as many as forty having been found at the end of April on one day; Patriki is another favourite area where we saw it ourselves. In spring it may be seen from early April to late May, occasionally from mid-June to August.

It occurs mainly in years when water is plentiful. Irregular on autumn passage it has been encountered between late August and mid-October, but mainly in September. Many winter in the Sudan where they are reported to be common visitors from October to March frequenting the sea coast and banks of main rivers. It is also resident there.

There is an old Cyprus breeding record when five nests were located by the lake at Famagusta on 14 June 1913. Eggs, two or three in number, are laid in a depression of the ground or an animal's hoof-mark without any lining, the nests all close together. Eggs have a buff or stone-coloured ground thickly spotted or marbled with black or brown with underlying purplish markings. The chicks are described in *Birds of Cyprus* p. 325.

BLACK-WINGED PRATINCOLE

Glareola nordmanni

Many systematists unite this bird with the last, considering it a colour phase only, following that suggestion in *Birds of Arabia* p. 474. The point is arguable, but I prefer to stick to giving a name to each, and have given my reasons fully in *The Birds of the British Isles* (1962) vol. xi, p. 18. This is not the place to argue the point. The two are so similar in colour and appearance that unless the bird we are here discussing raises its wings, which it often does when alighting, and exhibits the black axillaries and underwing, it is excusable to fail to distinguish it. But there is another character which may help in the field. The almost uniform upperparts, jet-black under wing-coverts and lack of white trailing edge to the secondaries, all of which help distinguish *G. nordmanni* from *G. pratincola*. There is much more *contrast* in the wing-pattern of the common pratincole when seen in flight.

To see these birds and the last mentioned at their best a bush-fire is the medium as they dart in and out of the smoke in their chase after fleeing insects of all kinds. They are birds which do an infinity of good, could but the fact be recognised!

To Cyprus the black-winged pratincole comes at the same time as the common pratincole, but the numbers which have been identified are smaller. It has been recorded in Cyprus in mid-March, but otherwise as given for the last species from mid-April to mid-June. In autumn it has been identified from late August to early October, mainly in September, as with the previous species.

Order LARIFORMES

Family STERCORARIIDAE

The family which holds the skuas (or jaegers as the birds are named in America) is usually placed with the gulls *Laridae*, but well deserve family rank which Dr. Wetmore accords them. They are the highwaymen of the sea, robbing the gulls and terns of their spoil and by their habit of making their prey disgorge their catch which they then appropriate, are not looked upon with much favour by their neighbours. Armed with very sharp claws on their webbed feet and a powerful hooked beak, they are capable of attacking even birds the size of *Larus marinus*. Their wings are long and their flight swift. Sometimes we have seen them following ships. They will attack migratory birds in difficulties and ailing birds of any size.

Skuas are very rarely seen in the Eastern Mediterranean but have been recorded off the Arabian coasts, in the Gulf of Suez and off Aden, but to the Middle East they are usually rare. Both the Arctic skua and the pomatorhine skua (recognised by its long *twisted* tail feathers) figure in Kasparyan's *List of the Birds of Turkey*, but only the Arctic skua has been recorded from Cyprus (see Appendix p. 217). Unidentified members of the skua family have however been seen off the Cyprian coast on several occasions and both the above are quite possibly vagrants to these seas on occasion, but at a distance are not easily identified.

Family LARIDAE

This very large family which more than almost any other lends itself to sub-family division (i) Larinae the gulls, (ii) Sterninae the terns, is well represented in the Cyprus seas, ten species of gulls are recorded on the Cyprus List and nine species of terns. Of this assembly six will be found in the *Appendix*, where birds which have been rarely recorded from Cyprus find their place, while some of those dealt with in our main text are only saved from relegation to that section by having a dozen or more records. Winter *human* visitors to Cyprus will find that the gull family is numerically very poor. Only in the harbours, in search of ship's garbage do they congregate in any numbers. Terns are more often seen in the vicinity of the Salt Lakes.

Sub-Family LARINAE

No group of birds is more easily identified as a family, the adults with white underparts and grey of varying tone to slate or blackish upperparts (in *L. marinus* and *L. fuscus*). Some of the Larinae (*L. ridibundus, L. melanocephalus L. ichthyaëtus* and *L. minutus*) assume chocolate-brown or jet-black heads in the summer dress, but lose them in winter when a dark spot behind the eye is (in some species) diagnostic. Black wing-tips with white "mirrors" are commonly seen, as in the herring and lesser black-backed gulls, but in the greater black-back the primaries are black and only the tips white.

In the European black-headed gull the head is chocolate-brown, in the slender-billed gull wings are black-tipped, but the *mirrors* are absent, and in *L. melanocephalus*, the Mediterranean black-headed gull, black tips to the wings are entirely absent, as they are in *L. minutus*, the little gull. In adult dress the legs are either various shades of dark red, or yellow; only in *L. marinus* are they pink and in *Larus tridactyla*, the adult kittiwake, black. The black triangle on the wing-tips (without mirrors) of the kittiwake is a sure mark of identification in addition to the dark collar.

The ten gulls which figure on the Cyprus List range in size from the little gull 11 ins (28 cm) in length to the rarely seen greater black-backed gull, 30 ins (76 cm), but an average size varies from 15 ins (38 cm) in the black-headed gull to 21 ins (53 cm) in the lesser black-back. The beak is powerful in the larger species but much more attenuated in those which habitually hawk for insects and are less powerfully built. In the herring and black-backed species a brilliant vermilion spot on the gonys ornaments the bill, which is thought to be of some significance in the ritual behaviour indulged in when the breeding season arrives. Some, like the slender-billed gull, assume a lovely salmon-pink blush on the white breast and underparts at this season which is retained throughout the summer but quickly fades after death. Full maturity is not reached for three to five years; the juvenile dress is brown or mottled brown and in consequence of this slow maturing many intermediate plumages may normally be seen in a gathering of gulls. The only species known actually to breed in Cyprus are: Audouin's gull, very sparingly on the Klidhes islands off the tip of the Karpas Peninsula, and the Mediterranean race of the herring gull. All the rest are winter visitors or vagrants, some, like the slender-billed gull, being mainly passage migrants, especially in the spring.

From the above resumé, it will be seen how important it is when attempting to identify gulls to bear in mind some of the small points here enumerated.

LESSER BLACK-BACKED GULL

Larus fuscus

The representative of this gull which visits Cyprus mainly in the spring months, is the typical subspecies originally described from Scandinavia, whose breeding range extends to the White Sea and the Lakes Ladoga and Onega in U.S.S.R. In winter these birds range south to the Mediterranean, and the great lakes of Kenya and Uganda. Its back is as black as that of the greater black-backed gull; head, tail and underparts are white; the bill is yellow with a bright red spot, the eye lemon-yellow and the legs and feet bright yellow. Immature are mottled brown with dark brown to flesh-coloured legs, according to age, and a dark horn-brown bill. Adult plumage is not fully attained until the fifth year. It is 21 ins (53 cm) in length.

A passage migrant principally in spring, this gull is occasionally seen in small numbers in winter and it is probably true to say that a few are present off the coast all the year round but only common during the two periods of migration. Very seldom in summer. We gave a number of instances in our larger work where birds were seen prior to the date of publication 1958. Since then much more attention has been paid to migration of sea birds by the then formed C.O.S. They summarize the results of their observations as follows: "In spring from early to mid-March until mid-May or early June, mainly seen in the first half of April. In autumn from late August to late October, rarely from the beginning of August. The main passage occurs from mid to late September, with odd birds or small numbers staying around the harbours in the late autumn and winter: November to February. Only rarely observed in larger numbers."

NOTE

The **Greater black-backed gull** (*Larus marinus*) has seldom been recorded see under Rarer Visitors p. 217 and *Birds of Cyprus* (1958) p. 337. Its considerably larger size, 29 ins (73 cm), huge wing-span and pinkish flesh-coloured legs should proclaim its identity.

EASTERN MEDITERRANEAN HERRING GULL

Larus argentatus michahellis

The account which we published in our *Birds of Cyprus* (1958) does not require much amendment. It is the Mediterranean race: *L.a. michahellis* of this widely distributed gull which, in Cyprus, is the local *breeding* bird; but there are other races of *Larus argentatus* not as yet locally recognised, which could well occur in the island on passage. Without the recovery in Cyprus of ringed specimens – and gulls are one of the few Cyprus birds *not* shot, there will remain a doubt from which geographical area the migratory birds have come. The *Caspian Sea* race (*cachinnans*) – very pale grey, with wing 421–476 mm, and the base of the outer primary white, is almost certain to be one of these. Only a *collected specimen*, sent to the British Museum for

Lesser black-backed gull

identification, is likely to prove it.

The breeding bird *has* been collected already, and is that named above, which nests on most of the islands from Corsica and Sardinia to Cyprus. It has a pearl-grey mantle, white head, tail and underparts. The wing is grey, tipped with black and white; the powerful bill has a vermilion spot, the legs are chrome yellow and the iris lemon with orange orbital ring. Immature are mottled brown with a dark bill, the plumage is not so dark as in the immature *Larus fuscus*. The adult is 22 ins (56 cm) in length.

Gulls are colonial nesters and this one is no exception, laying their two or three eggs on the rock ledges on dried grass stems or other debris, no real nest is made. There are colonies on the Klidhes islands, on Cape Gata and Cape Aspro and on similar rocky promontories or islets around the coast. There is a colony at Paphos on the main island among other well-worked areas. Breeding is reported to occur from early April to May. The eggs of all herring gulls have much the same pattern of heavy blotches, spots and lines of umber-brown and blackish-brown on a paler ground, which varies considerably (even in the clutch); dun brown, pale olive or greenish-blue are equally common in *Larus argentatus* in Europe, but the eggs of the Cyprus population have not been studied with any care. There is no cause for them to differ materially, if at all.

There is no very marked migration from a herring-gull's breeding grounds – rather there is a wide dispersal in winter which takes them far afield.

As a migrant to Cyprus, herring gulls are very common birds. Passage migrants are mainly in evidence in March and early April at the Salt Lakes and again from July to September. Winter visitors in hundreds around the harbours between November and April, their numbers fluctuate according to circumstances. There is no doubt that shipping attracts them to the harbour and when overseas commerce falls off, so do the gulls.

AUDOUIN'S GULL

Larus audouini [Plate 13, facing p. 65]

Previous to one of us (W.M.B.), discovering a pair of these rare gulls on the Karpas Peninsula on 19 March 1954, no-one had ever heard of them so far east in the Mediterranean, and the possibility of their breeding in the vicinity, (for we eventually saw three pairs) appeared more than probable. Our guess was confirmed when a small colony was discovered by members of the C.O.S., nesting on the Klidhes islands, in May 1960. Whether they have colonised those islands in the near fifty years which have intervened since the Klidhes had been visited (in the spring months of 1911, 1912 and 1914) by an extremely competent resident ornithologist, no one can say, but it is odd indeed that he never saw them, nor were they reported by other leading ornithologists who wrote on the birds of Cyprus in earlier days.

Audouin's gull is slightly smaller than a herring gull some 19½ ins (50 cm) in length. In breeding plumage the head, neck, tail and underparts are pure white; the mantle and wings bluish-grey; the primaries black with a white terminal spot on the tip. Iris brown with red opthalmic ring; legs and feet olive-green and, most characteristic of all, a massive vermilion bill with the tip yellow and subterminal black band, which at once betrays the species among herring gulls. In flight the white tips to the flight-feathers are reported to be "barely noticeable" seen from below. This also helps to distinguish these two gulls which often select the same uninhabited islets on which to rear their young, but keeping strictly to themselves, *L. audouini* nesting apart from *L. argentatus*, though on the same small island. Immature specimens have a grey crown and the neck and upperparts are pale brown.

The year following the discovery of Audouin eggs in 1960, a second C.O.S. party investigated the Klidhes islands on 1 and 4 May 1961, when a small Audouin colony of six nests in close proximity was located. Clutches of two and three eggs were examined. All had been laid before 4 May, two eggs certainly between first and fourth being singletons and quite fresh. the largest eggs measured 65 × 42·5 and

63·5 × 46 mm; the smallest 63 × 41 and 61 × 44 mm. In comparison the smallest egg of the herring gulls on the island measured 66 × 47. Audouin's gulls eggs, in addition to being appreciably smaller, were also more olive-green in ground-colour, and decidedly darker than the herring gulls eggs, which were of a pale green colour with dark blotchy markings. All but two of the six pairs of Audouin's gulls had used a small amount of nesting material on which to lay the eggs; the other two had laid in a scrape without any lining. In 1960 the eggs discovered had all been laid on bare rock with only a pretence of a scrape visible. In the Bird Report of the C.O.S. for 1968 we learn that two chicks of this species were found on the Klidhes in mid-June both of which suffered the usual fate at the hands of local fishermen.

Audouin's gull now nominally enjoys the "protection of the Law" in Cyprus, but it is unlikely that Cypriot fishermen when collecting the eggs and chicks of the herring gull, which they do regularly, will differentiate between the eggs of the two species. The colony is too small to enable the birds to increase to any extent, quite apart from the ordinary hazards of life which Cypriot birds encounter. To enable it to be more generally known, the Cyprus Government have issued a stamp to the value of 15M upon which its image appears, but unless a statute is passed forbidding all landing on the Klidhes in the breeding season, we can see no hope of Audouin's gull surviviing.

The birds may be seen occasionally all the year round and visit the other bays and ports in the winter months.

SLENDER-BILLED GULL

Larus geneï [Plate 13, facing p. 65]

Approximately the same size, 17 ins (43 cm) in length, as the common black-headed gull from which, in winter dress, it can be distinguished by the slender and, for a gull, rather long bill, which is dark red in colour, and by the very white primaries. It lacks the spot behind the eye which is such a distinguishing feature of *Larus ridibundus*. The wing-pattern is much the same in both species, black at the tip but no white mirrors; the three outer primaries almost entirely white with only black tips and a blackish margin to the outermost. The rest of the plumage is pure white, the head and neck remaining so in winter, with sometimes a pale grey-blue mark round the eye. Legs and feet are red.

In summer the adults have a strong rosy blush on the breast and underparts.

Immature examples have the white tail tipped with black, the legs and feet yellowish, and the bill yellowish with a black tip.

In our larger work we classed this gull as a passage migrant, probably regular but overlooked. We recorded a number ringed on Orlov Island, in the Black Sea, which had been recovered in Cyprus, pointing to the direction of their annual migration or dispersal. Others have now been recovered. Another breeding colony is on Bahrein Island in the Persian Gulf. It is not surprising that it is now discovered to be quite a common migrant especially in spring, a marked passage taking place along the south coast of Cyprus from early March to early April, mainly noted in mid-March onwards. It is also a winter visitor which

Plate 16 (opposite)

European bee-eater

Hoopoe

Roller

D.M. HENRY.

C.E.Talbot Kelly

becomes scarcer after mid-winter. The autumn movement may begin with a few about the middle of August but normally is first noticeable from late October and in November.

MEDITERRANEAN BLACK-HEADED GULL [Plate 14, facing p. 80]

Larus melanocephalus

There is no difficulty in recognising this Mediterranean species in summer plumage from the so-called European black-headed (*ridibundus*), for the local bird really *has* a black head in summer, extending well over the nape, whereas *Larus ridibundus* has a dark chocolate-brown head, which does *not* extend over the nape. Another very obvious difference is the lack of any black at the wing-tips in *melanocephalus*. Seen side by side, the bill of the Mediterranean gull is stouter than the European species. The tail in adults, is pure white in both, like the breast and belly, but in immature examples the Mediterranean gulls are mottled brown, and have a dark edge to the forewing, whereas in the European black-headed the forewing edge is white. In the immature of both there is a black tip to the tail. There is little to choose between them in size – the present species is 15½ ins (39 cm) in length, the European bird half an inch shorter.

The breeding grounds of *Larus melanocephalus* lie in Greece, Rumania, the Crimea and Asia Minor. It winters largely in the Mediterranean basin from the S.W. Coast of France to Egypt and we have seen many in the Black Sea and Bosphorus in the early months of the year, thronging the harbours and earning a living among the anchored shipping.

This gull assumes its black head very early in the year. In the distant past reliable observers of whom details are given in our larger work, reported enormous numbers of these gulls in April off the Cyprus coast in the years 1875–87, but with the exception of a small flock in 1927, no such large numbers have been reported. The C.O.S., since its formation in 1957, can find only thirteen records, covering almost every month of the year, and sum up its present day status in the island as "normally very irregular and very scarce".

Plate 17

1. Calandra lark
2. Wood lark
3. Red-spotted bluethroat
4. European rock-thrush
5. Blue rock-thrush ♂
6. Blue rock-thrush ♀
7. Isabelline wheatear
8. Alpine ring-ouzel
9. Arabian chat
10. Black-eared or Spanish wheatear

EUROPEAN BLACK-HEADED GULL

Larus ridibundus

This is far the most numerous of the gulls which assume a black (in this case dark-brown) head in summer plumage, and in winter a prominent dark spot behind the eye, the brown hood being lost. The crown is then mixed with grey or brownish and the forecrown is white. It can be distinguished from the Mediterranean black-headed gull by the *chocolate* rather than black hood and the black on the wing-tips; see also under *Larus melanocephalus*.

The European bird is a medium-sized gull, 15 ins (38 cm) in length, with no difference in size in the field between it and the Mediterranean black-headed. It has a crimson bill, legs and feet. One other gull which assumes a black head in summer is the little gull (*Larus minutus*) but its much smaller size totalling not more than 11 ins (28 cm), saves confusion. At the other extreme, but rarely recorded from Cyprus, is the great black-headed gull, 29 ins (73 cm) in length, with greenish-yellow legs and feet (see Appendix p. 217). It too assumes a black head in summer.

The European bird is a numerous winter visitor, coming to Cyprus harbours and the various lakes, arriving towards the end of September. In late October and more especially in November swarms are to be seen around the shipping on the lookout for garbage. In 1961 for instance 100–200 were present all the winter in Famagusta harbour and much greater numbers came in December. The passage migrants continue their journey to Egypt and the Red Sea, ranging to Aden, but they do not wander far south beyond the Nile Valley. We have found them still around the Cyprus Ports in February by which early date some have acquired their chocolate hoods in which they are known to be erratic. Most of these gulls have gone by the end of March, but exceptionally up to 100 have been seen in early May. It is rarely seen in summer.

LITTLE GULL

[Plate 14, facing p. 80]

Larus minutus

Of all the gulls which visit Cyprus this is the smallest not more than 11 ins (28 cm) in length. It is one of those which in summer assumes a black head, sharply defined from the pale bluish-grey mantle, white body and wings. There is no black in the wings on the upperside, but the underwing is dark slate-grey with a broad white rear edge, a character which is noticeable when the bird is flying, if one knows what to look for. In summer there is a rosy flush on the underparts when close enough to observe it. The black head is lost in winter when the very small size is probably the best guide to identification. In breeding dress the bill is reddish-brown (blackish in winter), the legs and feet bright vermilion and the eye dark brown.

Birds in first year plumage have the underwing *white* (not slate) until the third year. Juveniles have a blackish crown and ear-coverts, sooty upperparts and completely white underparts, except for a dark patch on each side of the breast. There is a black diagonal band across the open wing and a black subterminal band on the white tail.

To Cyprus the little gull is irregular in its appearance. Up to a 100 have been reported visiting the salt lakes in mid-winter. South-westerly gales in winter, between December and March, result in their appearance in the bays of the island and in some of the ports, where their rounded wings and buoyant flight as well as their unusually small size, draws attention to their presence.

The largest numbers are noted from late December to mid-February; smaller numbers through March and early April. One flock was reported at the end of June, an exceptional occurrence.

Sub-Family STERNINAE

The terns, in the sub-family Sterninae, with few exceptions, need just as much attention to detail – particularly the marsh terns of the genus *Chlidonias* – before they can be certainly identified. As a family the small and medium sized members are distinguished from other sea birds by their graceful swallow-like appearance, tapering medium-length, sharp-pointed bills (except in the gull-billed terns), long pointed wings, sharply forked tail and grey plumage with white underside, having generally a black cap in summer dress only. In particular their habits betray them from a distance, hovering with beating wings above the water or diving with a splash to capture the small fish upon which they habitually feed.

The nine species on the Cyprus List vary from the little tern 8 ins (20 cm) in length, to the huge Caspian tern, 20 ins (51 cm) in total length, as large as a big gull, with a wing-expanse of over 4 ft from tip to tip, and very heavy bill. It has been recorded rarely but may escape notice. Its large size should betray it at all seasons.

The marsh terns represented by three species in Cyprus: the black tern, whiskered, and white-winged are more addicted to fresh water than salt and in summer plumage are not difficult to recognise from one another by the individual features to be described under each species. In the winter however they are nearly impossible to recognise, so much alike are they at that season. They are among the most graceful of all to watch.

A member of the family which visits Cyprus seas commonly in winter, but does not conform to the above general description, is the gull-billed tern which has a shorter and stouter bill *black* in colour, not red or orange-yellow, a less forked tail and size more approaching the sandwich tern. In flight it is tern-like and wonderfully buoyant. On the ground it stands higher owing to its longer tarsus. It is a common winter visitor to Sinai, Palestine and Egypt as are many of the other terns in the above short list.

The only terns which have bred in the distant past in Cyprus are the common tern and the little tern some sixty years ago or less. No tern breeds in Cyprus today and there is little to induce them to do so.

BLACK TERN

Chlidonias nigra

There are three terns placed in this genus which are on the Cyprus List, but whereas they are easy enough to recognise in their breeding plumage, the reverse is the case in autumn, when most of them occur. The black tern in winter is mainly white. The forepart of the head is sometimes flecked with black with some white mottling on the nape. In front of the eye is a narrow rim of black. Collar and sides of the neck are white. Underparts are white with a blackish patch on either side of the breast. Upperparts are pale grey.

In summer the head and whole underparts are sooty black except for white under tail-coverts; wings slate-grey, a slightly forked grey tail and black bill. Legs and feet are dark reddish-brown. It is 9½ ins (24 cm) in length.

There is an enormous migration of black terns from Europe and western Asia to their winter quarters in Africa. Cyprus then comes in for its share of passage migrants during the autumn passage. In the spring far fewer are to be seen and seldom before May when some are in summer dress. As the fresh-water lakes dry up in May there is little to induce these marsh terns to tarry on their way. Very few are to be seen in the early summer months until the autumn passage sets in again from the middle of July lasting to early October with the main body August and September. The difference in the numbers in spring and autumn is very marked. In some recent springs none have been seen at all at places such as Akrotiri where numbers pass through in autumn.

WHITE-WINGED BLACK TERN

Chlidonias leucoptera

[Plate 2, facing p. 4]

In summer dress this is a strikingly beautiful bird, the whole head, mantle, back and breast black. A white patch on the carpal joint of the wing is then very noticeable in flight. The wings are grey; the tail, upper tail-coverts and under tail-coverts white, in strong contrast to the dark body. The under wing-coverts and axillaries are black. Bill and legs are red, of a vivid colour.

In winter this tern is very difficult to distinguish in life from the black tern at the same season. The head, neck and underparts are white, except for the black on the nape; the upperparts slate-grey; the tail is greyish and there are *no dark patches on either side of the breast* as in the black tern. In front of eye a small black spot, ear-coverts blackish. The bill in winter is blackish. First winter birds, which are frequently seen in Cyprus, closely resemble adults in winter dress, but the brown feathers of the juvenile plumage often remain on the upperside, the rump is nearly white, the bill reddish-black and the legs and feet dull reddish-yellow.

All the three marsh terns (black, white-winged and whiskered) have a characteristic slow flight, especially when hunting for the insects and small fish upon which they mainly feed, the first two stooping to the water to pick the food from the surface rather than plunge which is a habit more connected with the larger whiskered tern.

Of the three marsh terns on the Cyprus list the white-winged is the more numerous arriving in April and remaining till late May, occasionally to the third week of June. As many as 250 together have been counted at Akrotiri on 23 April. The return passage lasts from the first week of August to mid-September, seldom seen after 1 October, when single birds may sometimes be encountered.

WHISKERED TERN

Chlidonias hybrida
(formerly Chlidonias leucopareia)

This is the largest of the three marsh terns, almost 10 ins (25 cm) in length, but not so much larger as to enable it to be recognised for its size alone from the other two. It is however, far the rarest and barely found its way into the main text of this book. Southern Europe and northern Africa are its breeding grounds. In summer plumage it may be recognised easily from the other two by its all-grey uppersurface, white face, black crown and dark crimson bill; the throat is pale slate, darker on breast and blacker on the belly. Axillaries white; legs and feet crimson.

As it is seldom seen in Cyprus before May, some of the records apply to birds in summer plumage. In winter the forehead is white, the crown streaked black and white, the nape black with white tips to feathers. Entire upperparts and tail-coverts ash-grey. Underparts of body and underside of wing are white. No dark spots on either side of breast.

When we were engaged in the preparation of *Birds of Cyprus* (1958) the whiskered tern had only been recorded on two occasions giving a false idea of its rarity. Since the C.O.S. came into being, its energetic members have given us a truer perspective of its status, summed up in their latest check-list 1970 as follows: "Rare but almost regular now, between twenty and thirty records, nearly all since the formation of the C.O.S. in 1957. Occurs from late April to early

October. Some birds staying for periods at the same place". The records refer to from one to eleven birds at a time covering all the months mentioned to 1970 inclusive. Most of the records mentioned were, not surprisingly, from the Akrotiri lake.

This is a common visitor in winter to the Sudan from October to the late spring when numbers may be seen in summer plumage. As Cyprus lies on the direct route to Europe they may be expected to occur on passage more regularly than they have been recognised at Akrotiri where military observers have been stationed.

GULL-BILLED TERN [Plate 14, facing p. 80]

Gelochelidon nilotica

As its Engish name implies the bill of this bird is very different in shape from those of the *Sterna* or *Chlidonias* species – black in colour (with no pale tip) and much deeper and heavier in appearance. The bill is also shorter. In colour its plumage is silvery-grey above, the rump and tail paler grey; entire underparts white. In summer it has a completely black crown, in winter the black is lost but many birds retain black shaftstreaks on the head and nape. A blackish auricular patch is present behind the eye and a black ring nearly encircles the eye. Iris dark brown; legs and feet black.

Compared with the other terns it is larger than any except the Caspian and Sandwich, measuring 15 ins (38 cm) in length with a wing expanse of over 40 ins. It has appreciably longer legs and stands higher. Its flight is more tern-like than gull-like, though perfectly distinctive. Its less deeply forked tail and heavier shorter bill give the gull-billed tern a stocky appearance, and compared with say the common or Arctic tern, a less graceful flight. It obtains most of its prey hovering over water, diving upon it and occasionally completely immersing.

To Cyprus it arrives occasionally late March, and in April, May and June, most frequently in April. There are a number of summer records in August but it is definitely scarce in autumn or hardly ever recognised. It migrates down the Nile to reach the Great Lakes and breeds in Asia Minor and various localities in southern Europe.

The latest record to hand is of a bird on the Akrotiri Salt Lake on 4 July 1970.

CASPIAN TERN [Plate 14, facing p. 80]

Hydroprogne caspia

This is the largest of the terns on the Cyprus list, quite 20 ins (51 cm) in legth with a wing span of 50 ins. The very heavy bill measures up to 78 mm in length and is bright vermilion, becoming dusky towards the tip. Legs and feet are black with a reddish tinge. In summer the bird has a black cap to the level of the eye; the whole upperside of the body and wings being silvery-grey; tail and rump are white as are the entire underparts. Seen from below the primaries appear very black, but this is not noticeable on the upper surface. In winter the black crown is lost and the head becomes streaky on a pale ground. It retains its vermilion bill in the winter. It can be mistaken for a gull – being about the size of a common gull – by anyone unacquainted with it, though it is tern-like in its habits and is a wonderful diver. Its cry is a hoarse croaking *kraa* on a low key.

There are only a few sight-records for Cyprus of recent years since we published our larger work in 1958. Previous to that date it had been recognised near Limassol in May 1875, near Famagusta 26 April 1887 and 9 April 1909. No more were recorded, doubtless for lack of observers, till the last few years of the British occupation when two were seen off Famagusta 17 April 1962, and two more off the Klidhes islands on 8 April 1967 "flying north east". There is also a record in September. Finally, in 1970, one was found dead by Akrotiri Salt Lake, believed to have died the previous December, as the body was decomposed; the first ever to have been handled. Identified at British Museum. Other records were sightings.

The Caspian tern is a summer visitor to northern Europe especially the Baltic coasts of Sweden and Finland, ranging to the Mediterranean and eastwards to eastern Siberia. There are colonies on the Black and Caspian Seas. There are many recoveries of ringed birds from the Delta of the Nile, so that it may be expected in Cyprus waters more often than records would suggest.

COMMON TERN

Sterna hirundo

In winter when it is sometimes present in Cyprus in small numbers (in January and February in certain years) but by no means regularly, the common tern is almost certain to be noticed if present, for there are no resident terns in the area and the visitors soon call attention to themselves when they first arrive. At that season the birds are dove-grey on the upperparts and entirely white on the underparts with a dark diagonal shoulder-patch, an incomplete black cap and broad white forehead. The bill is then mainly black with a red tip.

In summer the black cap covers the crown and the sharp pointed bill turns completely orange-red with distinct black tip, the legs vermilion of even brighter hue. In length it measures 14 ins (36 cm). Its long narrow wings and forked tail, the streamers of which do not project beyond the closed wing-tips, together with its bouyant graceful flight, proclaim it to anyone faintly familiar with the sea shore. Its voice is a harsh *Kree-ah*.

To Cyprus it is mainly a spring passage migrant never in any great number in April, May and occasionally June. A few may be seen on the reservoirs in summer in some years, and there is even an ancient breeding record as we recorded in our larger work, when eggs were found at Acheritou reservoir (no longer in use) in May 1905.

The autumn passage seems to miss Cyprus, very few having been recorded in September and October, seven records in all up to 1970.

NOTE

The **Arctic tern**, *Sterna paradisea*, has been reported on at least two occasions, see List of Rarely-recorded Visitors p. 217; in summer its bill is deep blood-red without a black tip. In winter very difficult to distinguish on the wing. The call is often a monosyllabic "*keer*". The report of a considerable number – up to sixty – being present on the Akrotiri Salt Lake for the first seventeen days of May 1969 is a very extraordinary record, but we have much to learn about the route taken by this tern on its journeys to and from winter quarters, and, the occurrence mentioned is of great interest.

LITTLE TERN

Sterna albifrons

This is yet another of the tern family that in the not too distant past could be classed as a breeding bird in the island, both at Famagusta and Larnaca, but is now only rarely seen in summer and has quite ceased to breed. What is the primary cause of so many birds ceasing to lay their eggs in Cyprus and rear their families in this island? There can only be two answers, great changes in the ecological conditions or excessive disturbance of the nesting grounds. Even terns are not sought after by Cypriot gunners, but the constant discharging of firearms in the nesting season which certainly occurred until quite recently, and the increase in coastal dwellings, may well have had an adverse effect on birds which would otherwise have remained to rear their young.

Common tern

The little tern's small size (8 ins (20 cm) in length) broad white forehead, black crown and nape, pearl-grey upperparts and white underparts, yellow bill with dusky tip and dull yellow legs, are the points to observe. A black band passes through the eye extending from the base of the bill to join the black cap. Tail and upper tail-coverts are white.

Nowadays in Cyprus the birds are passage migrants only, mainly in spring, but of uncertain number. Very seldom in autumn. They are very irregular on spring passage from mid-April to late May; sometimes common in mid-May. It is now very rare in summer, despite having bred in the past, (1910–12). In autumn it is only occasionally seen in August and September.

The little tern ranges to European Russia, the Caspian and Black seas and Asia Minor and is identical with the bird which breeds in Great Britain.

Order COLUMBIFORMES

Family PTEROCLIDIDAE

The sandgrouse which form this family are today allied with the pigeons as their nearest relatives and placed in the vast Order Columbiformes. Their true home lies in the deserts of the Middle East, Arabia, Africa and central Asia. The numerous species are birds which assimilate closely to the ground which they inhabit and are renowned, in desert countries where water is scarce, for the immense distances covered to their drinking places and the punctuality in which their daily journeys are performed. Of the several species found in the Middle East only one is (today) a scarce resident in Cyprus i.e. the black-bellied sandgrouse, a species which is less attached to absolute desert than most of its family and which occurs in semi-cultivated areas. One other species – the pintailed sandgrouse (whose half-tone portrait appears on Pl. 24 of *Birds of Cyprus*) has been shot on the island between 1820 (skins in Berlin Museum) and possibly in 1910, but no later record has been reported (see Appendix, p. 217).

Sandgrouse have very long pointed wings, a small head somewhat reminiscent of the European partridge; a short bill, lacking the soft membrane of the pigeons; and short legs, the tarsi feathered to the toes. The formation of the tail is distinctive as witness the two species on the Cyprus List. They fly at great speed and usually in small to medium flocks. They lay, usually, two eggs in a scraping on the bare ground and the eggs are as difficult to find as any, so closely are they camouflaged. Both the species instanced here occur in Asia Minor and Iraq.

BLACK-BELLIED SANDGROUSE

Pterocles orientalis

[Plate 14, facing p. 80]

It is unnecessary to give a detailed description of this bird here. It is the only sandgrouse ever likely to be encountered in Cyprus at the present day by a visitor and is becoming increasingly scarce. The marbled appearance of the upper-parts (brown, grey, orange buff and isabelline), the black throat, grey and isabelline breast and black belly, serve to distinguish the male, which is about 14 ins (36 cm) in length. The female is slightly smaller, its plumage sandy-isabelline closely barred and spotted with black and, like the male, has a black belly. The head is pigeon-like, the wings long and pointed and the flight exceedingly swift. The legs are short and feathered. It has a pretty rippling liquid note which carries far.

On the ground owing to its protective colouring it is very difficult to see until it moves and it moves on the first sign of danger, taking wing and covering a long distance before alighting. It lives on the plains and on arable land and is very dependant on fresh water to drink. The Mesaoria plain used always to be a favoured locality and also Athalassa but it turns up unexpectedly in many places.

At one time, circa 1910, sandgrouse were comparatively common in Cyprus and many were shot. Today it is a breeding bird locally in the southern Mesaoria where it is resident. As a passage migrant it was formerly more common than today, mainly September to November and in April, but now it is clearly scarce both as a passage migrant and as a breeding bird.

This sandgrouse lays two eggs on the bare earth, sometimes in a depression or scratching made by the bird. Eggs are pale-buff to coffee-colour, occasionally cream, the ground covered with ill-defined blotches of amber-brown. Some eggs have spots of rufous and underlying markings of stone colour.

The account of the older naturalists in Cyprus who reported large flocks of autumn migrants from mid-September to mid-November, with "hundreds coming to drink at a river near Nicosia", reads today like a fairy tale, so greatly has the scene changed.

At least one other sand-grouse visited Cyprus prior to 1910 at rare intervals, i.e. the **Pin-tailed sandgrouse** (*Pterocles alchata*) of which we gave a description in our larger volume and a full paged plate op. p. 289. It must be relegated in this Handbook to the Appendix in which Rarely Recorded Species are briefly listed. See p. 217. An inhabitant of Asia Minor, Iraq and Syria where it is very numerous, the pin-tailed sandgrouse is a likely visitor to occur. The only accepted record is of two birds collected in 1820. It may, or may not, have appeared again around 1910 but no specimen was preserved.

Family COLUMBIDAE

The pigeons and doves in this family on the Cyprus List require little introduction for with the exception of two quite accidental vagrants the other five species are widely distributed European birds.

Pigeons have small heads in comparison with their bodies, weak bills with a fleshy cere covering the base of the upper mandible, short legs, bare of feathers, three toes directed forward and one well developed hind toe. Their bodies are copiously covered with feathers loosely attached to the skin. They build flimsy stick nests through which the white or cream – coloured eggs may be clearly seen. Young pigeons are naked and exceedingly ugly with an almost reptilian appearance. Most pigeons are strong fliers and some of the doves, like the European turtle dove, are strongly migratory. Others like the wood-pigeon are more given to settling down, but all pigeons in northern latitudes are usually forced to make considerable journeys in the winter.

Of the pigeons on the Cyprus List three now breed regularly in the island: the wood-pigeon and rock-pigeon are resident and the turtle-dove a summer visitor; the collared dove had ceased to do so but is now trying to re-establish a town colony; the stock dove comes from Asia Minor to spend the winter and there is likewise an influx of migrants from the continent of European wood-pigeons to swell the small resident population. Such is the not very interesting pattern which the Cyprus *Columbidae* present, unless it be the brave attempt of *Streptopelia decaocto* to make a come-back.

WOOD-PIGEON [Plate 14, facing p. 80]

Columba palumbus

Often named the ring-dove, this fine pigeon is known throughout most of Europe and indeed has become almost a pest in the British Isles, such numbers descend upon the crops. In Cyprus, although still, surprisingly, to be reckoned among the resident breeding birds, it is looked upon locally with benevolent eye, as it affords good sport and excellent eating to the multitude of Cyprian sportsmen. Restricted in its breeding mainly, but not entirely, to the high mountain area of the Northern and Southern Ranges, it descends in flocks to the arable land for feeding purposes, while in autumn: October and November, its numbers are augmented by flocks from overseas, which are common on the low ground, and, when winter sets in the mountains, by the resident population from the high forests.

The wood-pigeon needs little description to Europeans for there are no other pigeons in Cyprus with which it can be confused. It is a heavily built bird, slate-grey in colour with a bluish-grey head, the neck glossed with violet and green, with a conspicuous white patch on either side; the mantle tends to brownish, wing-coverts grey broadly edged with white, forming a white bar on the open wing. Rump slate-grey, the tail blackish; underside of body rich vinous–purple, merging into ash-grey on the belly, more bluish on the flanks. Bill basally pink, yellow towards the horn-coloured tip. Legs and feet coral red tinged with mauve. Iris pale straw yellow. Total length 16–17 ins (41–43 cm). Immature are much duller than adults and lack the white patch on sides of neck. The five-note-cooing of this pigeon is known to most countrymen.

The wood pigeon in Cyprus lays its one or two white, slightly glossy, eggs on the small flimsy platform of fine twigs for which it is renowned, building at varied heights in a variety of trees: pine, olive, alder or in creepers. One nest was 8 ft. up in a smilax, growing on a pine on the Karpas Peninsula. Usually the nests are between 10 and 30 ft from the ground.

In the quiet valleys of the Southern range these pigeons were more numerous in the early spring months than we found them anywhere in the island – the majority still in flocks in February and March, when the migrants from overseas are leaving the lower ground for Europe.

STOCK DOVE

Columba oenas

This is a smaller pigeon than the last described, circa 13 ins (33 cm), about the same size as the rock dove, and is generally darker than either, darkish blue-grey which pales on the rump and darkens on the tail which shades from lavender-grey at the base to blackish at the tip. The grey wings with slate-coloured quills are crossed by two imperfect black bars. The breast is vinaceous, below which the body is pale blue-grey. On each side of the stock dove's neck is a patch of metallic green shot with purple. The underside of the wing is grey. Eye brown, surrounded by a pink rim; bill red at base, horn colour at tip, the fleshy portion white. Legs and feet pinkish-mauve.

With the wood pigeon it should never be confused. Smaller in size, less bulky body, and quick movements, should serve to identify the stock dove at all ages. The lack of any white in the wing precludes any mistake with the *adult* wood-pigeon in flight. The stockdove is also distinctive in having no white on the sides of the neck.

With the rock-dove there is more chance of confusion, usually the rock-doves in Cyprus have white rumps, we have never seen one without. The stock dove's rump is pale blue-grey; the stock dove has a dark brown eye and the rock dove a yellow eye. Again the stock dove is grey under the wing, the rock dove white. One more point – in flight the two black bars on the wing of the rock dove are always conspicuous, in the stock dove the two interrupted bars made up of spots, are barely noticeable. The gruffer voice of these birds, when known to the observer, is also diagnostic.

The stock-dove comes to Cyprus in winter in some years, arriving in variable numbers in October, few remaining till the end of January (uncommonly later) on the plains, but it can only be described as an erratic visitor as our own experience, related in *Birds of Cyprus* pp. 281/2, foretold. A pair shot near Kyrenia 24 April 1970 – an unusually late date, suggested they may have intended to breed.

It is an abundant visitor to Sinai in winter and many breed in Asia Minor but Cyprus does not appear to be on any regular route and their visits to the island must be governed by other factors. Inclement weather in Turkey may bring the birds over the intervening sea.

ROCK PIGEON [Plate 14, facing p. 80]

Columba livia gaddi

The subspecies of the rock-pigeon breeding in Cyprus is that named *C. livia gaddi* of S.W. Persia, which inhabits the adjoining countries, Asia Minor and the island of Crete. It is a short-winged race (210–240 mm) and has whitish, more rarely grey, upper tail-coverts. The terminal portion of the grey tail is broadly tipped with blackish. It is blue-grey in plumage with white rump and axillaries and two prominent black wing-bars. There is a metallic green and purple patch on the sides of the neck and on the grey breast. Bill lead-grey, legs and feet red, eye orange red with a yellow inner ring; cere white. Total length 13 ins (33 cm).

Comparison with the other pigeons is given under the stock-dove.

This dove or rock-pigeon is exceedingly numerous in the island, considerable flocks being seen in the crags and precipices of both mountain ranges as well as in the sea-cliffs where it breeds abundantly on the ledges and among the rocks. It also breeds in the Klidhes islands and other off-shore islets round the coast.

It has a lengthy nesting season lasting from February until May. As recorded in our larger work nests have been found in holes and crannies of the cliffs and in ruined buildings and even in disused wells. In the late summer and autumn it collects into large flocks which move around from one locality to another in search of drinking water.

In our last visit to the island, after twelve years interval, we believed the rock-doves had greatly increased in numbers and it is a pity that the Cypriot gunners do not pay more attention to them in preference to the much smaller "game" – hoopoes, cuckoos, etc., one sees dangling from their belts.

TURTLE DOVE

Streptopelia turtur

A small slenderly-built dove, 10½ ins (27 cm) from bill to tail. The upperparts rust-colour with black middles to the feathers. Forehead pale grey, crown ashy, nape browner. Neck, throat and breast pinkish-vinous. On each side of the neck a patch of black and white feathers. The inner coverts, secondaries and scapulars

black, margined with cinnamon-rufous; outer-coverts blue-grey; primaries dark brown. The tail is prettily patterned when open, the central feathers dark brown, the rest black washed with grey and broadly tipped with white, the outer feather white on the entire outer web. Sides of body dark blue-grey with a vinaceous wash; middle of belly and under tail-coverts white. Eye yellowish-brown, eyelids red, bill blackish, legs and feet claret colour.

Immature birds are browner above and the breast much more brown than pinkish-vinous which is attained when mature.

This is the only member of the pigeon family which can be described as a summer visitor, arriving in the island to breed, and departing to winter in Africa.

European turtle doves migrating through Cyprus may be expected around the third week of March, and flocks are passing in hundreds throughout April and May. The return journey takes place during September and October, mainly early to mid-September. Nesting of the summer visitors begins on the lower ground in mid-April and continues in the higher altitudes into June, where eggs have been taken in the Troödos mountains on 10 June. Breeding should be at its height in the lower northern Range, 3,000–4,000 ft in mid-May. Whereever the country is wooded the turtle-doves are to be seen.

The Nórth African, more sandy-coloured, turtle dove (*S. turtur arenicola*) has been recognised and collected in Cyprus, but its status is uncertain. See Appendix of "Least Recorded Visitors" p. 217.

The Senegal palm dove (*S. senegalensis*) has also twice been reported (See Appendix p. 218).

COLLARED DOVE

Streptopelia decaocto

[Plate 14, facing p. 80]

Once a breeding bird in the towns of Cyprus from which it had been wiped out, this most attractive and tame dove can hardly be mistaken if encountered. The whole upperparts are pale earth-brown, the head and neck grey tinged lilac, forehead pale mauve. A black collar bordered with white forms a half circle at the back of the neck. The wing-coverts are pale blue, the flight feathers dark brown. Middle pair of tail feathers are pale brown, the remainder grey and blackish-brown with broad white tips. Breast pale lilac, belly ash-grey, under tail-coverts slate-colour. The whole underside of the tail is black with broad white tips, quill-lining white. Eye crimson, eyelids whitish, bill black; legs and feet pinkish-red.

In size 11 ins (28 cm), slightly larger than the European turtle-dove; we have seen it succintly described as "a sandy-grey dove with narrow black half-collar, edged white, round back of neck, dark primaries and black and white under tail surface, particularly striking in flight".

It is sad this dove had been forced to retire from Nicosia where it was once a common sight in the secluded Old Turkish Gardens, even until 1912. There have been occasional records in recent years but the chance that these were escapes is greater than that they are genuine visitors, for doves of this kind – and the paler ring-dove – are often kept in captivity. We did not know in 1958 of a wild pair left in any of the towns or villages and believe the original stock was virtually exterminated as resident birds about fifty years ago.

Whether the "influx" reported to have occurred in the autumn of 1956 re-populated any places permanently seems doubtful. One bird was found dead in Nicosia in the summer and another seen on 4 October at Akrotiri. In 1957 one was reported in January from Limassol. It was seen again in Limassol in 1958. In 1963 four were reported from Nicosia in September. In 1969 two were seen in the summer in Nicosia and in the following year, 1970, one was reported on 19 February and *five or six pairs* located in the southern and western part of Nicosia (now a large town) in late February and early March, several of the males being seen in display flight. This certainly points to the bird re-establishing itself in the town of Nicosia, if permitted to do so, but how this stock originated can only be surmised.

Order CUCULIFORMES

Family CUCULIDAE

We cannot do better than repeat what we wrote in *Birds of Cyprus* when giving the principal characters of the cuckoo family, for whatever else changes, the habits of cuckoos do not, and what we wrote about them thirteen or more years ago is equally true today. Most Europeans judge the family by what they have seen of the species in their homeland, but cuckoos have a wide distribution and in Africa there are very small cuckoos and very large cuckoos, some of the Ethiopian species in the first named group being clothed in brilliantly metallic plumage. We divide the Palaearctic and Ethiopian species into two or more subfamilies in one of which the nesting habits are parasitic on other birds, in the other non-parasitic. The two species – the common European cuckoo, and the great spotted cuckoo – which occur on the Cyprus list, both belong to the first-named group Cuculinae, which lay their eggs in the nests of other species and leave their young to be brought up by foster-parents.

The true cuckoos have the zygodactylous arrangement of the foot with the first and fourth toes turned backwards and the second and third forwards. They are furnished with long pointed wings and long tails, which are graduated in both the cuckoos to be discussed hereafter. The bill is curved and is a great deal more powerful and more decurved in the great spotted cuckoo than in the common cuckoo. The tarsus is short with overhanging feathers, the feet furnished with sharp short claws.

All cuckoos are insectivorous destroying billions of injurious insects and caterpillars, even the hairy ones which most birds reject. It cannot be too strongly stressed how valuable cuckoos are on the land especially to the fruit farmers and the foresters. They are among those birds which any sensible Government should have near the top of their list of protected birds, and young Cypriots should be taught in the schools the good they do and the stupidity of shooting and ensnaring them. The great spotted cuckoo comes to Cyprus to breed, the common European cuckoo only as a passage migrant, but while guests in the island they should receive full Government protection and be given the welcome due to them – NOT shot.

EUROPEAN CUCKOO

Cuculus canorus [Plate 15, facing p. 81]

The general colour of the cuckoo is uniform leaden-grey, including wing-coverts and scapulars, but the primaries and secondaries are brown, the former heavily notched with white on the inner web. The long graduated tail is black, each feather with four diamond-shaped white spots down the middle at alternative intervals and a white tip. Cheeks, neck and upper breast are uniform ash-grey, the rest of the underparts white, heavily and closely barred with black. Eye bright yellow, bill horn colour, legs and feet chrome yellow. The sexes are much alike but the female browner. Total length 15 ins (38 cm) of which the tail alone is 7½ ins.

A colour variety named the hepatic cuckoo, is commonly seen in Cyprus on the spring migration. This variety has the whole of the upperparts rich chestnut barred with blackish-brown; tail barred black and chestnut. This colour phase is retained for life. The European cuckoo is a frequent spring migrant when a travesty of its well-known cry may be heard.

It arrives in the island on its return journey from Africa in mid-March and is common until late May, after which date it is only rarely reported. The main spring passage is in April. The autumn passage is for some reason negligible. There are only six September records with one in August and one in mid-October but doubt is cast on those outwith September by the Editors of the new Check-List, especially that in October.

The island seems to be avoided during the journey from summer to winter quarters, unless the birds pass over by night.

GREAT SPOTTED CUCKOO

Clamator glandarius

[Plate 15, facing p. 81]

This is a larger bird than the last cuckoo discussed, measuring about 16 ins (41 cm) from bill to tail, of which the strongly graduated broad tail takes up 8–9 ins from the base. The wings are long and pointed, about 2 ft across when open. The crown and cheeks are grey, the nape and back more ashy, a distinct crest overhangs the nape. Wings and scapulars are covered with large white spots which immediately distinguishes this cuckoo from all others; the wing-coverts are also tipped with white, as are the upper tail-coverts. The tail is dark brown with metallic gloss, all but the middle feathers broadly tipped with white, the middle feathers only slightly so. Entire underside white. Eye dark-brown, orbital ring reddish-orange, bill brown, legs hidden with white feathers, feet brownish-grey.

Young birds have a black crown, buff throat and chestnut remiges; they may be recognised by the five parallel rows of white spots on the open wing.

To Cyprus this bird comes as a summer visitor and passage migrant. Those which remain to breed scatter over the lower wooded plains and are especially to be seen among the olive groves. They are known to victimise ravens, crows, magpies and starlings on the continent of Europe but so far only magpies have so featured in Cyprus, in the nests of which, built in carobs or olives, the cuckoo eggs have been found. When we wrote our larger book, there was much still to be learned about this cuckoo's nesting habits in the island. Since then a British Officer, serving in Cyprus in 1958, found a magpie's nest in the

Karpas, 20 ft up in a Carob tree. This nest originally held eight magpie's eggs but on 9 April it contained six pies' eggs and two great-spotted cuckoo's eggs "from different hens". The latter eggs were identified in Britain by an Oological authority as those of *Clamator glandarius*. They were smaller than typical magpies and rather blunt-ended, with a pale greenish ground and violet shell marks with liver-brown blotches. The female cuckoos had, it seems, disposed in some way of two magpie's eggs between them, so that the number of eggs left in the nest was not altered. The European cuckoo (*C. canorus*) seldom deposits more than one egg in the nest of its victim.

The passage migrants which arrive in Cyprus may be encountered both on the plains and in the high mountains but do not remain in the latter to breed. The migrants arrive about mid-March – an early date was 3 March – and have been recorded on passage until mid-May, an even earlier arrival is on record on 21 February which is exceptional. The return passage in autumn begins in August, until which date the birds are to be usually seen each month. In 1968, the last was observed at Episkopi on 2 September, but that may be exceptional.

Order STRIGIFORMES

Family TYTONIDAE

The owls belong to an Order distributed all over the World, and is represented by two families, one of which Tytonidae is reserved for the barn owls of Cosmopolitan distribution. In Europe there is only a single representative of the Tytonidae, the barn owl, which has certain peculiarites entitling it and its relatives to family rank, distinct from the next family, the Strigidae. The barn owls have a highly developed heart-shaped facial disc which is never so pronounced a feature in the Strigidae, though present in all genera. In the genus *Tyto* the feathers above the bill meet to form an elevated ridge. The tarsi are slender and are *not* feathered to the toes as usually in the *Strigidae* (excepting the fishing owls) the feathering on the lower half more resembling hairs. Their legs are proportionately long in comparison.

Barn owls have another peculiarity – they appear to prefer to live in the proximity of man, spending the day in old buildings, lofts, barns and so on where they can remain undisturbed during the daylight hours. For other characters which they share with the next family, (see page 111). Barn owls should be accorded strict protection, for there is no bird more adept at killing rats and mice. They do no harm to man's interests in any way, but very much the reverse. This applies equally to the owls in the next family and should be born in mind by all legislators who have the interests of agriculture to safeguard.

BARN OWL [Plate 9, facing p. 33]

Tyto alba

The whole of the upperparts of this owl are golden-buff with pale grey mottling, and white speckles on the back, scapulars and wing-coverts. The facial mask, in which the large dark eyes are prominent, is silky-white, the underparts entirely white, shaded with greyish and very sparsely flecked, more so in the female than in the male. The legs are covered to the toes with white feathers and are long in comparison with the other owls of its size to be encountered in Cyprus.

On the wing the barn owl is easily recognised as it looks as if it was an all white bird when seen in poor light quartering a field or hillside in search of its prey. Known commonly in Europe as the screech owl, its cries are so weird: hissing, snoring and screeching as to defy description. It is a bird which does an enormous amount of good its principal prey being rats and mice. The barn owl is very seldom seen in Cyprus and can only be described as a scarce resident. It is as likely to be heard in the vicinity of the towns as in old ruined buildings or precipices in the interior. There are a number of records from Nicosia itself and the fact that, in October 1967, barn owls were caught on lime-sticks at Paralimni, Limpia and Akrotiri suggested to some a possible migratory movement through the island, though in our view it seemed more likely the owls were attracted to passerine species already so entangled, for barn owls are among the most sedentary species in their large family. No-one appears to have found its nest in Cyprus but the barn-owl has itself been taken in mid-June among other dates, which point to some being resident, a view which we believe is shared by those responsible for the last Check-List. Local movements in Cyprus may take place, especially in the autumn but we do not believe there is an overseas passage from Europe, a very difficult point to prove.

Family STRIGIDAE

This family includes all the owls in the World bar the barn owls (and some might except the fishing owls!). The Strigidae have round rather than an oval facial disc, very highly developed ears, and very soft plumage including the wings, which enable the birds to come upon their prey absolutely silently, a character they share with the last family. Legs are strong and the feet specially adapted for seizing and carrying their prey, the claws curved and exceedingly sharp. The outer toe is reversible; the bill is weak except in the very large species. Eyes are large and forwardly directed. In most the wings are long in comparison with the bird's size, particularly so in the short-eared owl which is capable of long journeys over the sea when it waylays the smaller migrants. Some species, notably among them the long-eared owl, have a tuft of elongated feathers over the eye, which are usually held erect. The eagle-owls are prominent among these "horned" owls. They occur in Turkey and neighbouring countries of the Middle East but not in Cyprus.

Owls are nocturnal in habits spending the day in hiding but coming out to feed as darkness is gathering; the little owl however may often be seen in daylight and even in bright sunlight sitting on some vantage point by the roadside. Owls can see perfectly well in daylight but Dr. Voous has told us what is not usually recognised; they cannot see in total darkness. They prefer moonlight nights and to hunt for their prey in what we may term a half light or "the gloaming".

The larger owls may occasionally be seen flying against a darkening sky or in the glare of headlights, but viewing the family as a whole they are much less often observed than birds which feed in broad daylight and both their status and their numbers are difficult to assess. There are today five members of the Strigidae for certain on the Cyprus List, two of which are resident and breed regularly, two other species have been found nesting but their real status is unknown, and another species is purely migratory, for the details of which the following pages must be consulted. One or two others, doubtfully recorded, are mentioned on p. 218 in the Appendix.

CYPRUS SCOPS OWL

Otus scops cyprius

[Plate 20, facing p. 128]

Apart from field observations by many naturalists, the number of specimens from Cyprus in the museums of Europe point to it always having been an abundant resident in this island, where in course of centuries, a well-established subspecies, *Otus scops cyprius*, has evolved. A very beautiful picture of this owl, by a world-famed artist, is given in this book on the plate reproduced from our earlier volume.

When seen at rest the Scops appears rather long and narrow in body with short erect ear-tufts. Its plumage is dark grey above with prominent white markings and fine vermiculations of grey-brown. The grey underparts are covered with broad black shaft-streaks and black cross-bars. Its eye is bright yellow and very arresting. The open wing has a wonderful pattern especially if exhibited on the underside, covered as it is with round white spots arranged in symmetrical lines. It utters a flute-like call. This owl is only 7½ ins (19 cm) in length.

The indigenous bird is to be found all over the island more especially in wooded areas. It may be found from the coastal belt to the Troödos mountains. It has a particular liking for olive trees in the hollows of which it sometimes chooses to nest. Breeding takes place from late March to mid-May. In addition to laying in hollow trees, roofs of houses, in wells and empty buildings, it also utilises the old nests of magpies built in olive or juniper trees, some 15 ft from the ground. The eggs are white and glossy and up to six eggs have been found in a nest.

Whether the **European Scops**, *Otus scops scops*, passes through Cyprus on migration is not certain. In 1968, 129 Scops owls were taken on lime-sticks by the Paralimni limers between 5 March and 11 May, which certainly points to a considerable influx either of continental birds on passage or of the local scops owl which had been attracted to the place by the countless small birds caught on the lime-sticks. In any case a most deplorable loss of a species which does nothing but good in the island, living mainly on insects, mice and lizards and perhaps fruit-bats. It seems extraordinary that when such numbers were available at Paralimni, the race to which they belonged was not determined. In the new Check-List it is suggested it is most likely to be the nominate form from Europe, with which we agree.

LITTLE OWL [Plate 9, facing p. 33]

Athene noctua

The Cyprus examples of the little owl are slightly intermediate between the two races *A.n. glaux* of the maritime zone of

Cyprus pied chat

Masked shrike

Golden oriole

Plate 18

Plate 19

northern Africa and *A.n. indigena* of S.E. Europe and Asia Minor. In our larger work it is indexed as an intermediate, not as a cross. For details see *Birds of Cyprus* (1958) p. 185, but in the new Check-List *indigena* is preferred.

The head, nape and back are brown, the crown streaked and spotted with white; facial disc white, eye very large and lemon-yellow. Underparts dull white profusely streaked with brown; tarsi covered with dull white feathers, the toes with bristles. The tail has four dark bands across a dull white ground. Total length 8 ins (20 cm). Its image appears on many Greek coins.

When encountered in broad daylight they usually remain where they are, but bob in a grotesque manner as if dropping a curtsy. If alarmed they fly fast, when the white spots on the wings and scapulars, and the bands on the tail, are noticeable. It is a resident species in all the wooded areas of Cyprus. Its call note is a softly repeated *quew*, that of the male uttered in a different key to the female. To what altitude breeding takes place needs to be discovered.

It nests on the plains in a variety of situations – in holes in walls or trees, in houses or ruined buildings, in wells and in low cliffs. One bird was extracted from a hole in a wall three feet deep when it promptly laid an egg in a nest-box and then disappeared. Another was "sitting" in an inaccessible fissure at Curium on 4 May. They are reported to be especially common around the ruined ancient city at Famagusta where the old crumbling walls bristle with inviting nesting places. Breeding occurs from April to June; full grown young have been seen on 26 May, and highly incubated eggs on 10 April. The eggs are white and rather small, circa 34 × 28·5 mm if a Cyprus taken egg is typical.

LONG-EARED OWL

Asio otus [Plate 9, facing p. 33]

This is one of the larger owls some 12–14 ins (30–36 cm) in length notable for the long ear-tufts, dark brown in colour with whitish edging. The ground colour of the upperparts is golden-buff, streaked with black and dark brown and finely vermiculated with white. Facial disc is pale brownish-buff with a blackish rim, while the forehead and chin are white. Underparts are golden-buff, broadly streaked with dark brown on the upper breast with a greyish edging. The lower part of breast is more lightly streaked and has dark wavy markings with transverse barring and varying amount of white edging. Middle of belly pale buff to whitish. Tail buff or grey barred with brown. Eye golden-orange, bill black; tarsus and toes covered with buff feathers.

In flight the ear-tufts are not visible, but when the bird is at rest, these erect tufts are very prominent. It is a bird with a huge distribution over the whole of continental Europe and over Asia. It is migratory in the north of its range.

It had until quite recently been considered mainly a winter visitor in very small numbers to Cyprus, but the discovery in 1968 of two breeding pairs in a fir plantation at Salamis – only present from December to May – which had made use of Cyprus

Plate 19 (opposite)

Cyprus jay
Cyprus great tit
Caucasian dipper
Grey wagtail

crow's nests in which to rear two or three young respectively, put a different aspect on the bird's status. The old birds of both pairs were seen in the vicinity and on the nests. Whether this is a case of isolated breeding of two pairs, or whether the birds have been overlooked by earlier naturalists is uncertain, for apart from under a dozen records between 20 October and 7 May, there is nothing to confirm earlier nesting. Being nocturnal it may easily have escaped notice hitherto. We gave what scanty information was available in our *Birds of Cyprus* (1958) p. 184. The breeding records were first reported in the fifteenth *Bird Report* of the C.O.S p. 21. Nesting took place in February and the owlets had reached the flight stage on 7 April. In 1969 two pairs again bred at Salamis and were present until July when they all disappeared.

SHORT-EARED OWL

Asio flammeus

This owl may be distinguished by its large size, 14–15 ins (36–38 cm) in length, and exceptionally long wings and, when examined closely, by the short ear-tufts which are difficult to see in life. The ground-colour varies individually from cream or buff to pale rufous, the feathers profusely mottled with black or dark brown with pale fringes. There are large white spots on the outer web of the greater wing-coverts. Facial disc dirty white or buff, the eye bordered with black feathers. Ruff shining-white, each feather tipped black. Underparts vary in same way as back, the breast prominently marked with dark brown shaft-streaks. Belly uniform, flanks finely streaked. Thighs, under tail-coverts and legs cream or buff, unmarked. Legs and toes feathered. The tail is crossed with dark brown on a pale ground.

In flight the head appears large and round and the exceptional wing-span is then noticeable. Bill horn-colour, eye yellow.

The short-eared owl has not been found breeding but is a regular passage migrant to Cyprus in the autumn and has also been taken by the limers during the spring. It is generally believed to be a common winter visitor on the lower elevations. It is one of the largest birds to have been caught on lime-sticks, which give some indication of the strength of this locally-made deadly substance. It is most frequently seen in spring, mainly in late March to early April. It is considered to be a rather scarce winter visitor, but few autumn records are available, recorded from mid-September to mid-April, rarely later.

NOTE

The **Tawny owl** is reported (Check-List 1971) to have been discovered *breeding* near Lefkoniko, 2 April 1966, where two fully grown fledglings were seen later on 30th. If true this is a very extraordinary record – the species having been reported only once previously and then unsatisfactorily. (See Appendix p. 218 under *Strix aluco.*) Text-fig in *Birds of Cyprus* 1958, p. 187.

Short-eared owl

Order CAPRIMULGIFORMES

Family CAPRIMULGIDAE

The nightjars, sometimes called goatsuckers, are a cosmopolitan family of wide distribution but in Europe and Asia Minor represented by only two species the common nightjar and the Egyptian. All nightjars are remarkable for an extraordinary similarity in colour-pattern and plumage which closely resembles the ground they inhabit, whether it be woodland, scrub or desert or sandy areas of the earth. The eastern European and S. W. Asian population winter in Africa and great numbers of *Caprimulgus europaeus* cross the eastern Mediterranean from their breeding places in Europe.

The plumage is exceptionally soft and the feathers loosely attached to the skin; in consequence nightjars are among the most difficult birds to preserve. The bill is short, weak and broad, the gape very wide, enabling the birds to capture insects on the wing with the minimum of effort. The tail of ten feathers is of medium length. The feet are very weak and the tarsus short; three toes are forwardly directed, one anteriorly. The third toe has the claw pectinated. The eyes are large and luminous.

Owing to their crepuscular and nocturnal habits they are only seen in flight as dusk is falling or if accidentally flushed in daylight. They are among the most difficult to locate on the ground. Consequently to what extent Cyprus can claim a breeding population is very difficult to assess, but as a migrant the birds are abundant on both spring and autumn passage. Eggs are laid on the bare earth and are wonderfully camouflaged.

Until specimens have been collected it is useless to speculate whether the Egyptian nightjar which breeds in Turkey is among the regular migrants to Cyprus or whether it takes a more eastern route to winter in Arabia and the Sudan. Passage of all nightjars when migrating is by night.

EUROPEAN NIGHTJAR

Caprimulgus europaeus

[Plate 15, facing p. 81]

About 10–11 ins (25–28 cm) in length with a very short weak bill, long pointed wings and a long square-tipped tail, the nightjar is one of the most difficult of all birds to see when on the ground, or lying along a lichen-covered bough. The general colour of the upper surface is grey, vermiculated with black; the underparts are mostly buff, the breast grey-brown barred and vermiculated with black; chin and throat are rufous finely barred black. A patch of cream or white adorns the lower throat, and there are buff patches on the outer web of the scapulars. Wings are dark grey-brown, the three outer primaries having a broad white patch on the outer webs. The outer tail-feathers are conspicuously tipped with white.

The female differs from the male in having no white patch on the primaries and no white tips to the outer tail-feathers, characters by which the sexes can be distinguished even in the lights of a car as the bird rises from the track.

A night-flying bird, as its name proclaims, feeding from dusk to dawn, the wide gape of the nightjar is well adapted for the purpose. We have seen the mountain tracks in Cyprus alive with nightjars on 30 April and 1 May, their large eyes caught in the gleam of the headlights, shining in the dark before the bird rises, absolutely silently.

To Cyprus the nightjar comes in large numbers in April and May, some arriving earlier, mid to late March; there are records in varying numbers until October and occasional sightings in November and December. In summer they are scattered over the forest area, and in the foothills, and in some years are very common all through the summer.

Breeding has recently been reliably confirmed at Polemidhia and Cape Andreas, the nesting birds belonging to the race *meridionalis*. No nest is made and the two eggs normally laid are as difficult to distinguish from the ground as are the birds themselves and are seldom found, so closely do they assimilate in colour. Its churring note in the summer months may be the first indication of its presence. We are tempted to consider the nightjar, a numerous spring and summer visitor to Cyprus, a number remaining to breed, some staying in the island until December. We have reliable records of nightjars seen crossing the eastern Mediterranean as late as the third week of November, observed from ships at sea, so there is nothing strange in finding odd birds in Cyprus up till Christmas. The main autumn passage occurs from late August or early September to the end of October. It is probable that the passage migrants belong to the nominate race but specimens have not been collected to establish this.

NOTE

We accepted the record of an **Egyptian nightjar** *Caprimulgus aegyptius* as a vagrant in *Birds of Cyprus* p. 163 and see no reason to retract it, for so striking a bird could not be easily mistaken for any other. See Appendix p. 218.

Order APODIFORMES

Family APODIDAE

Swifts have a purely superficial resemblance to swallows and have the same habit of hawking insects on the wing, but in structure they differ widely from the Hirundinidae. In outward appearance swifts may be recognised by the striking formation of their narrow pointed wings. The peculiarly flattened inner edge of the anterior part of the wing is a character which attracts attention when the bird is handled and the wing extended. The head is flat and broad, the bill very weak, but the gape wide as in the swallows. Swifts possess remarkably weak feet, the tarsus being very short; thus the bird has difficult in rising if placed on a flat surface. The toes are directed forwards.

The tail of the swifts varies in shape in the different species: in those which occur in Cyprus it is moderately forked and unlike swallows the outer feathers are never elongated into streamers; the tail is composed of ten feathers only. All members of the family are sombrely coloured – those in the Palaearctic region being grey-brown, brown, blackish or mouse-colour, often with some white on the chin, or, in one species which breeds in Cyprus, on most of the underside of the body. The family is poorly represented in the island, only three species being found there in the summer months, all three of which nest in the island, and depart with their broods after the breeding season. One of the small white-rumped species has been recorded as an accidental vagrant. Cyprus is one of the best places in which to study the three breeding species: common, pallid and Alpine, all nesting in apparently amicable competition.

EUROPEAN SWIFT

Apus apus

The entire plumage, save for a white patch on the throat and chin, is dusky black, with bottle-green reflections on the mantle and back. The belly is black, feathers of flanks and ventral region with pale fringes. Under tail-coverts lighter brown with dark tips. An adult swift measures about 7 ins (18 cm). The bill is very small and weak, the gape wide, the eye sunk deep in the socket; the tail is moderately forked and the wings long and pointed. The head is large and rather flat in appearance. Both by its shape and flight a swift is easily recognised, but in Cyprus care is required not to confuse it with the pallid swift, both of which are summer visitors, the European swift by far the more numerous of the two.

Both a breeding bird and passage migrant in large numbers, the main body arrive in Cyprus early in March with small numbers in February or even in the last week of January. Enormous numbers are present in the summer, breeding in all the towns. Nesting is in full swing in April. Swifts prefer the lower altitudes but nest at all elevations. Birds found nesting under roofs of houses at 5,500 ft in Troödos village had small young on 20 May.

The majority which nest in Cyprus do so in holes of town-buildings and ruins, usually laying two or three white eggs on a shallow nest of feathers, dead grass and leaves, and other similar material, even adding scraps of paper and flower-petals etc. during incubation.

Most breeding birds of this swift leave before mid-July and are usually all gone by end of the month. Autumn passage migrants have been noticed in August and September, but are generally very few in numbers. Occasional flocks seen in November and early December must have made very late departure from localities in southern Europe or Asia Minor. The breeding birds are allied with the nominate subspecies but are not absolutely typical according to recent investigation.

PALLID SWIFT [Plate 15, facing p. 81]

Apus murinus pallidus

Very similar in size and appearance to the European swift but slightly smaller and much paler in plumage, greyish-mouse colour, with a larger white patch on the throat.

It is a summer visitor to the island breeding in distinct scattered colonies at all elevations. They are not usually seen before the beginning of March and remain in the island until the young are able to leave. Its numbers are small in comparison with the darker common swift, but they may be seen in the same areas, hawking over the lower levels and while consorting with the common swift when feeding, they nest apart from it in scattered pairs and small colonies.

They are reported to breed in the Troödos mountains two or three weeks later than the common swift, but two nests of faeces, feathers and bits of rubbish found under the eaves of a roof at Troödos, circa 5,500 ft, held respectively two newly hatched and two small young on 27 May and were only one week later than *Apus apus* in the same locality. High altitude nesting is likely to affect both birds in the same way and on an average may well be two or three weeks later than colonies on the plains.

When the common swift has left Cyprus in June and July after nesting, the pallid swift stays on and is then more easily recognised around the towns. Autumn passage of the pallid swift has been noticed up to late September, by which time the breeding population have all departed.

ALPINE SWIFT [Plate 15, facing p. 81]

Apus melba

This is another, and most important, summer visitor to breed in the island, and also passage migrant. It is a much larger bird than either of the other two breeding swifts, and apart from its size is easily recognised by its all-white underparts with a band of brown across the chest. Head and back are pale brown, the wings and tail darker brown. Feathers of the crown and cheeks are narrowly bordered with white only noticeable when in the hand. The bill is very weak but the gape very wide; the legs are feathered to the tibio-tarsal joint. From bill to tail the Alpine swift measures fully 8 ins (20 cm) and the wing is 9 ins in length. the tail is forked.

This swift has its breeding colonies in Cyprus in immense cliffs, the nesting holes being quite inaccessible. The steepest precipices are chosen and returned to year after year. The nesting birds return to the island mid to late February, the main body arriving by mid-March at their nesting holes. In the breeding season the old birds descend to the lower ground over which they may be seen hawking high in the air and sometimes coming to drink at freshwater pools on the plains. They are especially common in the Northern Range where there are precipices of immense size and grandeur at Buffavento and Pentadactylos. Visitors to Kantara Castle and the cliffs above the Forest station of Aronia, where other colonies exist, cannot ever fail to be delighted by the aerial evolutions of these fine birds at their nesting sites.

There are also colonies at Episcopi and Cape Aspro among other sea-cliff sites. Whether there are breeding places in the Troödos mountains has not yet been confirmed but Alpine swifts have been seen among these heights in the summer.

Alpine swifts, believe to be *Apus melba melba* from northern Europe also pass through Cyprus on their autumn journey to Africa. Those which have bred in Cyprus have mostly vanished by the end of September. Recently a party of twenty-six appeared at Limassol on 21 November, a late date for so many before crossing the sea. These would more likely be of the nominate subspecies.

Order CORACIIFORMES

Family ALCEDINIDAE

In the kingfishers we have some of the most gaudily coloured birds in the world typified for British ornithologists by the common blue kingfisher of Europe, *Alcedo atthis*, which has its representatives in Cyprus and the Middle East, but not apparently, as we were once given to understand, as a breeding bird in the island. At least one other genus *Ceryle* is represented in Cyprus by the pied kingfisher *Ceryle rudis* as an occasional visitor and possibly in the distant past the genus *Halycon* by the Smyrna kingfisher, but if so it was a chance visitor whcih has not repeated its visit. The other two however, we have seen for ourselves.

The chief characters of this family are to be found in the long straight bill with keeled or flattened culmen, terminating in most species in a sharp point; and short weak tarsi and feet, the third and fourth toes being united for most of their length. The reversed hind toe is well developed and the soles of the feet are broad and flattened. The primaries are eleven in number, the wing rounded with the outermost primary falling far short of the next. The tail is fairly short and is composed of twelve feathers. Some species have well-developed crests. The brilliance of their plumage is renowned.

An attempt was made at one time to separate the kingfishers into two groups – first the Alcedininae, with perceptibly keeled bill, being mostly fish-eaters, obtaining their living by diving for fish and consequently being dependent on water. To this group belong the brilliant European or common kingfisher and the black and white pied kingfisher. The other group, having generally a rounded or flattened culmen, are mainly insectivorous and fish do not figure in their diet. Consequently they occur far from any water and are content to find their food supply in cultivated areas or even in perfectly dry country. The Smyrna kingfisher, so brilliantly garbed, is one of these and as it inhabits the surrounding countries of Asia Minor, Syria and Palestine it may surely be expected someday to grace Cyprus with a passing visit. From an anatomical point of view the existence of these two groups cannot be recognised, and consequently in modern classifications all are included in the family Alcedinidae.

EUROPEAN KINGFISHER

Alcedo atthis [Plate 15, facing p. 81]

The whole upperparts of this brilliant bird are cobalt blue, brightest on the rump. Feathers on crown greener, each with a bright blue subterminal bar. Wings are brown but the outer webs of the primaries blue-green, the wing-coverts with pale blue tips. Tail greenish-blue and very short. Underparts and ear-coverts orange-chestnut, a patch of white lies behind the ear-coverts. Below these coverts a broad blue streak extends from beneath the eye. Bill fairly stout and long (1·60 ins in length) and sharp-pointed, is black in colour, the under mandible reddish at base; tarsus and feet are sealing-wax red, the legs very short. In total length bill to tail is 7 to 7½ ins (18–19 cm) in all.

We cannot claim that the kingfisher is a breeding bird in Cyprus at the present day whatever it was in the past. One well-known naturalist resident in the island on Government Service from 1903–1946 is responsible for the statement (in writing) that a pair bred in the Othello Tower, Famagusta but gave no supporting details perhaps inferring breeding from their actions. The statement in our book *Birds* of *Cyprus* (1958) p. 171 that one had a nest in a sand cliff at Athalassa was a sad error, caused by a misplaced card in our card-index. The nest reported was that of a roller and we apologise for having attributed it to the subject of this essay. There is no satisfactory nesting record as yet for the island.

Kingfishers of the south European race *A. atthis atthis* are to be seen all the year round, but only a few in number both on the coast where we have seen it several times in unfrequented places, in the ports and on the reservoirs. It is very scarce from May to July inclusive. An entry in the C.O.S. Report for 1967 sums up its status as succintly and accurately as possible: "Ones and twos around coast and inland waters throughout the year; most numerous in March and April and again in September to mid-October. A party of six at Polemidhia Dam on 7 September". This points to regular spring and autumn migration to Cyprus waters annually, a few of the birds electing to remain in the island. Breeding has yet to be confirmed. We have been astonished to read in the new official Check-List of Cyprus Birds that an example of *Alcedo atthis ispida* has been taken in Cyprus. No details are given of the capture of this north European bird which includes the British Isles in its breeding range.

PIED KINGFISHER

Ceryle rudis [Plate 15, facing p. 81]

This is one of the rarer visitors to Cyprus which we have been able to watch in the island for long at a time when a pair spent December and January in Famagusta harbour and the neighbouring coast. Easily recognised by its entirely black and white pattern, black bill and feet, and large size 10–11 ins (25–28 cm), a glance at the figure on Plate 15 will imprint it on one's mind. On the upperside there is more black than white in the plumage but on the underside the reverse, a heavy black patch on either side of the white breast in both sexes and – in the male – a narrow band beneath the patch, entirely crossing the breast.

This is one of the fish-eating kingfishers (as opposed to the kingfishers found in dry country but not in Cyprus which live on mole-crickets and insects) and is entirely dependent on water for its habitat, both fresh and salt. The pied kingfisher has occurred irregularly but uncommonly in Cyprus and we were indeed lucky to see it in 1957–58. It captures its prey by diving, first hovering over the clear water with fast beating wings before plunging to capture a passing fish. It will at times desert the coast for inland waters – even a roadside ditch may attract it. The pair we observed so closely spent much time sitting quite comfortably on telegraph lines crossing some casual water. It has only been seen in Cyprus in the winter months 1902 (1) November Larnaca; 1906 (1) February, Larnaca; 1924 (3) November to spring of the following year, Famagusta; 1944 (1) November, Nicosia; 1957–58 (2) December–January Famagusta: all definite dates accepted by the compilers of the latest Check-List. The statement that it has bred in Cyprus has no foundation. It is a very uncommon visitor, but one that should be easily recognised.

NOTE

Smyrna Kingfisher: *Halcyon smyrnensis* reported in the past (1887–88) to have occurred rarely in Cyprus. See Appendix p. 219.

Family MEROPIDAE

The bee-eaters are among the brightest coloured of all the birds which visit the Middle East, and Cyprus is fortunate in lying on one of their main routes between Europe and Africa of the so called common bee-eater of southern Europe. A glance at Plate 16 in this book will enable the reader to form his own opinion as to their beauty. Colours of the various species blend perfectly with one another but the feathers are not metallic. For the most part bee-eaters are slim birds, the common bee-eater not more than 10½ ins (27 cm) in total length, with a fine gently down-curved bill and very short legs. The wing is long and narrow and double pointed, the inner remiges abnormally long. The tail is of twelve feathers and varies in structure in the different species. In the common species (*apiaster*) in Cyprus the central pair of feathers extend beyond the others as shown so clearly in the Plate. This character is also present in the blue-cheeked bee-eater which is a much rarer bird in Cyprus and unlike the commoner species, has not been known to breed in the island. It is mainly green in plumage, the colour which predominates throughout the group.

Colonial builders excavating holes in banks of rivers, quarries or sandpits, the tunnels running in from 3 to 6 ft, they lay two white eggs. Summer visitors in the Middle East these attractive birds migrate in large flocks and draw attention to their arrival by their loud twittering notes. Living entirely on insects which they capture on the wing they are beneficial to all but the bee-keeper with whom they are, with good reason, very unpopular.

Unfortunately hundreds fall victim to the lime-sticks and other means of slaughter so prevalent in the Middle East.

COMMON BEE-EATER

Merops apiaster [Plate 16, facing p. 96]

The bee-eater can be recognised by its voice, its graceful gliding flight – the long narrow wings appearing to have two points – the shape of its tail, square at the end with two narrow central restrices protruding about ¾ in beyond the others and by its gently curved black bill. The entire forehead is white, the head, neck and mantle chestnut, fading to buff on the scapulars. In winter the mantle is strongly washed with green; the back is green washed with blue; the rump golden and the tail green. On the face a black band extends from the gape to the ear-coverts, passing below the eye. Throat bright yellow and rest of underparts green-blue the two colours separated by a narrow black bar. Wings are bluish with black tips to primaries and secondaries. Total length 10–11 ins (25–28 cm).

To Cyprus it comes in considerable numbers during both the spring and autumn passage, vast flocks passing over the island high overhead. Their numbers on these occasions have been reckoned in thousands. The spring migration which begins in early April is at its height in late April and early May and again in mid to late September. Not a great number descend to spend the summer or rest on their way, but birds are fairly general from mid-April till second or third week in May, occasionally later.

There are a number of breeding sites in Cyprus mainly in the southern hills but they do not appear to have received the attention they merit and breeding data of some species in Cyprus is entirely wanting. The earlier naturalists recorded colonies of bee-eaters near Paphos, and others were reported from the hills, but with two brilliant exceptions between 1948 and 1958 the breeding biology of Cyprus birds has been sadly neglected within recent years. Readers who possess our *Birds of Cyprus* will not find it difficult to discover to whom the "two brilliant exceptions" refer – the first and last references to "Recorders of Cyprus birds" of the two years giving him the answer on pp. Lvii and Lviii.

The common bee-eater is a colonial nester, the nesting holes being excavated in sandbanks or river banks when these are suitable. At the end of the burrow which they excavate themselves with their feet, they deposit their two white eggs. It is not recorded when the summer residents depart but they no doubt join the autumn migration from Europe to Africa, which lasts from mid-August to late September.

In the autumn passage as many as 500 birds have been seen on one occasion in a Eucalyptus grove at Phassouri, obviously resting, at the end of September, on their way to Africa. Birds may be seen passing up to the first week of November. Many pass over at night and in the early morning, especially in September. Ringed birds from the Ukraine and Bulgaria have been caught in Cyprus on their way south. Fortunately very few bee-eaters fall victim to the lime-sticks but they are regularly shot by Cypriot gunners who esteem them as an article of food.

BLUE-CHEEKED BEE-EATER

Merops superciliosus persicus

[Plate 15, facing p. 81]

Almost completely bright green above in colour, the adult Persian bee-eater, as it is often named, should not be confused with the much commoner *M. apiaster*. A blue band across the forehead and blue streaks (or patches) above and below the eye, have suggested its colloquial name, and are the only relief to its general green appearance, bar the black lores and black ear-coverts which are joined by a black stripe passing below the eye. In adult birds the frontal band is *white*, becoming blue on the forehead which merges into the green of the crown. Some of the primary coverts are blue on the outer web and the scapulars, rump and upper tail-coverts often have bluish tips. Primaries are green, washed with blue terminally, and have blackish tips. The tail is green with bluish outer edges, the central feathers elongated beyond the others up to 2½ ins and tapered to a fine point. The chin is yellow, throat bright chestnut, the rest of the underside green but axillaries and under tail-coverts pale chestnut. Eye crimson, bill black, legs and feet brownish pink.

Originally described from the Caspian area, the Asiatic birds migrate through Egypt to pass the cold months in tropical Africa returning to their summer quarters from the edge of the Syrian grasslands eastwards across Iraq and Persia. Not many had been reported from Cyprus previous to 1958 when our book was published but there have been a number of spring records since, which may be summed up as follows: Within the lifetime of the C.O.S. 1957–1971 there have been twenty records of the blue-cheeked bee-eater, suggesting that it may be considered a rare but annual visitor during the two periods of migration. Full data will be found in the new *Cyprus Check-List* for those who require details. Birds seen varied between singletons and four, and cover the years mentioned above. The spring months include March, April and May, the autumn months September and October when birds were seen. The first – and only – record previous to 1957 was of a single bird in 1901, pointing to the excellent work which the members of the C.O.S. have accomplished in a comparatively short time.

Family CORACIIDAE

The rollers which are grouped in this family are in Cyprus represented by a single species, *C. garrulus*, which is the only member of the family which breeds in Europe. It is almost a counterpart of the Abyssinian roller of the Sudan, from which it differs by lacking the elongated streamers on the long outer rectrices. The colours are practically the same (see Plate 16). Rollers are rather heavy looking birds with powerful beaks hooked at the tip and a wide gape. They vary in length from 10–15 ins (25–38 cm). They are locust eaters *par excellence* and when locusts are present feed on nothing else. Their relatives in Africa are noted for their aerobatics during bushfires, darting through the smoke and flames to snap up the insects fleeing from the conflagration. Were Cyprus to be attacked by locusts the rollers would no doubt arrive on the scene as if by magic, but normally they are only scarce summer visitors to breed.

For their nesting habits see under the species heading. The family is of African origin and their one representative is only to be found north of the Mediterranean in the summer months. There is an Asiatic roller in India but the family is entirely confined to the Old World.

EUROPEAN ROLLER

Coracias garrulus [Plate 16, facing p. 96]

About 12–13 ins (30–38 cm) in total length and somewhat jay-like in appearance, this bird together with the bee-eater and the oriole, are the most gaudily coloured of Cyprus birds. The head and breast of the roller are azure-blue, the back tawny brown and the rump purple. Flight feathers are purplish-black, the lesser wing-coverts and a patch on the bend of the wing deep purple and the rest of the wing-coverts greenish blue. Central tail feathers dull green, the remainder dark blue basally, light blue terminally with all the shafts black. In flight a deep purplish-blue band across the primaries and secondaries becomes visible and is a most prominent feature. A roller's flight is distinctive, extremely buoyant but difficult to describe. The rolling action, to be witnessed only in the breeding season, has provided the roller with its familiar name.

Considerable numbers arrive in Cyprus in early and mid-April and may be seen commonly in that month till mid-May. A great many are caught on lime-sticks for food. The birds will sit for hours on telegraph wires or posts from which they pounce down upon insects or small creatures like frogs. Locusts and large grasshoppers are greedily devoured and this is yet another beneficial species to the land of which benefits the shooting fraternity in Cyprus apparently cares nothing. It is good to eat and that is the end of it!

They do not breed in the higher elevations but lay their eggs in late April and early May in cliff holes and in soft banks of marl and sand in the then dry river-beds; birds have been seen feeding young in late May and in June. Hundreds pass through as passage migrants on their way from Africa in spring. The following dates are supplied by the members of the C.O.S., as collated in recent years: After breeding, never in any but sparse numbers, the rollers leave once more for their winter quarters in Africa, reaching the Sudan with the European passage migrants in October. Autumn migration through Cyprus may be witnessed from late August to the end of September, a few into October. Breeding in Cyprus in the plains and foothills, the roller may excavate a hole for itself in a dry river bank or in a hole in a ruin or old timber, but only the first named site has been found in Cyprus. Four to five glossy white eggs is the usual sett.

Family UPUPIDAE

The hoopoes are represented in Europe and Africa by two different birds *Upupa epops* and *Upupa senegalensis* but some modern taxonomists treat the latter as a subspecies of the former in the rush to eliminate one species after another and reduce them to subspecific rank. A *true* subspecies of *Upupa epops* inhabits the Nile Delta, *U. e. major* but only the typical subspecies occurs in Europe. It is a very beautiful bird (illustrated on Plate 16) and typical of its family in possessing such strikingly patterned plumage. The long decurved bill, barred black and white wings and banded black and white tail would alone attract a watcher's attention to it, but in addition its crown is adorned with a long crest which hangs over the nape and can be raised at will when the bird is alerted. It has rounded wings and a butterfly-like flight. An insect eater doing nothing but good, which comes to Cyprus to breed, but in small numbers, it is in danger of being exterminated by wanton shooting as it has already been exterminated from Crete and southern Greece according to reliable accounts. Gunners in the Middle East are all too often seen with hoopoes strung on their belts and the Cyprus Government should take heed lest the island loses one of its tamest and most attractive birds and a special delight to tourists by their pleasing habits.

HOOPOE [Plate 16, facing p. 96]

Upupa epops

The general colour of this widely recognised bird is cinnamon-brown. A long crest tipped heavily with black and with a considerable amount of white on the anterior feathers next to the black tip; the conspicuously banded black and white wings and a black tail crossed by a broad black band are the main points to be observed in this strikingly patterned bird. The long fine bill is 50–60 mm in length and brown in colour; the eye brown and legs and feet slate-grey.

The female is slightly browner and duller than her consort. The fine crest, with which the crown is adorned, is often raised and expanded, a habit which it exhibits on first alighting. It has various notes but that usually heard is an arresting *oop oop oop*. It is usually encountered in pairs. Exceptionally tame until alarmed, its flight when not frightened is wavering but it has a surprising turn of speed if genuinely alarmed or suddenly disturbed. It makes one sad to see this bird dangling from a hunter's belt, but one which is all too often met with in the Middle East.

In the spring months the hoopoe may be encountered scattered over the wooded country breeding in May and June in holes in trees or in walls, using very little nesting material upon which to lay its four to six eggs. It has been seen feeding young in low lying areas in late May, and in Troödos in early June, the latter perhaps an early brood at that altitude. Another Troödos nest in the hole of a pine contained five heavily incubated yellowish-olive nest-stained eggs on the 24 May. It is believed to prefer the higher elevations in both ranges in which to nest rather than the lower ground.

From an economic point of view if from no other the hoopoe is of value to the community and is one which merits complete protection. As a passage migrant the numbers which pass through Cyprus from early March onwards appear subject to considerable fluctuation and one is left with the impression that this most useful insect-eating bird is becoming much scarcer in recent years. The latest reports of its migrations which have reached us are as follows: Common on both passages, especially in spring. First arrivals early to mid-March, common from late March to early May, main passage late March to mid-April. In autumn from mid-August to early or mid-October, occasionally to early November and rarely to the end of that month.

Order PICIFORMES

Family PICIDAE

In this large family spread throughout the world in a great variety of genera we place three sub-families: the true woodpeckers *Picinae*, the piculets *Picuminae*, and the wrynecks *Jynginae*, the first and last groups forest-frequenting birds known to most people. It is a matter of great regret that Cyprus lacks any representative of the true woodpeckers and that is not for the lack of suitable terrain. The forests of Cyprus are extensive and those which clothe the Southern (Troödos) mountains are of ancient growth and support fine specimens of the Aleppo pine *Pinus halepensis* and of the Cyprus cedar, *Cedrus libani* var *brevifolia*, as well as the endemic golden oak *Quercus alnifolia* among much lesser growth. There is moreover no lack of deep ravines and river bottoms supporting broad-leaved riverine trees. In such forests in northern Africa we have never failed to find woodpeckers of at least two species and their complete absence from the older Cyprian forests is not easily explained.

The family is represented in Cyprus by the last sub-family mentioned above in which are grouped the wrynecks, believed by some to represent the ancestral type of the family. The contortions of the wrynecks head when alarmed accompanied by a snake-like hissing is responsible for the English name, as well as the specific *torquilla* i.e. twisted. To add to the delusion it has a long serpent-like tongue which it extends when taken by surprise.

Wrynecks so inconspicuously coloured in soft grey, pale rufous, black and brown plumage, blending to match the bark of deciduous trees it prefers, are not attracted by coniferous growth and the European migrant – the sole representative in Cyprus – only visits the island on migration, for which the main account of the species must be consulted. It can cling to a tree-trunk with facility with its sharp claws but does not run up and down the exterior of trees like a woodpecker but rather perches across the limbs, instead of clinging to them as a tit might do. Nor are the tail-feathers stiff as in the woodpecker. In appearance there is nothing to suggest that the wryneck is a member of the woodpecker family. The Romans named it *verticalis* for they believed it was subject to "fits"!

WRYNECK [Plate 15, facing p. 81]

Jynx torquilla

Six to seven ins (15–18 cm) in length, the wryneck at first acquaintance seems to be very unsuitably placed in the woodpecker family, so unlike those birds is it both in plumage-pattern and in making its long journeys overseas. It has the honour however of alone representing the great family with which systematists have allied it, for there is no true woodpecker in Cyprus, and even the wryneck can only be listed as a fairly common visitor which has never been known to breed. It winters largely in eastern Africa north of the Equator and its migration takes it, from all over Europe, in a S.E. direction, the majority of the European population crossing the Mediterranean east of Greece. It is one of the commonest migrants through the islands of the Aegean Sea and even deserts hold no terrors for it.

In appearance it is dully coloured – a mingling of streaks, bars and vermiculations of greys, browns and rufous. The middle line of the mantle and back is streaked prominently with black. The wing colour is subdued, the primaries barred rufous and blackish; the grey tail, closely vermiculated with dark brown is crossed by five narrow blackish bars. The wryneck's underparts are seldom seen, so closely does it cling to the treebark; when a sight is obtained – for it will often feed on the ground, it will be seen to be pale rufous, narrowly barred with black on the throat and breast; the belly white with spots or broken bars and the under tail-coverts buff, also finely barred.

Very rarely seen in Cyprus before the beginning of March, though some early dates in February are on record, the main body arrive in the island in April, a few in early May. Being passage migrants only, with no intention of breeding, they do not tarry in Cyprus and are not seen again before August when the forerunners of the autumn migration arrive early in that month, the main body once more in September, when they are fairly common up to mid or late October. Occasional late-comers into November or even to the end of the year. A S.E. course is followed in autumn by the European population, as the bird winters largely in eastern Africa.

Order PASSERIFORMES

This great Order contains more than half the birds of the world. They are land birds noted for perching and singing. The Order is divided by Dr. Wetmore into four Sub-Orders but only the last, the Oscines, comprising some forty families, concerns us here as it is the only Sub-Order represented in the Palaearctic Region.

Sub-Order OSCINES

Family ALAUDIDAE

The larks which are comprised in this family are widely distributed birds of the open spaces renowned for their sweet song and may be typified by the well-known sky-lark *Alauda arvensis*, a bird with an exceptionally long hind-claw which is nearly straight, unlike the hindclaws of most passeres which are short and abruptly curved. Another characteristic is in the fact that the hind part of the tarsus is scutelated (covered with scales), the opposite to the pipits (*Anthus*) which have the hind tarsus smooth. The habit of soaring while uttering their song is common to the group. Mostly dull-coloured, brown, buff, russet and grey, they harmonise closely with the earth. Larks are inhabitants of open grassy or arid regions and in desert areas blend to a remarkable degree with the colour of the soil upon which they live. In no species of lark is this more strikingly exemplified than in the crested lark (*Galerida*) of which Cyprus has its own indigenous representative in *Galerida cristata cypriaca*.

In all there are only six species of the family known from Cyprus three of which, including the Calandra lark – the largest member of the group, are known to have bred. They represent however, five different genera widespread throughout the Middle East.

CALANDRA LARK [Plate 17, facing p. 97]

Melanocorypha calandra

This is a large lark, 7 ins (18 cm) in length, with a heavy bill, long pointed wings and a very short tail compared with its body. The upperside blends closely with the colours of the ground, a mixture of brown, grey and buff with blackish middles to the feathers. On each side of the foreneck is a blackish patch which is very distinctive. The wings look black as the bird rises from the ground exposing the white tips to the secondaries and inner primaries. The middle tail feathers are black, the outer ones white and the rest are white tipped. The breast is buffish-white, prominently spotted below the breast band, the rest of the underparts and under tail-coverts being pure white. The bill is horn colour, the stout legs pinkish-flesh. The hind toe is furnished with an exceptionally long claw.

The cornfields of Cyprus swarm with larks among which the calandras are conspicuous for their size, even when the local crested-larks are present for those also are large birds at close quarters, dwarfing the short-toed and even the skylarks.

The calandra is resident all the year in Cyprus but is apparently rather local in its distribution. It nests abundantly on the Mesaoria plain, again near Larnaca, Dhekelia, at Kythrea and Kouklia and on the Karpas peninsula among other localities. Nesting is in April, the calandra building a nest on the ground often in a cornfield or under a tussock of grass or thistles growing in the corn. It is constructed of grass bents and lined with fine grasses. The eggs are distinctive with their bold blotchings of olive-brown and, when fresh, greenish shading; the ground colour varies from greyish-white to a very pale greenish-white. Many eggs have underlying blotches and smears of purplish-grey in addition to the spots and blotches already described.

Passage migrants occur in large flocks, in spring from late February to early April and in autumn in September and October. The breeding birds gather into flocks from midsummer onwards. The possibility of winter visitors also must be borne in mind, but difficult to establish.

SHORT-TOED LARK

Calandrella cinerea brachydactyla

We had been uncertain which of the races of this lark is the breeding bird of Cyprus. In our larger work we believed it to be *brachydactyla*, a bird with sandy-rufous plumage, whereas the eastern race named *longipennis* is browner and greyer. In a series the differences are not difficult to distinguish but seen singly it is impossible to do so and only the collecting of breeding birds will settle the point. The difference is most marked when the crown of the head is compared, for the crown of *longipennis* is always like the mantle, never redder. Larks are prone to live upon soil with which their plumage conforms, and there is much to be said for the theory that some larks are plastic species varying in colour according to the ground they inhabit, without regard to geographical distribution, in its wider sense. The short-toed lark is exceedingly difficult to see when

Plate 20 (opposite)

Cyprus tree-creeper
Cyprus scops owl
Cyprus coal tit

Plate 20

settled; more "sandy" than a skylark, despite its white underparts *with a patch of dark brown on each side of its neck* – a most important feature to observe. The tail is short and the feet remarkable in having no long hind toe. In flight the tail feathers are nearly black except the near-white outer one. Legs are brownish flesh-colour and the bill yellowish-horn. Its body is 5½ ins (14 cm) long.

While there must be more than one race of short-toed lark passing through Cyprus on migration it is the bird named *brachydactyla* which has been recorded breeding in April and May, when eggs may be found. The nest is a shallow scrape lined with hairs and soft vegetable material. Eggs are pale green in ground colour with dense mottling of brown and freckling of brown and violet brown. They no doubt vary considerably in a series.

Of its migrations through Cyprus and its status generally the following is a summary:

The short-toed lark, *brachydactyla*, besides being a breeding bird, is believed to be the principal passage migrant, although examples of other races have been collected, e.g. *longipennis* at Famagusta. (*artemesiana* is one which probably occurs according to the *Cyprus Check-List*.) Migrants begin to arrive in February and are common from early March to early May, when large numbers are reported. The autumn passage takes place from August, usually late in the month, to October, with small flocks into November. Systematists now consider *brachydactyla* a subspecies of *cinerea* and it so appears in the *Cyprus Check-List* 1971. In our *Birds of Cyprus* (p. 42) we retained *brachydactyla* as the species name.

LESSER SHORT-TOED LARK

Calandrella rufescens

This is a very small bird 5½ ins (14 cm) in length and differs from *C. brachydactyla* in having no dark neck patch or spots on either side of the neck. It has a noticeably streaky upper breast, the rest of the underside white. The upper-parts are reddish-sandy streaked with dark brown. The tail shows much white on the outer retrices when fanned.

Both species of short-toed lark mingle when feeding but keep in their own species if they rise. The lesser is much the more uncommon. It has a different voice from *C. cinerea*. It is satisfactory to have had our identification of this lark confirmed since 1958 and we should like here to emphasise that although we heard it singing we did not even tentatively suggest breeding. To behave in a suggestive manner in spring does not necessarily imply that birds are on their breeding ground!

We saw a mixed flock of *bachydactyla* and *rufescens* come in over the sea and alight near Cape Andreas on 19 March, but much remains to be learned about the migrations of the lesser short-toed lark in Cyprus before we can be sure of its status, or even of its subspecies. It seems to us very little use to speculate on the probable origin of these migrants until specimens are collected and critically examined. Otherwise it is a matter of guesswork. Those responsible for the latest Check-List mention *aharonii* from Asia Minor as a likely immigrant, owing to its geographical position. In our former work (1958) we allied it with *rufescens minor*. Its status is now considered to be "an irregular and very scarce visitor" – much scarcer than we had imagined when we were working in Cyprus on our bird survey in the years prior to 1958, from our much shorter experience than the compilers of the new Check-List. Records fall between late September and early May.

CYPRUS CRESTED LARK

Galerida cristata cypriaca

The general colour of the crested lark is grey-brown, the upperparts streaked though less obviously than in the skylark, to cite a well-known example. The underside is creamy-buff with broad, but ill-defined, streaking. No white is present on wing or tail. The most prominent feature is the crest on the crown of fairly long feathers which, if the bird is alarmed or excited, it can raise. From bill to tail the bird measures nearly 7 ins (18 cm) – it is the largest of the Cyprus larks with one exception. In our larger work, from personal examination of skins, we wrote that the Cyprus lark appeared to be (*in series*) darker in general colour and in breast markings than north African birds. It was separated as a distinct race long ago, but its distinctness has been disputed recently. We prefer to adhere to our own opinion, while conceding that too many subspecies of *G. cristata* have been described. As *cypriaca* is an insular race there is all the more reason to recognise it, even though Cypriot specimens *can* be matched on the mainland, that in itself does not invalidate it, but is applicable to other recognised races. The fact that it is a resident and non-migratory bird in Cyprus adds weight to this decision in face of opposite views held by some workers in America. Hartert recognised the subspecies in *Vögel Palaarktischen Fauna*, and his opinion will always carry weight.

Cypriaca is the breeding bird and is widely distributed on open ground but dreadfully persecuted. It is in smaller numbers in the hills. We have never seen it at anything like the altitude of 4000 ft mentioned in the new Check-List as its upper limit.

Breeding is mainly from late March to mid-May. Nests are deep scrapes in the dry earth in which the nest is made of dry grass and plants or woven of bents and thistledown lined with rootlets and vegetable down, occasionally a little wool. A good deal of variation occurs in the materials used for a foundation – Juniper bark figured in one instance. Eggs which number from four to six also show much variation, the ground dead white or creamy white spotted with light brown and ash-grey, sometimes a few large blotches. A set tinged with green has been found with olive-brown markings.

If the name *cypriaca* is not acceptable to modern workers then the lark from Cyprus must, it seems, be allied with the Caucasian race *caucasia*.

WOODLARK [Plate 17, facing p. 97]

Lullula arborea

Those who are familiar with the lark family will be able to recognise an adult woodlark in flight by its very short black tail, which when seen from close quarters, is tipped with white. On the ground the tail is difficult to see as it is almost concealed by the very long upper tail coverts of plain brown. Again at close quarters, a pale band across the nape is noticeable which is usually obscured by the crest feathers, for the woodlark's crest is a notable feature, longer in the male bird than in the hen. The upperparts are warm brown, heavily streaked blackish-brown; the underparts yellowish-white, the breast narrowly streaked with the same colour as the mantle and back. Legs and feet flesh-colour, bill brownish-horn.

In the breeding season – and the wood-

Cyprus crested lark

lark is now known to nest in Cyprus more generally than it was thought to do – it has an entrancing song of very great variety. Young woodlarks are very attractive, all the feathers having black centres, buff fringes and white tips, with a white patch showing on each side of the neck.

In Cyprus it is both resident and passage migrant but it was not until 1954 that eggs were actually indentified on 15 May in a nest near Platania forest station; juvenile woodlarks had been discovered some years earlier.

Woodlarks are also winter visitors to the island arriving from Europe occasionally from mid-September, but usually late October to early November and are fairly common till about mid-March. At that time breeding birds are reported to move from the lower ground to the higher levels and the winter visitors depart. The low ground is then deserted. There is again uncertainty as to the breeding race which may be *pallida* (as suggested in the Check-List) i.e. the Asia Minor subspecies. On the other hand September collected specimens were identical with west European examples, *arborea arborea*. The name of the breeding population must remain in abeyance.

SKYLARK

Alauda arvensis

This winter visitor to the Cyprus plains arrives in the island in great numbers and few can then be unaware of their presence, even though their plumage is so subdued. We have already expressed the opinion that both the west European form and the eastern Mediterranean skylark winter in Cyprus, but by far the greater number belong to the latter subspecies *A. a. cantarella*. This bird has been defined as having the whole upperparts grey-brown, red-brown or plain brown, sometimes rather dark and sometimes paler, the centres of the feathers almost black; throat and breast spotted, abdomen whitish; nostrils concealed by plumelets; axillaries white, tail brown, the outer pair largely white. Hind claw always much longer than the hind toe and fairly straight.

It is generally agreed by those systematists who have studied series of Middle East skylarks that it would be impossible to pick out individual specimens of wintering birds and to say from where they had originated. There is too much variation *inter se* but it appears there is a very slight dominance of grey in the dryer areas and of the red phase in more humid areas. Ringing on the nesting grounds is the only sure way to discover whence they have come.

Skylarks winter in Cyprus in abundant flocks and are especially numerous on the central plains thoughout the winter but by mid-March the flocks have all disappeared save for a very few. The passage migrants and winter visitors appear about mid-October, some from mid-September, and are numerous all winter from November to February. The numbers fluctuate from year to year but are always in tolerable numbers, sometimes in large numbers. In addition to the race named above, the typical *A. arvensis* from northern Europe has been collected in the spring but its status is uncertain.

Family HIRUNDINIDAE

The swallows are always a very favourite group of birds for as in our country of Great Britain they herald the spring throughout Europe, spending the colder months in their winter quarters in Africa. Moreover swallows are easily recognised for they do not shun the dwelling places of man but rather the reverse and so are in constant view, gaining their livelihood in the air in their endless search for insect life upon which they exclusively feed. Their form of flight, nesting and feeding habits are all characteristic of the swallows and martins which are known to most people and generally universally welcomed back to their breeding places when the winter is over.

Swallows and martins have broad flattened bills and very wide gapes, enabling the mandibles to be widely extended, which allows the bird to catch its insect prey more easily. The wings are long, pointed and powerful, all the swallow family being capable of sustained flight for their bodies are light. Swallows have variously shaped tails; often the outer tail feather is furnished with elongated pinions, as in the common barn swallow of Europe which visits Cyprus on passage and also breeds. The martins for the most part have narrowly forked tails but no streamers. The feet are weak and the tarsi short. In swallows the tarsus is bare, in house martins the feet are feathered and in the sand martin there is a tuft of hairlike feathers above the hind toe. Their toes are furnished with very fine sharp claws enabling the birds to cling with facility to perpendicular walls and rocks.

The family is represented in the Middle East by four genera divisible into five species, two swallows and three martins, all of which are recorded from Cyprus, four as breeding summer visitors and one – the sand martin – as a passage migrant only, perhaps owing to the drying up of fresh water on the plains so early in the year, for it breeds commonly in Palestine, Syria and Asia Minor. There are few, if any, suitable nesting sites in Cyprus to induce it to prolong its visit in the spring.

EUROPEAN SWALLOW

Hirundo rustica

The common European swallow is so well-known that the briefest description will suffice: dark glossy blue upperparts and wings, a chestnut throat; white to buff underparts with blue breast-band; a forked tail, with long outer feathers, the whole adorned with white mirrors, only conspicuous when the tail is open. The sexes are alike but the tail-streamers are much longer in the male bird.

Considerable variation is apparent in the colour of the underside ranging from white to deep reddish-buff, the extremes sometimes exhibited in paired couples. We have personally seen several of these very dark breasted birds, but singly.

We believe it to be very unwise to unite these abnormally dark examples with either the Palestine or Egyptian swallow but see remarks in Appendix under *Hirundo savignii* p. 219.

The swallow is an abundant nesting species in Cyprus and also passage migrant; early arrivals have been noted in January, earliest third, exceptional before last week. Main passage usual from 20 February increasing daily. In full swing during March and April and passing till mid-May. The return passage is in September some remaining till late October, exceptionally till 10 November.

Breeding takes place on the plains earlier than in the mountains and fresh eggs may be found in April when other pairs are building. Their nests are built in all manner of situations as in England. In private houses, in verandahs and in churches in towns and villages; the same birds returning year after year to their old haunts. By late October all young birds are reared and have departed for Africa. Ringing has shown interesting results already.

The nesting birds are *H. rustica rustica*, but another race, *H. r. transitiva* which breeds in the Near East has been reported to occur in Cyprus from time to time; it is another of the dark reddish-buff-breasted subspecies which may occur in the island but the Editor of the new Check-List considers that its occurrence is not well established, while admitting a single record of the Egyptian race *H. r. savignii*, about whose identification we had previously expressed some doubt. See Appendix p. 219.

RED-RUMPED SWALLOW

Hirundo daurica rufula

[Plate 6, facing p. 16]

It is always difficult to carry colours in ones head and when two birds so alike in size as *Hirundo rustica* and *daurica* are present together, it is useful to concentrate on major points of difference. If the head alone should be visible the blue forehead (instead of chestnut in the common swallow), the cream throat (instead of chestnut bordered with blue), and the pale rufous-chestnut rump in place of glossy blue, will establish identity of the subject of these notes. The *lack* of white mirrors on the tail feathers in the red-rumped swallow, so noticeable in the other bird, is a splendid diagnostic character to observe, visible either from above or below. Breast and belly of *H. daurica* are pale rufous, (instead of cream) and the under tail-coverts are *dark blue* (not cream).

Both swallows come to Cyprus to breed, the red-rumped swallow is also a passage migrant, early arrivals appearing in March, the main flocks coming in during the last ten days when parties of sixty or more may be encountered. In April and May these swallows are widespread and abundant, breeding at all elevations including sea-caves, and up till June in the mountains, especially above 3,000 ft. The nests which are made of mud are retort-shaped with an entrance funnel below. They are much commoner in the hills and mountains except on the Karpas Peninsula where they breed commonly in the villages.

It has been found in Cyprus that if when examining a nest the funnel gets broken, the birds will not desert, as one might expect, but set to work to repair the damage, a remarkable example of their faith that all will be well in the end! (c.f. *Oological Record* XXXV).

While small colonies of two or three pairs or more may be the rule in sea-caves, buildings, or cliff-sites, single pairs (and never more) build under the road-culverts, which seems to be the most preferable situation of all. The nests are lined with dry grass and feathers and hold five or six eggs, white and unmarked, though a rare clutch or two may occur with fine red-brown spots. One such has been examined by the writer and is mentioned in our *Birds of Cyprus* p. 153. Two broods can be reared. These summer-visiting swallows leave Cyprus earlier than the common swallow, to winter in Africa; few remain after September. The passage migrants pass through Cyprus on their way south from early August to mid-September. They do *not* reach tropical Africa and their winter quarters, beyond southern Arabia and Egypt, are still a mystery; they have been seen passing up the Nile in numbers! From whence had they come?

HOUSE MARTIN

Delichon urbica

The pure white underparts from chin to under tail-coverts and the white rump are features not shared by any other of the swallow family in Cyprus. The rest of the body plumage, including the crown, is deep glossy blue; the wings are blackish-brown and the tail blackish faintly glossed blue. The tail is deeply forked but unlike the two swallows, it has no elongated streamers. Its legs are unique in that they are covered with white feathers to the toes. The long narrow wings when closed extend beyond the tips of the tail-feathers.

The summer visitors to Cyprus, where they stay and breed in colonies, arrive in early March, only a very few forerunners in February have been recorded. A few breed on houses or monasteries as they do in Europe, making their mud nests under the eaves, but the majority prefer cliffs and rocks at all elevations. We found several, high on the cliff-sides, in the Northern Range, but many, apparently ideal sites, where there were no nests at all. They are evidently very selective and return year after year to a few chosen spots, rather than breed haphazard. Kantara Castle has always been favoured and we have read (*Ool. Record* XXXV) of twenty-five pairs at Troödos nesting under the eaves of one house overlooking the Caledonian Falls, which had eggs with large embryos on 15 May. In a very different setting we found a large colony on the cliffs near the Paphos-Polis road and there was formerly a colony on the monastery of St. Neophytos near Paphos. The fifteenth *Bird Report* of the C.O.S. contains a referrence to *circa* 300 nests at "Tunnel Beach," Episkopi in 1968, an unusually large congregation for Cyprus at one locality.

Most house-martins have left Cyprus for their winter quarters in Africa by the middle of October, a few stragglers following later. The passage migrants in autumn are mainly to be seen during September and the early part of October. After mid-October only a few late stragglers have been reported, one in mid-November and three in December.

SAND MARTIN

Riparia riparia

The only member of the swallow family on the Cyprus list which does not breed in the island, the sand martin is a passage migrant only, arriving in the island with the swallows from March to May. It is easily identified and very dully coloured; pale brown above, dull white below with a pale brown band across the breast, which is difficult to see in flight. The tail is slightly forked. There is no white anywhere on the wings or tail. If handled a peculiar feature in its appearance is a tuft of hairs behind the hind toe. It is only 4¾ ins (12 cm) in length.

Sand martins are especially fond of open fresh water over which to hunt for insects, and as all open lakes and pools in Cyprus dry up long before the young could leave the nest, the sandmartins have wisely decided to give Cyprus a miss, so far as breeding is concerned.

There is a return migration to Africa from Europe, which brings a number of the passage migrants to Cyprus in August and September with late stragglers up to 22 October and an odd bird or two in November. An exceptionally *early* passage was observed at Akrotiri in 1967, when huge flocks appeared on 22 July.

As a point of interest, it is certainly for ecological reasons that the sand martin does not attempt to nest in Cyprus, and not a question of latitude, for it breeds in colonies in neighbouring Palestine, Syria and Asia Minor. It is doubtful too, in a land where sand-quarries are lacking, where it would find suitable soil in Cyprus for its tiny feet to excavate the tunnels, at the end of which it normally lays its eggs.

CRAG MARTIN [Plate 6, facing p. 16]

Ptyonoprogne rupestris

This is a resident bird in Cyprus, scattered pairs and colonies living in the more mountainous areas. A little larger than the sand-martin, the upperparts are light mouse-brown, the underparts dirty white with no breast-band. The tail is square-tipped and is ornamented with white spots, making a pretty pattern when the rectrices are expanded.

In Cyprus the crag martin may be seen to advantage in the Northern Range where the forest road runs along a narrow ridge with a steep drop on either side. There, as the bird skims along, often just below the onlooker, the spots on the square tail are clearly visible, and as the bird turns in flight, the plain buffy-white underparts help to distinguish it. It breeds very locally; a colony is easily located because of the many birds at the site. There are several colonies in the Northern Range in the west, at St. Hilarion, Halevka, Kantara, at Buffavento and in the Kyrenia Pass. There are also colonies on cliffs in the Troödos Range in the south where they breed at 5,500 ft and near sea level at Paphos.

When the weather is severe in the higher altitudes, the birds descend to the lower ground and under those conditions considerable numbers have been observed frequenting the rocky southern coasts throughout the winter. When the weather is less severe we have found them in early January at 4,000 ft at Stavros, where two small parties remained until the snow drove them to lower altitudes.

Breeding takes place in May. The nest is an open cup, plastered against the rock. Two nests found 9 and 12 ft up, cemented on stone walls at Troödos (5,500 ft), were built of layers of three different colours of mud, dark brown, grey and light brown. Each nest held four eggs with embryos, on 20 May. Another nest under the eaves of a building in Troödos Village, also at 5,500 ft, was nearly complete on 9 May, held one egg on 19th and four eggs by 26th. It was a deep nest lined with pigeon's feathers. Another bird was seen sitting on 10 July but was left undisturbed. (*Oological Record* XXXV p. 20).

Eggs are somewhat elongated and white, spotted and flecked with dark brown with small ashy shell-marks. One of the sets taken at Troödos had fine speckles forming a zone round the big ends.

As always when a species is both a resident and a passage migrant it is difficult to assess the true status of each one accurately, but careful observation points to the passage migrants passing in spring from mid-February to mid-April, and again on their southern journey in late October and early November.

Family ORIOLIDAE

Orioles are a group of beautifully coloured birds the size of a starling which inhabit the whole of Europe, Asia and Africa. Golden-yellow predominates in the colour scheme, set off with black in many of the species. In Europe they are inhabitants of broad-leaved woods within their breeding range, but only one species, the golden oriole is the Palaearctic representative and is the only species which passes through the Middle East countries, including Cyprus, at both seasons of the year.

Orioles have long pointed wings and tails which are noted for their black and yellow patterns according to the species; the European male bird, resplendent in its golden yellow dress having black wings adorned with a yellow alar patch and a black and yellow tail. The bill is powerful and coloured red in many of the species, the feet and legs strong. All are strong fliers and can migrate long distances between summer and winter quarters. They are fruit and insect eaters. The sexes are dissimilar.

Orioles are remarkable for their hammock-like nests which are suspended from the fork of a branch, but are very difficult to discover. The flute-like whistle of the golden oriole in spring is a happy reminder that the winter days are over in Europe and that summer will soon be here.

GOLDEN ORIOLE

Oriolus oriolus [Plate 18, facing p. 112]

The male oriole is about the same size as a song-thrush some 10 ins (25 cm) in length and will probably be heard before it is seen on the spring migration, for it is a secretive bird, preferring thick foliaged trees from which the loud musical whistle indicates its presence. Golden-yellow throughout except for the contrasting black wings with a pale yellow patch on the primaries, and the black and yellow patterned tail, the male is a striking bird and quite unmistakable with fairly long reddish bill and a crimson eye. The female is less decorative greenish-yellow above, whitish on the underparts, with faint breast streaking. Wings and tail are brown washed with olive. Immature birds resemble the female but have black streaks all over the underparts.

Of three of the best-known earlier ornithologists in Cyprus, all of whom were in official positions, spending much time in the forests or in search of birds in their spare time, only one had found an oriole's nest and seen the young birds abroad. That was near Platania forest station. By a curious coincidence it was near Platania again, in a fine wooded valley above that place at 3,700 ft, a half completed nest was discovered on 14 May, 1959 by a young officer serving in Cyprus with his regiment. The nest held four typical eggs, the first ever recorded for Cyprus, on 25 May. The nest was large, of white paper, wool, down, feathers and fine grasses. Typical eggs have a cream ground with grey shell-markings and are boldly spotted with reddish-brown or purplish-black. An oriole's nest, even half completed, can be recognised, usually woven at the fork of a branch from which it is suspended in hammock-like fashion, built of moss and lichens bound together by strips of grass and bark. The Platania nest was evidently exceptionally large.

The golden oriole is well-known to the inhabitants as a passage migrant which arrives commonly from early April to mid-May, some years rather later in appearing but rarely earlier. In the autumn orioles arrive from August to October but mainly in September on their way to Africa for the winter months.

Family CORVIDAE

The members of the crow family in Cyprus fall into three Genera: *Corvus, Pica* and *Garrulus*, in the last two of which we place the magpie and the jay respectively. Both are resident in Cyprus and non-migratory. They differ markedly from one another and from the true crows in the genus Corvus – all of which are black or black relieved with white or grey. Here we find the Punjab raven, Cyprus hooded crow and eastern form of the jackdaw among the resident breeding birds and the European rook as a rare winter visitor and perhaps a passage migrant.

The chief characteristic of the crows is the heavy powerful bill with stiff bristles at the base and very strong legs, much of their life being spent on the ground. The raven incidentally has the distinction of being the largest bird in the Order Passeriformes measuring 25 ins (64 cm) in length. The European rook is the same as the species of northern Europe and now comes rarely and irregularly to Cyprus. Finally the magpie is the same as the European bird and is both resident and increasing in Cyprus today. Both crow and magpie need keeping under control for the sake of the ground nesting game birds, if nothing else.

Of the above six species the hooded crow is the most widespread in the Middle East being abundant in the Egyptian Delta and in Palestine;

the magpie on the contrary is found in Asia Minor but not in Egypt, and is not a migratory bird, though it must have crossed the sea to get a footing in Cyprus.

RAVEN

Corvus corax

Identified by its exceptionally large size 25 ins (64 cm) from bill to tail tip, with wing expanse of 4 ft, the raven should not be mistaken in Cyprus for any other bird. The plumage is all black glossed with blue and purple; a heavy black beak guarded with bristles around the nostrils, is slightly arched. Legs and feet are also black and powerful. Its deep throaty call is likely to attract ones attention high overhead as the great bird leisurely wends its way from some rubbish dump in the plains to the high central mountains where this lord of the crow family betakes itself as the days draw to a close. We found it in the Troödos range above 6,000 ft and we found it on the refuse piles outside Nicosia, where at times a number will congregate but it is not a common bird in Cyprus either on plain, mountain or sea-cliff. Gatherings of ravens occur in the higher altitudes in the same way as they do in the British Isles but for some reason the raven does appear to be in lesser numbers than formerly. Is it being poisoned on the land? Many are reported still to breed around the Troödos heights and also on the sea-cliffs, but it would need a band of workers to compile a census.

Raven

A writer in the *Oological Record* 1961 describes several nests found in Cyprus, the first holding seven eggs on 8 March built on a hillside in the Mesaoria of dead vine branches, scrub-twigs and rootlets, lined with rags, hair, wool and moss. Another nest had three nearly fledged young in cliffs bordering Larnaca Salt Lake on 22 April. Other cliff nests were examined at Cape Greco and at Curium and finally a nest 50 ft up in a tall pine at Salamis containing three nearly fledged young on 6 May. These give a fair idea of the range and sites chosen. The writer – a member of the C.O.S. – records that there were fifty-one nests of the Spanish sparrow in the same tree! Eggs were reported to be large 50·2 × 34·6 mm. Usually raven's eggs are small for the size of the bird. Those taken were of two types, greenish and blotched with brown, or bluish and lightly spotted. All had violet shell-marks.

There has been so much difference of opinion as to the race to which the Cyprus raven belongs that we name it here binomially. It has even been given a local racial name the validity of which has been disputed. In our larger work we allied it with *laurencei*, and if in fact, as suggested in the new Check-List, it is an intermediate form between the nominate race and *subcorax* of Asia Minor, there is a new name available for it! The question requires much more study.

CYPRUS HOODED CROW

Corvus cornix sardonius

An ubiquitous species in Cyprus mainly to be seen on the lower ground but recorded up to 4,000 ft, it is a bird which cannot be missed, the almost cream-coloured (or very pale grey) mantle and nape and the pale grey underparts in sharp contrast with the glossy black head, throat, wings and tail, with purple and green reflections. A resident and useful bird *as a scavenger*, it should not be permitted to increase its numbers, for its scavenging must be set against the undoubted harm it does to ground-nesting birds: chukor, francolins and any ailing bird which comes within its range. It kills frogs, lizards, mice and large insects and has been seen to knock over a magpie and kill a nearly grown pigeon, as recounted in our book.

In the Mesaoria plain it is numerous round all the villages but especially so in winter. The nests are built in poplars, tall pines and in carobs and eucalyptus trees – the common tree of the plains, and nests may be in tamarisks, fig trees or junipers "if large enough". Nests may be anything from 13 to 30 ft from the ground, built of sticks, padded with earth and lined with some warm material; rags and scraps sometimes included. Eggs are more or less heavily spotted with different shades of brown and underlying markings of pale lavendar. Six eggs usually complete a clutch. Two exceptional clutches were described as taken in Cyprus one with a large number of violet shell-marks, the other heavily blotched brown and violet. The largest egg measured 47 × 31, the smallest 38 × 27 mm, both clutches taken in the island recently. Another small clutch recorded in our book measured 38·2 × 27 and 37·8 × 26·1 mm taken at Kakopetria. We found it very silent when near its nest. Normally it is a rather noisy bird. The nesting season lasts from early April to the end of May.

When the breeding season is over these crows gather into flocks and roam the lower ground in far too large numbers for the safety of other birds.

As with the raven the racial validity of the Cyprus crow has also been disputed. The name *pallescens* was given to a Cyprus bird by reason of its very pale mantle and nape, and we employed it in our *Birds of Cyprus*, but if in fact, as recent investigation is said to prove, the Cyprus *pallescens* is identical with the race from the East Mediterranean named *sardonius*, and the latter name has priority in age, then the Cyprian population must bear that name.

ROOK

Corvus frugilegus

Distinguished from all other *Corvidae* by the area of greyish-white skin at the base of the black heavy bill, which extends on to the chin. About 18 ins (46 cm) in total length the whole plumage is black with a strong blue gloss on all the feathers.

Cyprus hooded crow

Young rooks lack the greyish bare patch which area is covered at that stage with feathers.

An irregular winter visitor we discussed its status in Cyprus prior to 1958 in our previous work. Its visits to the island were formerly more common than they have been in the last 30 years. We will sum up its present status at the end of these notes. Many rooks in Europe remain near their breeding places all the year round but a considerable number migrate – the Continental bird being much more given to migratory movements than are our rooks in Britain. The rook has never bred in Cyprus and its arrival is certain to be unheralded and of spasmodic occurrence, should it come at all. Only three occurrences are mentioned in the latest Check-List for the last fifteen years; fifty rooks appeared on 9 February at Kolossi Castle and six on 7 April at Episkopi, both records in 1958. Two years later two were seen on 31 January 1960 at Kouklia.

JACKDAW

Corvus monedula

The jackdaw is a numerous *resident* bird in Cyprus but is reported to be decreasing in numbers. It is most often to be seen in the vicinity of the high cliffs in the mountain ranges which are such a feature of the higher altitudes. They breed in colonies and both in winter and summer are often to be seen in the vicinity of their nesting places. They descend to the lower ground to feed on the plains but are nothing like as numerous on the sea-cliffs of Cyprus as on the coasts of Britain.

Jackdaw

To anyone familiar with our bird in England, which is the jackdaw of western Europe, the bird seen in Cyprus is strikingly different. In colour pattern it is the same, but whereas the British race has the sides of the neck, nape and ear-coverts silvery-grey, in the Cyprus bird these areas are almost white, and even at a considerable distance this character of the pale collar is easily visible, especially when the bird is in flight. Another striking feature, common to all jackdaws, is the pearly-white eye of the adult bird. The crown of the head is glossy black with purple reflections and the rest of the body plumage, wings and tail, black also, generously glossed with purple. In total length the jackdaw measures 13 ins (33 cm), the bill being rather straight and stumpy compared with the other Corvidae.

Whether or not the name *pontocaspicus* can be maintained we do not propose to argue. However it is important that it should be mentioned, even if relegated to the synonymy. Formerly the Cyprus birds were allied with the eastern race *Corvus monedula sommeringii* which is known to be a winter visitor to Palestine from Turkestan, and is almost certain to be the same bird which visits Cyprus *in winter*. Whether or not the breeding population is distinct others must decide. If so, the name *pontocaspicus* is waiting for it.

Nesting begins early in March and young are abroad early in May. An enormous nest of sticks may be made when nesting in ruins but in cliffs a smaller nest is usual, the nest built in the crevices where space is more restricted. Four to six is the usual clutch of eggs with ground-colour of greenish-blue, spotted and blotched with black, brown and ash-grey, among which other variations have occurred. A fairly recent investigation (1959) revealed that scattered colonies were situated in all the lower parts of the island, including the Karpas Peninsula where we failed to find it a dozen years ago. We have recently (1970) seen them in the cliffs of the Nothern Range where they were so common in 1954. If indeed the jackdaw is decreasing in numbers the cause must be hard to discover. Most of their breeding places are quite inaccessible. The colony at Halefka (2,000 ft) is fairly typical.

MAGPIE

Pica pica

The magpie of Cyprus is indistinguishable from the same bird in the British Isles which has a huge range across Europe. The whole plumage at a distance appears black and white and on close inspection all the black plumage is strongly glossed with green and purple. The long black tail is irridescent with green and bronze reflections while the white scapulars form a noticeable patch at the base of each wing when the bird is in flight.

An inhabitant of the low ground where trees are plentiful the magpie shuns the larger towns but is often to be seen about the villages and in some districts as around Curium they seemed especially common. We did not meet with any above 2,500 ft but in the lower Northern Range were often encountered, and in the foothills of the Southern Range below that level.

Magpies increased very much in the island during the Eoka emergency, when guns were ordered to be handed in. The birds have in consequence spread since we wrote our book published in 1958, and are reported (in 1970) to be "common in most places". Whereas we seldom found them up to 3,000 ft or anywhere near that altitude they are now reported to breed up to 5,000 ft, a remarkable extension of breeding range. We suspect it still prefers the lower tree-covered elevations. Carob trees which give excellent shade and in which the magpies build their bulky nests are very common in Cyprus and wherever there were thick carob groves there we always found magpies. The big nests are built of sticks, lined with earth and covered with a layer of roots, usually placed from 12 to 35 ft from the ground. In the Tricomo-Boghaz district they were nesting in Aleppo pines and in large olive trees. Early April to mid-May is the height of the breeding season from five to eight eggs being laid. These varied much in size. In colour the ground is pale blue or green, uniformly spotted with brown or grey.

Great spotted cuckoos select the magpies nests in which to lay their eggs.

On the mosaics which have been excavated at Curium we found four birds depicted, one of which was clearly the magpie. It is a bird which should not be allowed to become too numerous, of which there is a distinct danger. It is resident throughout the year.

CYPRUS JAY [Plate 19, facing p. 113]

Garrulus glandarius glaszneri

The jay is one of the most colourful of Cyprian resident birds. Its most striking features are the white rump contrasting with the black tail and a large white patch on the wing, contrasting with the black and chestnut secondaries. The wing-coverts are barred alternately with pale blue, black and white. The body plumage is vinous the forehead light greyish-red with a black band passing back from the bill. Its total length is about 13 ins (33 cm).

It is a mountain species in Cyprus with rather an odd distribution restricted to the pine–and–oak forests of the Southern Range. We have found it in a valley below Stavros at 2,500 ft but its preference is for higher altitudes between 3,000 and 4,500 ft. On Troödos it has been seen up to 5,000 ft. There is one curious record from Nicosia in October but how it came there must remain a mystery.

Its absence from the Northern Range at first seems strange but may be due to the absence there of *Quercus alnifolia* and to the younger growth of the pines. We saw none in the cedar area of the Southern Range but that may have been coincidence.

In the Stavros forest parties of these jays may be encountered threading their way through the trees. Naturally secretive birds in life, they are not exceptionally shy in Cyprus, living as they do in sparsely frequented forests where they may often be observed at close quarters. They live principally upon vegetable food but also suck eggs and will destroy nestling birds and eat snails, worms, slugs and mice, insects and larvae of all kinds, for which, apart from it being an endemic subspecies which is restricted to Cyprus, it merits full protection.

It breeds from mid-April well into June making a nest of sticks, twigs and a little earth, lining it with roots. Five or six eggs are laid, greyish green, speckled with brown and mottled with olive spots. Its unpleasant harsh note *kraak kraak* usually betrays its presence in the vicinity.

Little was known about the nesting of the Cyprus jay when the *Birds of Cyprus* was written but since that date a Service member of the C.O.S. has published an account of his finding four nests of this bird in the Southern Range which he describes. One nest was at Platania 3,750 ft, 16 ft up in a small pine, built of twigs, lined with rootlets, the rim with lichens; it held six eggs with large embryos on 9 May. Another was 60 ft up at the top of a pine at Troödos and contained three chicks and an infertile egg; it was lined with black and red hair and a few bents with the underside and rim of lichen. A third nest 18 ft up on the branch of a pine held four eggs with small embryos on 26 May, and was built of grey twigs with many pieces of lichen round the rim and base, and lined with fine grass and a few rootlets. As the discoverer of these nests observed (*Öol. Record* 1961 p. 22) lichen seems to be almost a characteristic feature of the nest of this race. The eggs of C/6 were described as typical, but smaller than those of western races, but the C/4 clutch were as large as in other races. May is evidently the height of the egg laying.

We have quoted these descriptions fully as the first ever to have been written of the endemic Cyprus jay. The periodical in which the originals first appeared has now unfortunately ceased publication and sets are almost unprocurable.

Family PARIDAE

In this family we group the titmice – small birds ranging from 4½ ins (11 cm in the coal-tit) to 5½ ins (14 cm in the great tit) in total length. Both the above have been described as specialised races in Cyprus, but whereas the great tit varies imperceptibly from the Continental subspecies the Cyprian coal-tit is one of the best defined of Cyprian birds from the mainland stock and must have had its roots in the ancient Cyprus forests centuries ago. Fortunately tits do not offer very sporting shots to the "sporting" fraternity and even less of a meal! So the only real danger comes from the lime-sticks where migrating parties of great tits are the only ones of the family to figure at all prominently on the list of captures. These are probably not tits of the resident population (*aphrodite*) but of the European subspecies on its migration. Only the migrant titmice are prone to be captured in this way among which the penduline tit and the bearded tit are possible victims. In the forests sparrowhawks may account for some.

Tits have small but powerful bills, as they are hard-seed, insect and fruit-eaters; strong legs and very sharp claws enable them to hang up-side-down or at any angle from the branches while they hunt the leaves and crevices of the bark for insects and other food. Wings are round. The tail varies very much in the different genera, slightly rounded in *Parus*, strongly graduated in *Panurus*. Very interesting was the discovery that the penduline tit *Remiz*, which breeds in Asia Minor and in Greece, visits Cyprus as a winter visitor, for this diminutive ball of feathers to brave the crossing from Turkey in the winter gales is one of the marvels, among many others, which the Cyprus bird world has to offer.

GREAT TIT [Plate 19, facing p. 113]

Parus major aphrodite

The great tit of Cyprus was described as an endemic subspecies, restricted to the island, and while agreeing that its distinctions from *Parus major major* were very fine, we decided in our former work on Cyprus birds, to retain the name *aphrodite* for the breeding population, while the migrants, if any occur, will probably be of the typical race. This is far the largest member of the tit-family in Cyprus measuring 5½ ins. (14 cm) in length, easily recognised by its shining dark blue head and collar, prominent white cheeks and ear-coverts. The back is bright green shading to yellow at the nape. Wings and tail blue-grey, the former with whitish wing-bar. Underparts bright yellow, a streak of black, of variable length, down the middle of the breast. When the tail is opened, white is exhibited on the outer edge. Sexes are alike in pattern, but the female duller.

It is a very common resident in Cyprus nesting widely from sea level to the highest mountains in a great variety of situations. Nine nests found by a member of the C.O.S. in 1958/9 were built on the plains, in carobs and whitethorn; but in the mountains in holes in culverts, under wooden eaves and corrugated iron roofs, as well as in the cracks of plane and Troödos pine trees. Fresh eggs are commonest at the end of March on the plains, but at 5,600 ft at Troödos, a clutch of five, freshly laid, was found on 26 May. None of the nine nests had less than five eggs or young and the largest was probably C/8. Cyprus-taken eggs are typical of the species; i.e. white marked with specks, spots and blotches of two shades of chestnut.

The Cyprus great tits in winter join up with other insect-eating birds to wander through the forest in foraging bands, in the course of which they account for countless injurious insects and their larvae, and do an incredible amount of good which it beholdens the forester and agriculturalist to remember. They should have widespread protection. Commonest on the lower and intermediate ground it is nevertheless found nesting in the higher zones of the Southern Range.

CYPRUS COAL TIT

Parus ater cypriotes

[Plate 20, facing p. 128]

This very small tit measures only 4½ ins (11 cm) in length. It has a blue-black crown and a dark blue-grey back. The throat and chin are black, a white patch adorns the cheeks, and a white patch the nape. The underparts are dark buff with a brown tinge on the flanks. It is a darker bird than the Continental coal tit, a fact easily remarked in life.

No-one has disputed the fact that this is a well characterised endemic race which is restricted in its breeding range to the high pine and cedar forests of the Southern Range, moving about the trees in bad weather in little parties as is their wont feeding on conifer seeds, insects and larvae. We found them more numerous than the great tit in their respective habitats. Breeding is general in April and May, most clutches being full by the end of April. Five or six eggs are laid which have a white ground spotted and blotched with dark brown, often with spots clustered round the broad end. Nests which are built of moss, grass and bits of bark and lined with wool, with small entrance are placed in various situations, usually found in holes in the ground under a protecting bank of stones, in earth banks, or in walls. Holes in trees are more rarely utilised. Nests have been found at 5,500 ft altitude but probably occur up to the highest tree growth. The 6 April is an exceptionally early date to find young in the nest. A freshly laid C/5 found on 19 May at 5,500 ft on Troödos has been recorded.

It has been rarely met with in the Northern Range and then, not as might be expected in the depths of winter, but in May and September. There is only one ancient record, from Kyrenia district in late May, but in recent times in the year 1960, "many" were reported at Malounda on 15 May, and one at St. Hilarion on 3 September. Could the "many" have been of Continental origin? or a wandering band from the southern mountain forests when the birds should rightfully have been breeding.

PENDULINE TIT

Remiz pendulinus

To learn that this minute bird occurred in Cyprus came as a surprise for it had only been discovered there in 1957, the year before our first Cyprus book was published. It is difficult to credit it with a sea crossing even from Asia Minor, but these diminutive birds are known to wander in the winter months, and the few so far recorded from Cyprus to date, must be in the category of occasional vagrants. Their discovery was another feather in the cap of the founder of the C.O.S., who had a clear view of two near Akrotiri on the 25 January 1957, during which winter twelve were reported from the same area. It was later found to be a scarce winter visitor to marshes recorded between early November and early April.

The bird acquires its English name on account of the formation of its nest, a beautiful purse-shaped structure suspended from an outer twig of some tree or bush at any height from 6–50 ft above the ground. It breeds in both Greece and Turkey and has a wide distribution north of the Mediterranean and far into Asia, but is a newcomer to the Cyprus list.

It is not a difficult bird to recognise in the field: it has a whitish head with a broad black band running from the ear-coverts across the forehead. The back is chestnut nearest the head, shading off to a warm yellowish-buff over the rump. The tail is blackish margined with white, the upper wing-coverts chestnut and black tipped with ochreous. The chin and throat are white, the rest of the underparts ochreous white with some chestnut-red on the upper breast. The female is duller. It measures 4½ ins (11 cm) in length. Its call is a soft whistle.

It has been suggested that the penduline tits of Cyprus should be referred to the eastern Asia Minor race *R.p. menzbieri*, rather than to the typical subspecies of further west. It is little use speculating until specimens have been collected and compared, but I am ready to agree that *menzbieri* is the more probable. The C.O.S. have twenty-two records of this bird from Akrotiri, Morphou and Larnaca between November and April and believe it to be more regular than these records suggest, though scarce in numbers and irregular in appearance.

In the latest systematic acrobatics this bird has been placed in a distinct Family (!) Remizdae.

BEARDED TIT

Panurus biarmicus

It seem very extraordinary that the bearded tit of Cyprus as a migratory species belongs to the very same race as the bird which breeds in the Norfolk Broads and spreads right across Europe and Asia. No-one has dared to describe the Cyprus visitors as distinct and the only marvel is in the immense distances these tiny creatures travel to reach the eastern Mediterranean.

When we wrote our previous book on the island's birds we were able to cite only one record of a bearded reedling – to quote its appropriate English name – for Cyprus until, just as we went to press, a bird was seen on Larnaca marsh in December 1956, but not immediately brought to our notice. We had no knowledge of the five birds limed at Paralimni until we discovered two specimens in a school collection in Nicosia.

The following is an abbreviated description of its plumage: adult male: crown and cheeks dove grey, chin, throat and breast white. A black patch beginning from the bill extends to the eye and continuing down the sides of the throat ends in a point. Mantle, back, rump, tail and flank-feathers are tawny brown. Underparts grey, the sides chestnut. Bands of tawny, black and white on the wing, give it a remarkable appearance. The female lacks the black moustachial patch, her plumage is warm brown tinged with tawny; a pale throat and buff underparts complete the colour-scheme with a rosy wash on the flanks. The male is 6½ ins (17 cm) long and its strongly graduated tail accounts for half the bird's length.

A winter visitor to Cyprus, there is small hope of it ever breeding in an island where the lakes are so prone to dry up but it seems to be a visitor in larger numbers than was formerly ever believed, and is now recorded from Akrotiri, Morphou and Larnaca in small numbers reported between 1941 and 1946 – all between November and March.

Specimens examined belonged to the nominate race which breeds in Greece but the Asia Minor race *russicus* is even more likely to occur someday.

Family SITTIDAE

In this family we include the nuthatches and the rock nuthatch both of which are in the genus *Sitta*, the former typified by the European nuthatch of Great Britain, a race of which is found in Asia Minor but has never been found in Cyprus, while the rock-nuthatch, *Sitta neumayeri syriaca*, received tentative notice in our *Birds of Cyprus* (1958) by reason of a single ancient record from the island.

Nuthatches have the general appearance of small woodpeckers, but contrary to those birds have a short tail of soft feathers. They have a strong (for their size) wedge-shaped bill and their long and strong toes are furnished with powerful claws. The upperparts are bluish slate colour, the flanks chestnut and the rest of the underside white. Although not usually migratory, the Asia Minor race *S. europaea caucasica*, is a very possible visitor, for there is no lack of forest areas in Cyprus essential to its requirements. The terrain however is more suitable for the rock nuthatch, *S. neumayeri*, of which there are two races: *syriaca* and *zarudnyi* in Asia Minor, birds which have no chestnut on the flanks and under tail-coverts and no white spots on the tail. The former has once been recorded in the distant past, see Appendix p. 220. It is resident in S.E. Asia, Greece and Asia Minor.

As remarked under the last family the remarkable wall-creeper in the monotypic genus *Tichodroma* was formerly placed with the Certhiidae as we did ourselves in our former larger work. It is now generally considered more nearly allied to the Nuthatches and is so placed by Professor Voous in his *Atlas of European Birds,* who considers it replaces the nuthatches in the higher, colder and less sunny mountain zones.

Neither the tree-creeper nor wall-creepers are normally migratory and it must surely only be by accident that the latter occur as often as

Cyprus warbler ♂

Cyprus warbler ♀

Plate 22

C.E.Talbot Kelly

they do on the limestone precipices of Cyprus. Inhabitants of the cliff faces of the mountain ranges of central and southern Europe, these highly decorative birds occur in the Taurus Range which is visible on clear days from the Cyprus high ground. Their rounded wings and very short tail is not adapted for long flight, but in other ways they are fitted for the life they lead, their very long, gently curved bill can probe deep into the rock-crevices. Their feet are adapted for clinging but they obtain no support from their soft tails, as do tree-creepers with their stiff shafts. They progress on the rock-face in a series of jumps when the wings are brought into play exposing the rose-red on the wings.

Peculiarly sensitive to snow conditions when they seek lower altitudes, it is then that they must brave the overseas flight. The marvel is that they ever arrive, to give immeasurable pleasure to anyone fortunate enough to see them with their rose-crimson wings adorned with white spots. They are living gems in the bird world of Europe.

WALL-CREEPER

Tichodroma muraria

[Plate 23, facing p. 145]

The accompanying picture in colour of the wall-creeper will give the reader a better idea of this unique bird than any number of words. Its general colour above is pale grey, more slate on the rump. The tail is short and square tipped, blackish in colour with white tips to the outer pairs and the remainder tipped with grey. Seen from the underside all the tips look to be white. The wing is the brightest part of the bird. From the lesser wing-coverts to a distance of an inch to the tip of the quills, the

Plate 23

1. Thrush-nightingale or Sprosser
2. Goldcrest
3. Rufous warbler
4. Barred warbler
5. Fan-tailed warbler
6. Red-breasted flycatcher
7. Spectacled warbler
8. Wall-creeper
9. Pied flycatcher
10. Collared flycatcher

feathers are bright rose crimson. The four outer primaries are black, have a large white mirror towards the tip and a smaller white spot – markings which are very conspicuous in flight, but otherwise are concealed. In summer both male and female have a black chin and throat, but in winter these parts are white. Breast and belly are dark grey. The black bill is very fine, almost but not quite, straight and 25 mm in length.

It is fitting that such an attractive bird should live among lovely scenery for it is an inhabitant of huge cliff faces running up the perpendicular rock with the facility of a tree-creeper on a tree trunk. In Cyprus to which island it comes only on rare occasions, it must be looked for on such precipices as the cliffs below the ruins of Buffavento Castle in the Northern Range. The older naturalists recorded it from Stavrovouni and Tryparouna but since those days they have been seen at other places. There have been nineteen separate records since 1957, suggesting that it is almost a regular, but rare winter visitor.

The latest C.O.S. Check-list (1971) analyses the records and mentions the sort of place, where the wall-creeper has been actually seen. These include sea-cliffs (the majority), mountain peaks, tall buildings, and steep rock-faces. Birds were observed (when dates are known) from early November to late March.

An inhabitant of the great mountain systems of Europe and Asia and recorded from Algeria, the visitors to Cyprus are believed to cross from the Taurus Mountains in southern Turkey.

Family CERTHIIDAE

There are two tree-creeper species in the Middle East, the Asia Minor form *brachydactyla*, having a short hind toe and the more familiar European creeper appropriately named *familiaris* also found in Turkey, but the Cyprus bird has evolved from the Asia Minor short-toed stock and is sufficiently distinct from the nominate race to have been named *dorothea* in honour of a distinguished lady palaeontologist of the British Museum (Dorothy Bate) who first noticed its distinctions and close relationship to the Asia Minor bird.

Some 5 ins (13 cm) in length, camouflaged to resemble the bark of the trees upon which they climb in search of insect food, and roost between the crevices, their agility in this occupation is remarkable to see. They progress very fast by means of their sharp claws at any angle over the tree-trunk. Like woodpeckers they have a stiff sharp-pointed tail which they press closely against the bark and can support their light bodies. Although their undersurface is white they can make themselves quite invisible. Armed with very fine curved bills, needle pointed, they can extract the smallest insects and their long tongue does the rest, divided as it is at the extremity.

The chief danger with which the tree-creeper in the Middle East has to contend is the chemical spraying of trees, a danger which also threatens the food-supply of the Paridae or poisons them from the results of the chemicals in their insect food.

In our previous work *Birds of Cyprus* we included in this family

Tichodroma, the wall creeper, following the classification of Dr. Hartert's *Vögel Palaearktischen Fauna*, upon which our work was based. It will be found in this *Handbook* in the last family discussed.

CYPRUS TREE-CREEPER

Certhia brachydactyla dorotheae

[Plate 20, facing p. 128]

The Cyprus representative of the tree-creeper belongs to the species characterised by having short toes, our tree-creeper in Britain is another species and belongs to the *familiaris* group with *long* toes, but in general appearance they are very much alike. The Cyprus bird is a resident species in the forests and is rather darker than the British bird and has pure white underparts. Head and back are streaked dark brown, the wings barred and edged with white, rump rust-brown, tail grey-brown. The bill is rather long and very fine. In total length it measures 5 ins (13 cm).

This is another endemic Cyprus bird to be found only in the Southern Range in the high pine forests where the trees are of much older growth than in the Northern Range. Its nest and eggs have but recently been described from Cyprus by a member of the C.O.S. Breeding above 3,000 ft, of four nests found in May, two were under the eaves of buildings or huts the first composed of pine needles, some lichen and profusely lined with feathers, another was built of strips of bark and feathers, a third nest was largely of pine needles in a large hole 25 ft up in a Troödos pine. The fourth nest was 18 ft up behind the bark of a Troödos pine and again had a pine needle base. These nests had respectively five eggs on 29 May, three fully fledged young on 20 May, four or five unfeathered chicks on 25 May; the young had flown from the fourth nest on 26 May.

Eggs had a white ground tinged with pink with ashy shell marks and heavy brown blotches at the big end forming a zone. Two eggs were very lightly speckled but still showed a distinct zone. They possessed a lovely bloom and all were extremely pretty eggs. (c.f. *Ool. Record* 1961 pp. 33, 34).

A decrease in the number of birds seen in 1967 was believed to be due to anti-malarial spraying of its breeding haunts. In 1968 numbers again increased.

Family PYCNONOTIDAE

The bulbuls are an Old World family, mainly tropical or sub-tropical which occur in the Ethiopian, Indian and Malayan Regions and are represented in the Middle East by a single species of the genus *Pycnonotus*. There has been considerable argument as to how they should be classified, some authors regarding all the African bulbuls as conspecific. We followed that course in *Birds of Cyprus* 1958 where the Palestine bulbul was given as a subspecies of *Pycnonotus capensis* following the suggestion in *Birds of Arabia* pp. 177–180. We have since retracted that opinion and prefer the arrangement in which three distinct groups are recognised in Africa and the Middle East; *P. barbatus* the North African species, being the most widely distributed.

The Palestine bulbul becomes a subspecies of that bird and will consequently be referred to in this Handbook as *Pycnonotus barbatus xanthopygos*. It is one of the yellow-vented birds with an eye-wattle characteristic of a number of species in the family. Others have only a trace, others again no eye-wattle at all.

The African bulbuls are much alike in general appearance rather larger than a sparrow and are not brightly coloured as are some of the eastern members of the group. Their upperparts are mainly brown but the colour of the feathers in the ventral region is variable: white, yellow or even red in the numerous species.

The eye-wattle is also a characteristic of the bulbuls but is not always present. In the African birds the sexes are alike and all are noted for their pleasant song, the Middle East representatives being no exception.

PALESTINE BULBUL

Pycnonotus barbatus xanthopygos
[Plate 24, facing p. 160]

This is one of the *yellow*-vented bulbuls as opposed to the red-vented group, which has a wide distribution in Africa. A native of Palestine among other places, it was at one time a not uncommon visitor to Cyprus in the spring. Old accounts written in the early days of the twentieth century speak of it as found in May, especially in the Larnaca district. There is no record of it having bred in Cyprus though it does so commonly in Palestine and Syria. It was last reported in April 1929.

About 7½ ins (19 cm) in length, its appearance is easily described. The head and throat are black, the upper side of the body brown and the tail the same of a darker shade. Underparts are a pale grey-brown, the ventral region *bright lemon yellow*. A greyish-white ring which surrounds the eye gives the bird an inquisitive expression.

If allowed to do so, it would possibly breed in Cyprus, as it does in other areas of the Middle East, building a cup-shaped nest of small twigs in which it deposits from three to four eggs with white or pinkish-white ground, densely (or slightly) spotted with pale brown or lilac brown. It is a favourite bird to keep in a cage, as its song of rich flute-like notes has a particular appeal to the Arabs in whose countries it nests.

Family CINCLIDAE

The dippers form a well-marked group of birds which occur widely in the hill and mountain streams of Europe, northern Asia, northern Africa, western North America and the Andes. They are contained in a single genus *Cinclus* and are peculiar in many ways. In affinities the group shows relationship with the thrushes – the young in all forms have spotted plumage – but are probably more akin to the wrens than to the thrushes.

Dippers have rounded wings, a short tail, a plump body and a habit of bobbing up and down on a stone in the middle of a turbulent stream. These characteristics easily betray them wherever in the world they may be – and there are over a dozen species. Boulder-strewn fast-running streams are their favourite habitat, usually in mountain surroundings, though they may equally occur at low elevations. They make a rounded nest of moss, lining it with leaves. The young are said to be able to swim as soon as they leave the nest and the old birds are capable of walking below the surface of the water in very fast-running streams for which the eye is specially adapted. Dippers lay unmarked white eggs and are sombrely coloured. The plumage is heavy and they have an abundant coat of under-down, which protects the body from cold and wet. Their food is almost entirely aquatic – water insects, larvae and small fish. There is, or was, only one representative in Cyprus, a subspecies of *Cinclus cinclus* which at one time was believed to be an endemic race.

Dippers occur in Turkey where two distinct subspecies are reported to occur, one of which is the race formerly resident in Cyprus before extermination apparently has overtaken it. Details of the Cyprian representative are given under the species name. The bird is a great loss to Cyprus and the reasons for its disappearance are not at once apparent.

CAUCASIAN DIPPER

Cinclus cinclus caucasicus

[Plate 19, facing p. 113]

Once believed to be an endemic race and named *Cinclus olympicus* in consequence, it was later found to be indistinguishable from the dipper which inhabits the Caucasus and with that bird *caucasicus* we allied it in *Birds of Cyprus* after Hartert: (*Die Vögel der Pal. Faun.* p. 794). We see no reason to depart from Hartert's opinion. There is small doubt that the dipper in Cyprus is now exterminated.

First discovered by an Englishman in Cyprus in 1887, it was still a well-known but uncommon bird in Cyprus in 1910 above 3,000 ft in the Southern Range and probably for a number of years after. A *possible* sighting was reported in 1945, since when nothing has been heard of it – it appears just to have faded away, leaving no trace of when this sad event took place. Will it ever come back? Of its breeding biology in the island not a single word has been recorded.

It was never numerous, dippers seldom are anywhere, and being restricted to the mountain streams of the Southern Range it had a comparatively small area of distribution. It could not remain unseen for so many years as have now been the case for it has been searched for by a number of competent ornithologists within recent years. The last definite record is reported to have been in 1939.

A plump-looking bird with a short tail, measuring from bill to tail-tip 7 ins (18 cm), it is sufficiently noticeable from its habit of standing on a stone in mid-stream and bobbing up and down, then with fast-beating wings flying up or downstream but seldom leaving its course. The head is dark brown, wings and back slate-grey. Chin, throat and upper breast are *white* (and very noticeable); lower breast, belly and flanks blackish-brown. It has a sweet song which has been described as an airy warble. Young dippers are even more noticeable than the parents as they are copiously spotted with white.

The nest is a domed structure often built on a stone in mid-stream when it looks like a pile of moss. Eggs are white and unmarked. The birds are remarkable for being able to walk under the water.

Family TROGLODYTIDAE

The wrens which are placed in the above named family embrace a number of small birds spread widely over the globe, the best known of which is the species named *Troglodytes troglodytes* whose profile was at one time depicted on the farthing coin of Great Britain. Its distribution extends from western Europe to China and Japan.

Wrens are small or medium-sized birds 3¾–8¾ ins (10–22 cm) in length, the smaller measurement covering the only Eurasian representative, the main concentration of the family being in tropical America. The sexes are alike.

In the Old World wrens can be recognised by their diminutive, to small size, very short cocked-up tail, strong feet and tarsi, short rounded wings and thick soft plumage. All the species make round ball-shaped nests with the entrance at the side. There are no wrens in the Australian and Pacific regions. In America some of the species have much longer tails than the familiar European bird. As a rule they inhabit thickets, vines, weeds and other dense growths where they may have secure hiding places. From these shelters they appear to chatter at intruders or to sing, but at any alarm they dash back to cover. One of the most attractive features in the wren is to be found in the voice, our Cyprus wren having a sweet powerful song, despite its very small body.

Wrens are predominantly sedentary except for the population of the common wren living in the higher latitudes of Europe and Asia which have periodically to escape from the winter snows, possible explanation of their wide distribution, races of which have established themselves in the Mediterranean islands and in northern Africa. Mountainous areas attract them in particular.

CYPRUS WREN [Plate 25, facing p. 161]

Troglodytes troglodytes cypriotes

The wren is unmistakable, its actions, silhouette, voice and song all betray it as it darts from one hidden spot to another with tail cocked at an acute angle. Never still for a moment, or so it appears, the wren is not really a shy bird and close approach is possible before it darts into thick cover and is gone. The song is astonishingly loud for so tiny a bird, its joyous notes may often be heard in the depth of winter with snow on the ground – even in Cyprus!

On near inspection the nut-brown plumage will be seen to be closely but almost imperceptibly, barred. It is common enough in the Southern Range at all elevations but does not occur in the Northern Range, the absence of water and undergrowth in the latter would be sufficient reason for its absence. On the lower ground, between the sea and the foothills, it does occur very occasionally in winter but is distinctly rare. We have seen it there only once ourselves, on the banks of a stream near Pyrna. One was recorded from Famagusta Fort by a reliable ornithologist well-known to us – both records in February. Another single bird was recorded in January 1962 from Akrotiri, following the extraordinary winter of 1959–60 when wrens were reported to be "plentiful at Akrotiri". No specimen appears to have been collected and the race to which these lowland records belong must remain in doubt. It has been suggested they may have been visitors from Europe.

The true home of the Cyprus residents is in the Troödos mountains, where it has been described as plentiful in the vicinity of Platres, but its range in the southern mountains is a wide one, between 3,500 and 6,000 ft.

The month of May is the best time to find nests which are often, but not invariably, built into the banks of streams, extremely well hidden under bracken, rank grass and brambles overhanging the stream bank. Others have built in house verandahs, one was located in the fork of a pine, another in the cleft of a rock. The nest is built of bracken-leaves and moss – sometimes entirely of moss, and lined with feathers of wood pigeons, chickens etc. The entrance is rather smaller, and the nest shallower, than in the British wren.

The eggs are reported to be interesting from the fact that they are usually only very sparingly speckled with red, some being almost unmarked, one or two spotless, all three types often appearing in the same clutch (c.f. *Oological Record* XXXV 1961 pp. 34–35). As many as seven eggs have been found in a nest in Cyprus. One nest found at Trooditissa on 1 July 1967, containing six eggs, points to a second laying.

Male wrens build the outside of the nest and also build several other so-called "cock-nests" in the vicinity of the one which eventually holds the eggs. It is the hen who apparently selects the lining.

Although this wren was described from a specimen obtained from Cyprus the subspecies *cypriotes* is not indigenous, as the name has been accepted for the wrens inhabiting the whole of the eastern Mediterranean, a fact of which the writer was not aware when preparing *The Birds of Cyprus* (1958).

Family TURDIDAE

A large assembly of well-known birds can be grouped under this heading, which so far as the Middle East is concerned may be split into three sub-families: the true thrushes *Turdinae* embracing such popular birds as the thrushes, blackbirds, ring-ouzels and rock-thrushes; the *Saxicolinae* which include the wheatears and chats and the *Ruticillinae* in which the redstarts and blue-throats are found. All are medium sized birds in which with few exceptions the young have a first spotted plumage.

The chats and wheatears alone form a large group widely dispersed in the middle east, inhabitants mainly of boulder-strewn desert areas of which there is no lack in Syria, Palestine and Asia Minor, typical of which may be cited *Oenanthe oenanthe* or *Oe. deserti* and the beautiful *Oenanthe hispanica*. A summer visitor to Cyprus usually classed as a resident, is the remarkable Cyprus chat, a bird of very special interest whose status and affinities are not clearly understood. Finsch's chat is on the contrary a winter visitor only to Cyprus, while others of the family are seen only at the time of migration. Two must be classed as accidental, the white-crowned black chat of the Nile Valley (*leucopyga*) and the hooded chat (*monacha*) of Upper Egypt, which wanders to Sinai and has now been recorded from Cyprus. In addition to the redstarts (*Ruticillinae*) both red and black and the Persian race of the former, Cyprus is fortunate in having both blue-throats, the red-spotted a regular winter visitor and the white-spotted, a passage migrant. Only those ornithologists familiar with the island who know where to look, are ever likely to see them.

Finally both of Europe's celebrated songsters: the nightingale and the sprosser are among the Cyprian visitors, the former a summer resident which breeds in small numbers.

It is the fashion today to treat the thrushes and their allies, the warblers and the flycatchers as one enormous family under the title *Muscicapidae* – a classification which Dr. Wetmore ten years earlier had the very good sense to recognise as utterly unwieldy. How right he was.

MISTLE THRUSH

Turdus viscivorus

This, the largest of the thrushes which visits Cyprus in winter, measures about 11 ins (28 cm) from bill to tail and may be recognised primarily by its large size and by the light colour of its upperparts, very grey in comparison with the browner song thrush. The underparts too are more boldly spotted, the ground colour varying from buffish-white to yellowish-buff. The spots on the throat are wedge-shaped, those on the belly rounder. In flight the bird looks even greyer than when settled and the white tips to the outer tail feathers are very noticeable.

Many mistle thrushes come to Cyprus when the weather on the Continent is exceptionally severe; flocks of hundreds have been reported on those occasions in former days, but it is a long time since any large-scale movement has been brought to notice, such as occurred in the severe winter of 1910–11. In normal years it may be expected in mid-October, birds remaining in variable numbers, usually in small flocks, to late March, most prevalent during the months November to February inclusive.

FIELDFARE

Turdus pilaris

The ash-grey head and ear-coverts, with buffish-white eye-stripe, grey rump and a chestnut brown mantle and scapulars,

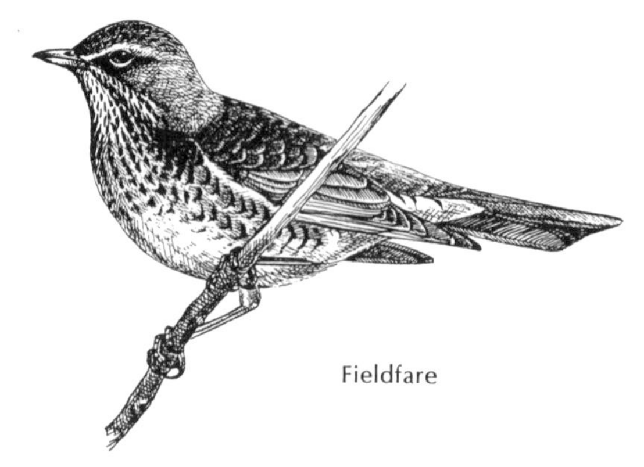

Fieldfare

should alone proclaim the fieldfares identity if only the upperparts are visible. When a full view can be obtained, the tawny throat and breast conspicuously streaked with almost black markings, the snow-white belly and the buffish flanks with black chevrons complete the picture of one of the most beautiful of its family. In flight the grey rump and white beneath the wings show clearly. The fieldfare has a yellow bill tipped with black, and dark grey legs and feet.

It comes as rather a surprise to a British ornithologist who is used to fieldfares invading his own country in the winter months, to find this Arctic-breeding species in the eastern Mediterranean, even as an irregular visitor. Highly gregarious by nature it is more likely to be seen in a flock than odd individuals. Feeding largely on berries it remains in its northern habitat so long as its favourite food can be found. In Cyprus it is reported to be especially fond of the berries of the Arbutus, so commonly seen when driving along forest paths. Parties of fifty birds have been seen recently in January and in that month, in 1957, a flock of thirty among others was reported when the winter was comparatively mild. It ascends to at least 4,000 ft in the Southern Range and occurs from late October to the end of February. Once to mid-April.

SONG THRUSH

Turdus ericetorum

It is the Continental race *T.e. philomelos* which on occasions invades Cyprus in winter in such huge numbers, a paler and greyer bird than the warmer coloured thrush with which British ornithologists are familiar in their home gardens. In total length it measures about 9 ins (23 cm), a good 2 ins less than the mistle thrush. The under wing-coverts of the song-thrush are buff, of the mistle-thrush white and the spotting of the breast of the former bird is less bold. The flight of the song thrush is also distinct, much more direct without the pauses so noticeable in the flight of the mistle thrush.

When first the flocks arrive mainly in November, some in late October, the birds make for the wooded areas but later in the season, when the snow covers the heights, they seek lower elevations, and may be seen in the plains hunting for snails. The year 1967 was one of those when the thrushes were reported by the C.O.S. to have been present "in thousands throughout the winter" – the first arrivals being noted on 24 October, the last half-dozen seen on 15 April. The next year, 1968, was even more remarkable and has been described as a "freak year" with "countless thousands reported from all over the island and more present on the Karpas Peninsula than ever within living memory". The numbers remained high from January to March, the last seen on 23 of the latter month until the return migration began on 28 October.

The extent of the spring passage can be gathered from the fact that from 5 March, 244 song thrushes were caught by lime-sticks at Paralimni Village alone. The last birds are usually seen late March to mid-April, very rarely later.

REDWING

Turdus musicus

A rarer winter visitor even than the fieldfare, it is worth examining any winter flock of those birds which may reach Cyprus to see if there are any redwings among them, for these two thrushes are very close neighbours in their far-north breeding quarters, and often migrate in company. In size, the redwing is a little smaller than a song thrush, i.e. 8¼ ins (21 cm) in length; the two should never be confused. The redwing can at once be identified by the warm chestnut flanks and the still more striking broad creamy-white eye stripe. The breast is streaked rather than spotted on a creamy-white ground. It is chestnut under the wings.

When it is said that the redwing visits Cyprus as a winter visitor in varying numbers there is no question of these numbers being large, occasionally up to a hundred have been recorded. Birds have been observed from late October to late February but normally are not seen before mid or late November.

During a visit to Cyprus the year that our

Birds of Cyprus was published, we found a bunch of redwings hanging in Nicosia market on 20 January 1958, which had been caught on lime-sticks. There is one remarkable instance of a redwing which had been ringed in Lincolnshire, England, on 1 November 1952, and was captured some sixteen and a half months later (13.2.54) at Kyrenia during a cold spell, a remarkable journey and direction for a redwing to have undertaken from the British Isles, which had probably started its journey from Scandinavia.

ALPINE RING-OUZEL

Turdus torquatus alpestris

[Plate 17, facing p. 97]

Two races of the ring-ouzel may visit Cyprus on rare occasions, the European and the Alpine, but to date only the latter has been recorded. Sooty black with a broad white gorget enables the male Alpine ring-ouzel to be easily recognised. The female is browner and her gorget less distinctive and more of a brownish-buff colour. In length it is 9½ ins (24 cm). The body feathers have pale edges and the wing-coverts and secondaries are paler than the rest of the plumage, a noticeable feature of the wing when closed.

The Alpine ring-ouzel can always be distinguished when handled from its better-known relative, the ring-ouzel of northern Europe, by the broader white margins to the feathers of the underparts, by the whitish centres to the feathers of the breast, belly and under tail-coverts and by the white margins to the secondaries and wing-coverts.

The one old breeding record near Kantara, as quoted in our *Birds of Cyprus*, has been disputed and has certainly never been confirmed by fresh evidence, but there seems no other valid reason to disbelieve in the record, given so convincingly in *Ibis* 1909 p. 584, and obviously accepted by other well-known ornithologists of the day. The old birds were reported to have been *seen* and both nest and eggs *taken*, but not (as they should have been) described.

It is a matter of individual taste very largely if we accept records made in all good faith at the time, or if, as is the modern trend, we discard them on the grounds that details were not supplied of the circumstances (which they seldom were in those days of which we are writing) a ridiculous excuse to discard anything it is impossible to prove sixty years after the event!

Normally this ring-ouzel is but a rare winter visitor which, on occasions in the past, has been reported in unusual numbers, perhaps driven by bad weather in mid-February from the Taurus mountains in Turkey. It has been seen in the Troödos mountian region of Cyprus and a pair have been reported from there in July, which may have intended nesting. The area is suitable, for the bird prefers high altitudes and builds a typical blackbird's nest in pine forests. Eggs are bluish-green with bold markings of brown and purple, but apart from the case cited, no nest or eggs have been located in Cyprus. Occasionally on passage ring-ouzels are caught by the limers, and should be examined by an ornithologist to discover to which race they belong.

BLACKBIRD

Turdus merula

When adult the male blackbird is glossy black including the wings and tail. The bill and eyelids in breeding dress are orange-yellow, the legs and feet dark brown. In first winter the bill is dark horn colour until autumn after which it gradually becomes yellow, the full bright colour being assumed by the early spring.

The adult female is umber-brown, paler and greyer on the throat, the breast inclines to rufous brown with dark streaks. Both bill and legs are brown at all seasons. It has been mistaken for a song thrush by the uninitiated. Female blackbirds throughout their range exhibit a confusing amount of variation in their underparts. In spring lovely mellow notes of the male may be heard.

To Cyprus it is a winter visitor and passage migrant in considerable numbers but oddly enough it does not breed in the island despite its enormous breeding range in Europe, extending as far east as the Volga. The numbers which pour into Cyprus in early November to winter in the wooded areas are considerable, but seem to vary greatly from year to year. We have seen it stated that "thousands" appear but that is contrary to our limited experience. The following more up-to-date appraisal is more likely to cover the blackbird's movements in Cyprus at the present day (prepared by the C.O.S. in 1970) for incorporation in this Handbook: Common winter visitor from mid-October, more commonly from early November to late March, but numbers fluctuate. The races visiting Cyprus are likely to include both the typical subspecies of northern Europe and the Caucasian form *aterrima*, the latter as reported by Hartert (*Vög. Pal. Faun.* p. 699) from the island.

EUROPEAN ROCK-THRUSH

Monticola saxatilis

[Plate 17, facing p. 97]

The European rock-thrush is a regular passage migrant at both seasons sometimes in fair numbers in autumn when owing to its conspicuous plumage and size – about 8 ins long (20 cm) – it is liable to persecution by local gunners. The male appears blue and orange. The head and neck blue-grey, the back dark slate with a partly concealed white patch, the wings blackish and the tail and breast orange chestnut. The female is mottled brown above, mottled buff on the underparts.

The largest numbers appear to have been noted in August and September and were to be seen in both ranges especially on Mt. Olympus, as well as at places near the coast. The latest information as to its status, prepared for the C.O.S. Check-List 1970, is that it is a relatively scarce spring migrant, reported mainly from the mountains notably Troödos, normally late March to late April, rarely in May. Reported in autumn from late August to late September.

The breeding record given in *Birds of Cyprus* pp. 122–123 should have been placed under the next species. This unfortunate error was due to the word "Blue" having been omitted in the handwritten note sent to me by the finder of the nest. It was therefore card-catalogued under *saxatilis*. It should, however, have been clear from reading the earlier context that the *Blue* rock-thrush was the species intended, and the fault for this mistake must remain with ourselves, an unfortunate error for which we offer our apologies.

No nest or eggs of this rock-thrush have *ever* been found in Cyprus. Normally, in Europe, this species nests in inaccessible situations between 4,000 and 7,000 ft in rocky gorges. From notes published by the C.O.S. it appears to be more numerous today than the older naturalists had believed, but only as a bird of passage. It is a breeding bird in the mountain ranges of southern and central Europe and migrates to eastern Africa in winter in huge numbers many reaching Kenya and Uganda. During the northern migration the sexes are said to keep apart, the males leaving first.

BLUE ROCK-THRUSH

Monticola solitarius [Plate 17, facing p. 97]

About same size as a starling with pointed wings and swift flight. As seen in winter the plumage is blue-grey in the male throughout but in its spring garb the feathers appear a darker blue. Any dark-coloured thrush-like bird, sitting quietly alone on the edge of a rock or cliff in hilly country, is most likely to be a blue rock-thrush; the female inconspicuous, much duller and browner than her consort; bluish brown above, paler and inconspicuously barred below. If alarmed they quickly disappear behind rock or cranny but otherwise they may sing a sweet short song which is very pleasant to listen to. It is usually solitary. Blue rock-thrushes are resident in the Northern Range but do not appear to have been found nesting in the Southern Range for some reason. Nests have been reported from quite low altitudes. From the numbers we have seen ourselves in coastal areas in spring there would appear to be a passage through the island as well as some remaining to winter in suitable areas.

Winter visitors and passage migrants occur from mid-September to mid-April, with spring migrants passing through from late February to early April. There are many winter records pointing to a permanent resident population. It is fairly common at that season on the southern sea-cliffs. Summer records at low elevations are very rare, but it was seen at Episkopi in the summers of 1968 and 1969.

Breeding takes place in the Northern Range in April and May; a nest of six eggs has been reported from Boghaz on the coast on 2 May. As it chooses holes in ruins as well as in cliffs in which to lay its eggs it may be found on quite low ground as well as in mountainous country.

Eggs are from four to six and are pale greenish-blue of a paler shade than in *M. saxatilis*, duller in appearance they are more often speckled with tiny brick-red spots which form a crown at the larger end, but some are immaculate and most delicately transparent. The nest is made of roots and fibres always in a most sheltered pisition.

The blue rock-thrush breeds in southern and middle Europe and in the mountains from Morocco to Libya. It migrates over the whole length of the Mediterranean to winter in the Sahara, N.E. Africa and southern Arabia.

COMMON WHEATEAR

Oenanthe oenanthe

The male common wheatear is a handsome bird with white forehead, pearl-grey crown and nape and a slightly darker grey mantle; ear-coverts are black and the eye-stripe is broad and white. Wings are black, the underparts cinnamon-buff fading to creamy-buff on the belly and under the wing. All wheatears have a black and white tail, the pattern varying slightly in the various species; the common wheatear's tail has the central feathers completely black, in some others they are white with a black tip. The female is a dull brown version of the male, but has the same tail pattern and white rump, which is very conspicuous in flight. It is 5¾ ins (15 cm) in length. Its call is *chack*.

These wheatears are passage migrants in numbers through Cyprus, the forerunners arriving the third or last week of February from Africa, but the main body in the second half of March, when they spread over suitable terrain on the lower ground. They do not however, remain to nest, but pass through the island in large numbers. Before April is out they have nearly all gone on their way. When we have been in Cyprus in those months, we found them all over the lower ground but seldom in the higher elevations. Once, on 16 April, we met with a party near Stroumbi, when several were in a mixed flock, evidently about to cross the foothills at that point.

The main return passage takes place from mid-August to the end of September when wheatears are again abundant returning to their winter quarters in southern Arabia and the Sudan, with stragglers passing till the second week of November. The autumn passage is more drawn out than the spring migration when the birds are hastening to their breeding quarters in northern and central Europe.

BLACK-EARED or SPANISH WHEATEAR

Oenanthe hispanica melanoleuca

[Plate 17, facing p. 97]

This is the eastern race of the black-eared wheatear and like its western representative it is dimorphic, that is to say it has two varieties, one with a black throat as well as ears, the other black ears only. The females are alike. It is a typical wheatear in appearance, and the males have conspicuous strongly marked colours. The crown and back are a warm cinnamon buff, and this colour can appear much brighter, almost a pinkish or sometimes golden-buff, in strong sunlight. The wings are black, the underparts whitish suffused with cinnamon. The rump is white, and the tail is white tipped with black except for the central feathers which are black. In the black-throated form the throat and the area round the eye to the beak are black. In the black-eared variety the throat is buffish. The female has a sandy-brown crown and back, with darker wings and a white rump like the male. The tail is like the male's but is brown where his is black. Its length is 5¾ ins (15 cm). In some males the crown is white.

The bird found in Cyprus breeds in southern Russia, western Iran, Asia Minor, Palestine and the Balkans. It is also found nesting in the Ægean and Crete. In winter its range extends to the southern Sahara,

Abyssinia and the Red Sea coasts.

The Spanish wheatear, to use its more familiar name, is a more regular spring migrant to Cyprus than it is in the autumn, when, in certain years, it seems to miss the island on its way south to winter in Africa. Never numerous, even in spring, its movements have been summed up as follows in the latest (1970) official Check-List of the C.O.S.: Occurs from early March to early May, the main passage late March to early April. There have been only sixteen autumn records between 1956 and 1970 between late August and late October, which emphasize its scarceness at that time of year. Both the black and the white throated form have been reported.

CYPRUS PIED CHAT

Oenanthe cypriaca

[Plate 18, facing p. 112]

The identification of the male bird in its summer quarters in Cyprus should be very easy. In the breeding season the male has the whole of the top of the head white, but the face, throat and upper breast are black. The back, wings and underwings are black. The rump and upper tail-coverts are white. The tail follows the usual wheatear pattern, with a broad black terminal band and mostly black centre feathers. The outer feathers and the remainder of the tail are white. The total length is 5¾ ins (15 cm).

The distinction in size, some aspects of plumage, habits and song all point to the Cyprus bird having evolved along lines of its own. The correctness of considering the Cyprus chat a subspecies of *leucomela* (as we did in *Birds of Cyprus* 1958) is still in abeyance, and for the time being it is wise to refrain from allying it with that or any other species. It has proved a puzzle to more than one ornithologist to determine its correct affinities, but a study of the bird has been made by a Danish ornithologist (Mr. Steen Christensen) whose conclusions have not yet been made public. Pending the result of his investigation we name it here binomially, though that does not imply we believe it must retain specific rank – the possibility however exists in Mr. Christensen's view.

On our first visit to Cyprus we were greatly intrigued by this delightful bird, the males arrive first, the females a few days later; one soon hears their rather harsh call-note in the early days of March and from mid-March onwards we saw it daily in ever increasing numbers. It is absent from the island in December, January and February. The song is uttered from tree-tops and in May several cocks, from their various vantage-points, will start a chorus, or even sing when in flight. They are very conspicuous and engaging birds, not a bit complying with ones preconceived idea of the wheatear family. At Stavros in the forest we used to see them perched on the topmost point of a pine uttering their *bizz-bizz-bizz*. They were not at all shy.

Although we found them extremely common on the hills and on rocky ground below, and exceptionally on ploughed land, they were uncommon after the end of April when the hens would be engaged in domestic duties, and the cocks in close attendance. The same gifted young soldier whose notes on the breeding birds of Cyprus were published just too late for use to be made of them in *Birds of Cyprus* (1958) studied this chat's breeding biology from the plains to the highest levels finding it an abundant and widely distributed summer visitor, breeding in the latter half of April on the plains, early May in the foothills around 2,000 ft, mid-May at 5,000–6,000 ft in the Troödos high forest. One at 5,000 ft with three eggs, probably a second laying, as late as 8 July.

In all twenty-three nests were found in two seasons. Three to five eggs formed the clutch (average 4·8). Nests were placed "in the earth-banks of mountain roads from 1 to 8 ft up; in stone walls averaging 3·3 ft from the ground, and two (at Troödos) in the eaves of wooden houses". Nests were usually rather loose, bulky and untidy but have a neat cup, usually lined with black and white, and sometimes red, hair, occasionally fine grasses, rootlets or (rarely) feathers. The cock's singing perch was sometimes 80 yds from the nest and is believed to be an average distance.

Eggs are exceptionally beautiful having a bright blue ground and show considerable variation in markings which usually form a zone round the large end. The red-brown spots are occasionally bright, but usually warm and dull, normally very fine and closely peppered. Both sexes incubate (for full details see J. F. R. Ashton-Johnson *Oological Record* XXXV, 1961, pp. 35–36).

The Cyprian chats leave the island when the young are fledged taking their departure in late September to early October, stragglers to late October, while occasional individuals have been noted in November. A few weeks prior to departure i.e. during September, most birds from the low ground move to higher ground when the birds become extremely abundant in both mountain ranges and in their foothills.

It is to be found in the north and north-east of the Sudan from October to April and has occurred as a vagrant in Arabia.

DESERT WHEATEAR

Oenanthe deserti

This is a true desert bird in its normal habitat and one which we should not usually associate with a verdant island like Cyprus except as a chance visitor. As it has more than a dozen records it is included with the main text in this book. It needs some care in identifying. The male is more easily recognised by reason of the black wings, the jet-black terminal half of the tail, the base being white, and the black cheeks and throat. The rest of the body plumage, except for the white rump, is isabelline, harmonising with the desert surroundings. The isabelline-buff female is less easily determined unless seen with the male. She too has a white rump but is otherwise inconspicuous.

Desert wheatear

The only wheatear in Cyprus with which the male desert wheatear may momentarily be confused, is the male of the *black-throated form* of the Spanish wheatear, whose tail pattern with the central feathers black and only the tips of the others black, should betray it.

The desert wheatear can only be described as an occasional rare visitor. Records are mainly in the spring and then range from 12 March to mid-April, most seen in March are nearly all singletons. All but one of the above have been recorded since the inception of the C.O.S., 1958–70, over which period there has been only one autumn record on 25 September 1969 at Paphos. All records but one come from coastal localities: Akrotiri, Paralimni, Larnaca and Paphos, the exception being the first for the island 7 April, 1929 at Athalassa. To which race these desert wheatears belong has not been ascertained.

ARABIAN CHAT [Plate 17, facing p. 97]

Oenanthe finschii

In autumn the adult male of this chat has the crown of the head to the mantle isabelline, the rump and upper tail-coverts white, the wings and under-wing black, the lores, orbital region, ear-coverts, chin and throat black. Rest of the underparts white washed with pale buff on chest. Central tail feathers black with white bases, outer tail-feathers white with a black terminal bar about 14 mm wide. In spring through wear the crown and mantle become pure white and the white underparts lose the buff wash.

The female is dimorphic, some examples having the chin and throat the same colour as the breast, others having these parts blackish with pale grey fringes to the feathers. The whole upperparts are hair brown, the wings dark brown with pale fringes, the underwing pale buff. The underparts are whitish with pale buff wash, darker on the breast. The bird measures 5¾ ins (15 cm) in length.

The white crown and white back of the male Arabian chat in worn plumage distinguish it from the Cyprian pied chat which has a *black* back, but care is required even so, during the short time both are present together; the one arriving, the other departing. The Arabian chat has been recorded arriving to winter as early as 1 September and staying as late as mid-April, by which date the pied chat should be nesting on the lower ground! But late September or early October to mid-March are more likely to be average dates of the Arabian chat's sojourn in the island. Its numbers vary from year to year. It frequents bare stony ground and we have seen it on the southern slopes of the Northern Range as well as on the low ground. It is also a victim in spring of the Paralimni limers.

After leaving Cyprus it migrates to its breeding grounds which embrace Asia Minor, Syria, Palestine, Sinia and Arabia.

NOTE

Two other members of this family have been recorded from Cyprus – the **hooded chat** (*Oenanthe monacha*) and the **white-crowned black wheatear** (*Oenanthe leucopyga*) for which see p. 220 of the Appendix.

ISABELLINE WHEATEAR

Oenanthe isabellina

[Plate 17, facing p. 97]

Another wheatear whose colouring makes it difficult to observe is the isabelline whose body plumage is entirely sandy-brown with a distinct grey tinge on the feathers. A pale cream stripe passes from the base of the bill over the eye. Primaries and secondaries are brown margined with pinkish-isabelline. The middle pair of tail feathers are black, the basal half covered by the white coverts. The rest of the tail feathers have the terminal half black, the basal half white. Throat and chin are whitish, merging into sandy-isabelline of a pinkish shade on the rest of the underparts.

A point worth remembering is that in the isabelline wheatear *the wings are brown*, not black as in most wheatears, but this is only really noticeable in flight. The isabelline wheatear is fairly large in size, 6 ins (15 cm) in length, a point which is likely to strike an observer familiar with most of the other members of the family we have been discussing. Only the Arabian chat approaches it in size. When handled infallible guides are the pure white under wing-coverts and axillaries. In the common wheatear for instance these parts are blackish, tipped and fringed with white.

It has now been proved to be a regular migrant to Cyprus in both spring and autumn, in variable numbers, but is generally tolerably common on the plains. It may be looked for from early March to late April, and on return passage from mid-August to possibly mid-November, mainly seen in September. As a pointer to the numbers which on occasion pass through the island, 180 isabelline wheatears were caught by the Paralimni limers in the spring of 1968.

This wheatear breeds in southern Russia, Asia Minor, Syria and eastwards, but does not nest in Cyprus.

STONECHAT

Saxicola torquata

This abundant winter visitor and passage migrant to Cyprus is a conspicuous bird well-known to most Europeans. Its head, throat, nape and back are black, though the feathers on the back have paler brown edges. The underparts are a rich chestnut, the under tail-coverts buff. The bill, legs and feet are black, the eye brown. The wings and tail are brown, with no white at the base of the tail. The upper tail-coverts are white streaked with black and buff. It is 5 ins (13 cm) in length.

The majority of those which pass through Cyprus in autumn, or those which remain to winter, will be the European bird *S. torquata rubicola*, but the Siberian race, *S. torquata maura*, has also been obtained in Cyprus in February and March. It has a trace of white at the base of the outer tail feathers and the feathers of the upperparts have longer and paler brown tips. Consequently, it has a paler general appearance. The underparts are rather paler; and there is also more white on the inner feathers of all the wing-coverts.

The status of the stonechats in Cyprus has been in dispute in the past, reports of adults having been seen with young lending colour to the opinion that a nesting pair may someday be found. Up to date there is no evidence that it breeds, but it would not be surprising, for it nests in the Mediterranean area. It must be remembered that stonechats almost certainly pair for life and take up territories in their winter quarters, as they do when breeding. It has never been recorded from Cyprus satisfactorily in summer. Birds arrive normally in October (rarely in late September) and are abundant by the end of the month. Departure takes place mainly in early March, some in late February, and all but an odd straggler have left by the end of March.

WHINCHAT

Saxicola rubetra

This is an altogether slimmer bird than the stonechat and in appearance less robust. The upperparts including the crown are streaked blackish brown and rufous-brown; the breast in the male is deep rich buff, in the female much browner and with some fine streaking. Both sexes have a prominent white streak passing from the base of the bill, above and beyond the eye. The male has a conspicuous white bar on the wing and a white patch on the lesser wing-coverts. In flight the white at the base of the tail is noticeable. The female resembles the male above but has considerably less white on the wing-coverts. The underparts have a pale buff patch on the breast unlike the deep rufous or pinkish buff of the male.

The only birds with which the whinchat can be confused are the female and young of the stonechat, but the buff or white eye-stripe of the whinchat and the *white* at the base of the outer tail-feathers, should identify it. In neither male nor female of the stonechat is there any white on the tail-feathers as there is in *both* sexes of the whinchat.

The whinchat is a numerous passage migrant in spring and autumn but unlike the

Plate 24

1. Red-backed shrike ♂
2. Red-backed shrike ♀
3. Woodchat shrike ♂
4. Woodchat shrike ♀
5. Palestine bulbul
6. Lesser grey shrike ♀
7. Lesser grey shrike ♂
8. Richard's pipit
9. Tawny pipit
10. Red-throated pipit ♂
11. Red-throated pipit ♀
12. White wagtail ♂
13. White wagtail ♀
14. Black-headed wagtail ♂
15. Black-headed wagtail ♀
16. Blue-headed wagtail ♀
17. Blue-headed wagtail ♂

E. Talbot Kelly '70

Plate 25

stonechat it does *not* spend the winter months there. In spring it is common from early April to early May. The autumn passage opens with occasional individuals seen in mid-August, becoming common from early September with peak numbers at end of the month. The migration may last to late October or early November. An early December bird is on record.

REDSTART

Phoenicurus phoenicurus

Two distinct races of the redstart occur in Cyprus – the typical European bird, known as the common redstart, and the northern Persian bird named Ehrenberg's redstart. The redstarts attract attention at once by their habit of shivering the chestnut-red tail. The adult male has a white forehead, and black cheeks and throat. The crown of the head is grey and so is the mantle. The breast and flanks are chestnut, the belly whitish. The female has the same bright tail, but she is a brown bird except for her buffish belly. Its length is 5½ ins (14 cm). The principal difference between Ehrenberg's and the common redstart is that the Persian form has a white speculum on the closed wing, caused by the white fringes to the secondaries. Unfortunately for the field observer there are intermediate examples, which show only a trace of this white marking. The females are greyer and darker in the Persian form, but it is not distinguishable from the common redstart in the field unless a close view is obtained. Their habits are similar but their breeding grounds distinct.

We should not normally stress the differences of closely allied passage migrants, but in this instance there is some excuse, for both birds have been reported to *nest* occasionally in Cyprus, and up to date this has not been confirmed by the discovery of a nest or eggs. We gave what evidence we had up to 1958 in the *Birds of Cyprus* where we hazarded the opinion that it was more likely the breeding bird would be Ehrenberg's redstart than its more western and northern relative. The last twelve years research by members of the C.O.S. has been unable to establish nesting of *Phoenicurus p. samamiscus* (i.e. Ehrenberg's) by finding its eggs, but it has been reported in late May near Paphos and a pair at Halevka; it has also been seen there in summer. As a passage migrant this race is recorded in small numbers from early March to mid-April and very rarely in September and October. The nominate form is a common migrant on both passages – in spring from early March to mid or late May and in autumn from late August to late October rarely to November.

Few species other than the warblers have suffered more than the common and Persian redstart at the hands of the Paralimni bird-limers. An accurate count by members of the Smithsonian Institute team, of the two races instanced, captured by this method *at Paralimni alone*, between 5 March and 11 May 1968 produced the staggering figure of 1,325 birds.

BLACK REDSTART

Phoenicurus ochrurus

There would appear to be at least three races of the black redstart on the Cyprus list if those critically examined have been

Plate 25 (opposite)

Guillemard's crossbill ♀

Guillemard's crossbill ♂

Cyprus wren

correctly identified. The commonest is probably the well-known north European bird *P.o. gibraltariensis* which arrives in Cyprus in autumn from early to mid-October (more commonly from late October to early November) remaining until March, only odd birds later. It is an abundant winter visitor most in evidence from November when there is a noticeable influx of passage migrants as there is again in March.

The male black redstart is easily recognised as such. It has the forehead, sides of the face, throat and breast black. The crown, nape, scapulars, wing-coverts and back are dark-grey. The under-parts are slate tinged with brown. The dark brown wings have a white patch, except in first-year males. The general appearance is of a very dark bird with chestnut rump and tail. The female is a brown version of the male and her tail is duller. The centre pair of tail feathers is brown in both sexes. Its length is 5½ ins (14 cm).

The Persian race *P. ochrurus* has also been collected in spring in the island. It breeds in northern Persia, the Caucasus and eastern Asia Minor. It may be distinguished from *gibraltariensis* by its *chestnut belly and axillaries*, the female is paler brown on the under-parts. A third race *P. ochrurus semirufa*, has also been identified from skins. This is the bird which inhabits Syria, Lebanon and northern Palestine. It has (in the male) the black of the breast reaching to about half way down the under-parts.

All three females are practically indistinguishable but the female of *gibraltariensis* is not so brown as the nominate form.

The status of the last two races is not clearly known except that both have been recorded during the migration period. The north European bird is firmly identified by ringed specimens from Germany and Poland having been captured in Cyprus. We found it most commonly among the tumbled rocks high above Ayios Chrisostomos Monastery and around St. Hilarion Castle. It is a species which has shown a remarkable tendency in central Europe to extend its already wide breeding range. Its population has been steadily increasing and the strength of its passage to the eastern Mediterranean is likely to increase also. In the vicinity of Paralimni Village in the spring of 1968, seventy-three black redstarts were caught on lime-sticks between 5 March and 11 May.

NIGHTINGALE

Luscinia megarhynchos

The nightingale's garb is disappointingly dull for one with so lovely a voice. Its entire upperparts are rufous-brown; the underparts and throat ashy-white, the breast pale brown. Tail chestnut brown. Legs are flesh-colour to grey-brown. It is in total length 6½ ins (17 cm).

Its voice is celebrated the world over for its beautiful liquid notes, which have a quality about them quite indescribable. When the song suddenly ceases one's attention is rivetted to catch again the opening notes. A solitary bird, shy by nature and given to hiding in thick tangled bushes, it is the song which betrays it.

When we read in the report issued recently by the Smithsonian Institute of Washington on the bird-liming carried on in Cyprus, that 357 nightingales and thrush-nightingales were captured in this way in *one single village* by the Paralimni villagers in a single spring, we realised to what extent this practice is robbing the countries in which these two species rear their young, of these incomparable songsters.

In Cyprus early arrivals are to be seen in mid-March the birds becoming more general in the last week. The passage continues throughout April, the main influx being in the middle of that month, later arrivals even to early May. When first they arrive they may be heard in the plains but as April draws to a close those birds which intend to nest in the island repair to the higher valleys, some breeding in the Troödos area in the young forest growth.

Nightingales are in full song in May and June. There are few instances of eggs having been taken but nests are usually well-concealed. We recorded one in our larger volume which was found near the Platania forest station on 16 May containing five fresh eggs; four or five is a normal clutch. In colour the eggs vary from olive-brown to olive-green. The nest may be placed in any sort of ground vegetation such as bracken and is a loosely made construction of dried grass and old leaves, usually lined with some finer material. Young abroad with their parents have been seen on 6 June in the Amiandos district. When the young are full grown the parents prepare for departure to Africa.

The autumn migration from Europe bears no relation whatever to that in the spring, and is almost negligible – the very few recorded passing have been in late August and September and the first week of October when birds have been captured and ringed.

THRUSH-NIGHTINGALE or SPROSSER

Luscinia luscinia [Plate 23, facing p. 145]

Only those already familiar with the sprosser – and few in Britain can claim that advantage – will be able to distinguish it in the field from the nightingale, so similar are they in appearance. Whereas the latter species is more *rufous*-brown above, the thrush-nightingale is more *olive*-brown, especially on the rump. A view of the breast is a helpful guide, for in the present species it is more mottled, and the middle of the throat is more definitely white, in contrast to the darker sides of the neck. If handled, the wing-structure at once proclaims the thrush-nightingale, for among other distinctions that of *L. luscinia* is longer (83–95 mm) and the first primary is minute, half the length of the primary coverts, whereas in *L. megarhyncha* the first primary is easily visible and usually longer than the primary coverts.

The voice of the two is entirely different, for while both birds are exquisite songsters, the notes of the thrush-nightingale are more powerful and contain marvellously pure bell-like notes, in place of the flute-like *piōō* of the better-known bird.

In 1958 when we collated all that was then known about Cyprus birds, we had very few records for the whole island of the "Sprosser" as the Germans name *L. luscinia*, but made the observation in our book that it was probably much commoner than appeared. How true that has proved is shown by the numbers caught in one short season by the Paralimni villagers on their lime-sticks: 245 thrush-nightingales as against 112 common nightingales! (see under last species). These figures, when combined with those of birds trapped for *ringing purposes* by the C.O.S. *and released*, point to a much heavier passage through Cyprus, especially so in autumn. In spring it passes through in April mainly in the latter half; in autumn from late August to late October, mainly in September as shown by those caught at the ringing station. Judged by the results of ringing alone, it appeared to be relatively scarce in spring and tolerably common in autumn, but this is evidently open to correction, when we recollect the large number caught on lime-sticks in the vicinity of one village in a single *spring* season. It may be that the bird is far more numerous on the east coast, and enters Cyprus by that route on its northward passage; unlike the nightingale none remain to nest and are never likely to do so for its southern-most breeding areas lie far to the north. The thrush-nightingale is an East European and Asiatic bird which traverses Asia Minor, Iraq, Persia, Palestine and Arabia to winter in the Sudan and tropical east Africa. It crosses the Mediterranean at its eastern end only, and then is met with so numerously in Cyprus, though for years it passed almost unnoticed.

BLUETHROAT [Plate 17, facing p. 97]

Cyanosylvia svecica

Here is another bird whose presence in Cyprus had been greatly overlooked by earlier naturalists and whose true status has now been discovered by members of the C.O.S. There are two quite distinct bluethroats which come to Cyprus: one with a red patch on the blue throat, the other with a white one. The latter, named *cyanecula* is now considered a subspecies of the red-spotted bluethroat. Their breeding ranges are different; the red-spotted nesting in sub-Arctic Europe and Asia, the white-spotted not breeding north of middle Europe. Both migrate south in the cold weather being dependent almost entirely upon insect life for their sustenance.

There should be no difficulty in recognising the adult males. Both have been recorded in the past.

1. The red-spotted bluethroat has brown upperparts, the crown rather darker than the mantle. The white eye-stripes meet on the fore crown, the ear-coverts are brown. The blue throat has a rufous-chestnut patch, and beneath this there are successive bands of black, white and dull chestnut. The remainder of the underparts are white, buff-tinged on the flanks and below the tail. The wings are brown. The centre feathers of the tail are brown, the others half-black with the basal half rufous-chestnut. The bill, like the eye, is dark brown. The bird is about 5½ ins (14 cm) in length. The female has the same upperparts, wings and tail as the male and also the white eye-stripe. Her chin and throat are buffish-white, the lower throat is crossed by a crescent-shaped dark brown band. The underparts are buffish-white, the sides of the body brown. This bird looks very like a robin and behaves in the same way. The chestnut base to the tail is a good field character.

The red-spotted bluethroat is a regular passage migrant and winter visitor in small numbers to the marshes and reed-beds, the latter occurring from late September, mainly from mid-October to late March, the last occasionally remain to April. Passage migrants are most common in mid-October to early November, and when returning north in March.

In the C.O.S. reports for the years 1967 and 1968 mention is made of *Cyanosylvia svecica* being "frequently seen in the Akrotiri reed-beds in January" and again "throughout the winter" – notes which obviously refer to the red-spotted bluethroat which finds in the reed-beds suitable roosting places and plenty of insect food.

2. The white-spotted bluethroat has a silky white spot on the throat, but this is sometimes entirely blue and the spot lacking.

The white-spotted bluethroat has been identified much less often; in *Birds of Cyprus* (1958) we could only trace three, since when seven have been recorded, i.e. ten in all. Undoubtedly many bluethroats of one race or the other pass Cyprus unseen by an ornithologist and the white-spotted race may be commoner on passage than the meagre records suggest. But whereas *Cyanecula svecica svecica*, with rufous spot instead of white, winters mainly in eastern Africa, *C.S. cyanecula*, with white breast-spot, winters throughout northern Africa and the Saharan oases but it is rare towards the east. It follows that Cyprus does *not* lie in its normal route. There is another white-spotted race which is more likely to occur in Cyprus than the last named. That is *C.s. volgae* (if recognised as a valid race) named from central Russia which winters in Egypt. In that race the white spot is smaller and may be mixed with rufous.

REDBREAST

Erithacus rubecula

The upperparts of the redbreast of continental Europe may be described as olive-brown and the breast as yellowish-orange, shades paler than the reddish-orange breast exhibited by the British breeding bird, with which many readers will be quite familiar. Moreover the continental bird has a whiter belly than its British representative, and the brown on the flanks and wings is of a paler shade. An arresting feature in all redbreasts is the large very dark brown eyes. Bill and legs are also similarly coloured. An adult bird measures about 5¼ ins (13 cm) from bill to tip of tail.

Young redbreasts have a spotted appearance and lack the orange colour on the breast, the general colour of that area being buff with dark brown tips and margins to the feathers.

It is to this, the typical subspecies, that the majority of the "robins" which winter in Cyprus have been referred, ringed birds from Sweden and Finland, recovered in Cyprus, proving the immense distances which some of them travel, though birds of the same race which have bred in central Europe are likely to come to Cyprus regularly when the cold weather sets in. The British robin (*melophilus*) we know to be largely sedentary, but there is a race inhabiting the Caucasus, named *E.r. caucasi-*

cus, which has definitely been collected in Cyprus (in 1938) and others from that source evidently occur in Cyprus annually. In the winter of 1969/70, at Akrotiri, birds caught for ringing showed that 25% of those examined were of the Caucasian race, distinguished from *E. rubecula rubecula* by being greyer and less olive above and the throat lighter yellow-ochre. The long upper tail-coverts and the outer webs of the tail feathers rust-colour. The bill is a little longer. It is intermediate in colour between *E.r. rubecula* and the Persian race *hyrcanus* which is deeper coloured on the breast and has the upper tail-coverts chestnut-brown and not *olivaceous*. This race too should pass through Cyprus but has not been recognised. It remains to be proved if there is a normal intake of *E.r. caucasicus* when compared with the better known subspecies.

The first migrants from Europe appear in autumn from early to mid-October and the winter visitors remain until mid or late March, some even staying until April. The passage *through* the island is at its height from early to mid-November. The spring passage is less in evidence and mainly in March. An occasional decrease in mid-winter of the wintering population may be accounted for by bad local weather. Both the races specified are likely to be affected in the same way.

Ringing of robins in Cyprus have given interesting results indicating that the birds are returning to the same wintering area year after year. One robin was re-trapped not only in the same area but *in the same building*, in which it had been caught the previous winter.

NOTE

An example of the **red-flanked bluetail** *Tarsiger cyanurus*, was found on 8 November 1957 on Mount Olympus at Troödos. See Appendix p. 220. It is fully described in *Birds of Cyprus* (1958) on p. 140.

An example of the **Persian robin** *Irania gutturalis*, occurred on 1 April 1962 at Dhekelia, the first and only record of this species in the island – For brief description see Appendix p. 220.

Family SYLVIIDAE

This is a family of small birds somewhat misleadingly named warblers, spread over the Old World which are mainly arboreal in their habits and with few exceptions are alike in sexes, the blackcap being a notable exception in which the male has a black crown and the female rufous.

As already remarked when writing of the *Turdidae*, warblers differ from the thrushes and flycatchers in having unspotted young, moreover they are restricted to the Old World. Those taxonomists who now reduce them to sub-family rank should reconsider such a retrograde step. The *Sylviidae* of the Old World constitute a complete family in themselves, and following the Wetmore Classification of 1960 we do not include within their ranks the firecrest and the goldcrest as some others would do. The Regulidae deserve the separate treatment we have accorded them.

Warblers are represented in the Middle East by all the well-known genera into which the Old World family is divided *Cettia, Locustella, Acrocephalus, Hippolais, Sylvia* (of which there are a dozen species on the Cyprus list), *Agrobates, Cisticola* and *Phylloscopus.* Thirty two species belonging to the above named genera have been recorded from Cyprus.

Of form and shape in the warbler family it is almost impossible to write, so diverse are the many species grouped in this assemblage. For the most part all are small or very small birds with fine straight bills and delicate legs. Rictal bristles if present at all are not conspicuous as in the flycatchers. The wing varies much but in the migratory species which pass through Cyprus it may be fairly long and pointed, in marked contrast to some African members of the family, which do not need to migrate and have short rounded wings. Colours are mainly subdued greens and browns and greys predominating, some have plain upperparts, some have streaky.

As they live so largely on an insect diet, the northern and central Eurasian population is forced to migrate in the winter months to countries wherein they can still obtain a living, thus accounting for the remarkably long journeys attributed to certain species. The majority winter in tropical Africa. Some of the Phylloscopine warblers though little more than 4 ins (10 cm) in length, make these annual flights twice a year, at which seasons the Middle East countries through which they pass have the woods and gardens filled with these minute birds of passage. Cyprus is in the centre of this migration and it can only be a matter of profound regret that literally thousands of *Sylviidae* are slaughtered by the inhabitants during the passage through the Middle East especially by the method of liming the bushes where the birds come down to rest. These are insect-eating birds which belong to Europe and Asia and *not* to the countries they are compelled to pass through on the way twice a year to winter in Africa.

The summer visitors which come to breed, as does the olivaceous warbler to Cyprus, and the European reed warbler for instance, are very much in the minority, while birds in this family which apparently remain all the year round, as for instance Cetti's warbler and the Cyprus warbler (though some emigrate in winter) are even fewer, but make up for that by their peculiar interest. All the rest must be counted as *birds of passage*. Cyprus owes them a better deal than they are receiving today and that applies to the whole Middle East.

Twelve years ago we wrote in *Birds of Cyprus* that there remained a great deal to learn about the status and migrations of the *Sylviidae* in this island. Today (1970) it is possible to write with much greater authority for much has been discovered in the intervening years especially by the mist-netting and ringing by leading members of the C.O.S. which adds to our knowledge without destroying life. Sergeant P. F. Stewart in particular should receive our thanks in this connection for the exemplary work he has done. Moreover a number of queries which we had raised have now been satisfactorily answered through careful observations, among them the status in Cyprus of the Sardinian and the spectacled warblers and of the fan-tailed warbler, one of the smallest of the birds in the island now proved to be locally resident. There is no end to the good work the C.O.S. and its energetic members have accomplished for the benefit of Middle East ornithology.

CETTI'S WARBLER

Cettia cetti

Cetti's warbler has the whole of the upperparts from crown to tail rufous-brown. The throat is whitish like the belly, while the breast and flanks are strongly washed with lighter brown. The bill and legs are brownish-flesh. At close quarters the narrow white line over the eye is conspicuous. The tail is much rounded, the ten feathers being graduated. It is 5½ ins (14 cm) in length. Cetti's warbler is difficult to see as it skulks in bushes, but its song betrays its presence. This is very loud and short and sounds unfinished, repeating something like *che wee* or *che wee ou* and stopping very suddenly, as if the bird had been scared into sudden silence. It usually spends its time in a thick shrub in close vegetation and is often near water. It is a difficult bird to identify by sight.

There has now been ample confirmation of the records mentioned in our *Birds of Cyprus* (1958) when the status of this warbler was still in question. There is no doubt that Cetti's warbler is resident in Cyprus the year round. Breeding was suspected in June 1909, when a juvenile was obtained on 6 June at Paphos, but actual breeding was not discovered until 13 May 1959, when a nest was found for the first time near Mandria, Troödos range at 2,850 ft.

Cetti's warbler

It has since been ascertained that it is a local bird found in valley bottoms in the Southern Range and also reported as "numerous in the Akrotiri reed-beds *from October*" and "from the end of the Karpas Peninsula". Birds are said to move "up hill" in summer, where breeding takes place. They are more widespread in winter but from ringing experiments it is believed to be stationary at Akrotiri all the year round. This requires more research, as well as its local movements. It is believed not to occur above 3,000–4,000 ft.

The nest near Mandria was suspended in mid-air 10 ft above a stream by three narrow strands of dead bramble – a typical large nest of reeds and grasses lined with hair and holding four young, recently hatched. Another nest was 6 ins up in reedy riparian growth and a third made of grass, tamarisk twigs, leaves and flower-down, lined with white hair, was 12 ins up in a growth of riparian plants at 2,000 ft altitude. Typical eggs are brick-red. May appears to be the month at which eggs can be found in the Southern Range between 2,000 and 3,000 ft. Nests at lower elevations (if any!) remain to be discovered. No overseas immigration has been reported.

RIVER WARBLER

Locustella fluviatilis

The first possible record of a river warbler

just crept into the *Birds of Cyprus* in a brief note on the strength of a bird said to have been seen at Akrotiri on 30 March 1957, but this record is described in the new Cyprus Check-List as "not acceptable" by the responsible editors. The river warbler's occurrence in Cyprus has since been established on a number of occasions, lifting it from its doubtful status.

A bird of this species trapped on 12 August 1962 – the only undisputable method – is the first certain record for the island. Again single birds caught and ringed on 14 April and 29 September 1967, and two more on 28 October, all in 1967 at Akrotiri or the vicinity, prompted the recorder to observe that they are "probably more common than previously believed... their skulking behaviour causing them to be easily overlooked". The year 1968 produced another record on 8 September, at the same place.

The sexes of this warbler are alike, the whole of the upperparts olive-brown, the underparts whitish tinged with buff, especially on the flanks and under tail-coverts which are tipped with white. The tail is strongly graduated; no white on wing or tail. Lower throat and breast distinctly spotted or streaked with brown, rarely without markings. First primaries always shorter than the primary coverts, second primary distinctly the longest wing 71–79 mm (after Meinertzhagen).

It breeds from northern Sweden to the Ural Mountains and in winter migrates to Africa, wintering south to the Zambesi but is not recorded from the Sudan.

NOTE

A dead specimen handed to a Greek Cypriot member of the C.O.S. of a **Grasshopper warbler** (*Locustella naevia*) on 22 September 1968 is the first definite confirmation of this warbler (reported in *Birds of Cyprus* 1958 p. 92 of a bird *heard* but not seen on 9 April 1957) by another member of the C.O.S. and reported as such. The latter record has not been accepted as more than "a possible occurrence" by those responsible for the 1971 Check-List.

The bird is listed in the Appendix of this book p. 220.

SAVI'S WARBLER

Locustella luscinioides

The discovery that no less than twenty-two Savi's warblers were caught on lime-sticks at Paralimni in one spring (1968) between 5 March and 11 May has put a very different complexion on the supposed rarity of this bird in Cyprus. Previous to 1958 there had only been three recorded, 21 April 1875 (Larnaca), 13 April 1909 (near Nicosia), and an autumn sighting 20 October 1957 (Nicosia airfield). There was good reason to consider it a rare accidental visitor in those days. Between 1958 and 1970, both dates inclusive, there have been fifteen records of single birds, three of two birds and one remarkable record when twenty-two were limed at Paralimni, between 5 March and 11 May 1968, during the spring bird-liming "season". March, April and May were the months of the spring captures or sight records; August, September and October the autumn records. The appearance of Savi's warbler at Paralimni and Akrotiri, which account for all but three of the records, suggest that it may fittingly be described as a rather scarce spring migrant, much rarer in the autumn.

It is not an easy bird to recognise: Uniform earth-brown above, with no spotting or streaking the underparts are non-descript but the throat and the middle of the belly are white, the breast and flanks light brown, washed with buff on the flanks and under tail-coverts. The wings and tail are rounded, the tail strongly graduated but uniform in colour without paler tips. The wings match the back in colour. The bill is rather long and slender, dark brown on upper mandible, paler below; legs and feet light brown.

Savi's warbler is a summer inhabitant of the vast reed-beds of central Europe, with a breeding range from Holland to the Volga river. It is a not uncommon winter visitor to the Sudan from October to March at least, frequenting swampy localities.

MOUSTACHED WARBLER

Lusciniola melanopogon

About 5 ins (13 cm) in total length, the

upperparts are russet brown, streaked on the mantle with black and it has an almost black crown; a prominent white eyebrow broadens into a small white patch behind the eye. Belly and throat are pure white, the breast and sides washed with russet. The bill is rather short and fine and the tail is noticeably graduated, blackish-brown in colour fringed with chestnut brown. The tail does *not* contrast with the back. Superficially it is not unlike the sedge warbler in appearance but has the wing much more rounded, a blacker crown and whiter eye-stripe.

This is yet another bird to which the status "rare passage migrant" no longer is applicable for since 1958, owing to the much greater ornithological activity in the island, we have learned a very great deal about the migratory birds of Cyprus.

First recorded for the island from the Famagusta freshwater lake on 19 March 1911, when a male bird was collected, no more was heard for over forty-five years when on the formation of the C.O.S. 1957–58 during the emergency, Service personnel accumulated many more records, twenty-two – twenty-three in all up to the winter of 1968–69 between early October and mid-March. In the winter of 1969–70 it was fairly common at Akrotiri Salt Lake. It was also reported from Athalassa and the Kouklia reservoir. It may be classed today as a scarce but probably regular winter visitor to the Akrotiri and Morphou areas, scarce elsewhere.

GREAT REED-WARBLER

Acrocephalus arundinaceus

It is the western representative of this fine reed-warbler which comes to Cyprus on migration, distinguished from the eastern form by wing-formula alone, a rather unusual distinction. The large size sets it in a class by itself for no other member of the family approaches 7½ ins (19 cm) from bill to tail. Robust of bill and legs, the latter bluish-grey in colour, its body colouring is dull, the upperparts all light brown without any streaks, the underparts pale orange-tawny except for a very white throat and a whitish belly. The tail is noticeably broad and is often spread in flight, it is dark brown, the tips of the rectrices paler. Its loud guttural voice has been described as "almost froglike"!

The western form ranges from the Baltic States to western Siberia and over the whole of central and southern Europe to the Mediterranean. In winter it migrates to tropical Africa and it is then, and on its return journey that it is frequently seen in Cyprus; in spring from early March throughout April to late May and again in late August, birds passing until the third week of October, rarely to November. It has been described as "abundant" at Bishop's Pool – a favourite locality on the Akrotiri Peninsula – from 3 to 6 September and then in smaller numbers till 4 October.

REED WARBLER

Acrocephalus scirpaceus

There is nothing very distinctive about the reed warbler's plumage. It is a *plain-backed* bird whose upper parts are *brown*, and paler on the rump. The underparts are dull white, washed with buff on the sides and flanks. The bill is brown above, flesh-coloured below. Legs and feet are brown. In the flesh it measures 5–5½ ins (13–14 cm) in length. Its *unstriped* crown and mantle distinguish it at close quarters from the streak-backed sedge warbler and if unseen the song of these two birds is a sure guide to their identity (if known to the listener) as they are very different; moreover the sedge has a prominent white eye-stripe. More easily confused with the reed warbler is the marsh warbler (*A. palustris*) as it too has a plain back but is more olive above and brighter buff below than the reed warbler.

To Cyprus the reed-warbler is both a passage migrant in spring and autumn and a summer visitor to the reed-covered lakes where it is now known to breed much more extensively than formerly believed. It occurs in Cyprus from early in mid-March, more usually late March with passage continuing into mid-May. In autumn the migrants return from mid or late August, according to the season, and may be seen until late October or even later into November, the main autumn passage taking place in September and early October.

As a nesting species – the race has not been subspecifically determined, but is believed to be *A.s. fuscus* – it is locally common. It bred abundantly at Akrotiri in 1969 and over thirty-five birds were captured in various stages of moult in June and July. Kouklia reservoir and Larnaca lake, where we found it commonly near the Turkish monastery garden, are two other very favoured nesting places, but wherever reeds are prevalent after a wet winter, the birds are likely to be found.

Reed warblers nests are works of art, usually firm structures of flowering grass with odd bits of wool and moss woven into a circular shape, the whole then woven to reeds standing in the water. Eggs are greyish-white to pale green densely mottled and blotched with greenish-brown and underlying lavendar markings. The clutch is from three to five. Eggs seen in Cyprus are like those in Europe but one set of two found at Akrotiri was said to be unusually pale.

MARSH WARBLER

Acrocephalus palustris

We have written in another place that unless the marsh and reed warblers can be captured and handled – and even then care is required – they are virtually impossible to name with certainty in the field by the ordinary observer, particularly when the birds are in winter dress. This is another plain-backed warbler, uniform olive-brown from the crown to the rump and showing no contrast between the rump and the back. A pale eyestripe extends from the base of the bill above the eye. Underparts are rather bright buff from the breast to the under tail-coverts, the throat being pure white. Wings and tail are brown. The wing formula is diagnostic. The second primary equals the fourth in length and is always longer than the fifth. The third primary is emarginate on outer web, but the fourth and fifth are not.

Known for its exceptional power of mimicry of the songs of other birds, the marsh warbler may draw attention to itself by this trait.

It was with the greatest surprise we discovered from the reports of the C.O.S. that the marsh warbler has now been recorded so often during migration in the last twelve years that it can no more be classed as an accidental visitor. The figures supplied to us – with which we shall end these notes – have perforce revolutionised our previous conception of its status. In 1958 we could trace but one single record – and that of exceptional interest – a bird ringed in nest at Ypres, Belgium 21.6.52, recovered at Nicosia in the last week of October of the same year, having covered a distance "as the crow flies" of 3,000 km. There have now been ringing returns from West Germany. Marsh warblers have been trapped in both seasons and as proof of the value of this work may be cited twenty-seven marsh warblers captured and ringed in autumn 1967 between 23 August and 5 November. *None* were trapped that year in the spring.

The latest assessment of its status in Cyprus is "a rather scarce spring migrant in the latter half of April. Often on autumn passage from late August into October, with most birds in September when it is tolerably common, rarely but occasionally recorded in late October or early November. All records obtained from ringed birds".

SEDGE WARBLER

Acrocephalus schoenobaenus

Similar in size to the reed warbler 5–5½ ins (13–14 cm) in length the sedge warbler is at once recognised from it by the *striped dark crown* and streaky mantle, the dark streaks on the mantle blurred, but very heavy and prominent on the crown, causing a distinct contrast between them. The rump is tawny and unstreaked contrasting with the earth-brown tail with its pale tips. The best character to observe however is the very prominent *yellowish-white eye-stripe*, made all the more noticeable by the almost black marginal edge of the crown immediately above it. The underparts are creamy-white, shading into yellowish-buff on the flanks.

There can be no confusing this bird with the reed or marsh warblers, neither of which has a prominent eye-stripe, while both have uniform backs. The sedge warbler unlike the reed warbler does *not* nest in Cyprus but passes through commonly both in spring and autumn to and from its winter quarters in tropical Africa. In spring from early April to late May and in the autumn from early August, occasionally late July, to early or late October. A December record and some in early March are suspected of possible error in identification with the exception of one found dead on 2 March. Sedge warblers do not breed in Cyprus.

Sedge warbler

NOTE

Two other species in the genus *Acrocephalus* have been recorded from Cyprus, the uniform backed **Blyth's reed warbler** (*A. dumetorum*), and the streaky-backed **Aquatic warbler** (*A. paludicola*). Both are rarely encountered and are mentioned accordingly in the Appendix p. 220.

ICTERINE WARBLER

Hippolais icterina

A handsome warbler with a striking song the icterine has noticeably long pointed wings and measures in length 5½ ins (14 cm). Its plumage is clear olive above, uniform in shade from crown to tail-coverts. A narrow yellow stripe passes over the eye and a yellow circle of minute feathers surrounds it. The underparts are pale yellow from chin to under tail-coverts. Wings are medium brown. The bill of the icterine is on the heavy side, not fine and sharp-pointed as, for instance, in the chiffchaff; the upper mandible is brown, the lower yellow. Legs and feet are greyish blue.

It is usual to compare the icterine with the very similar coloured Melodious warbler, but *H. polyglotta* is never likely to occur in the area, and consequently the icterine in Cyprus should not be mistaken for any other bird. The yellow underparts of the icterine should alone save it from confusion with the slightly smaller, but numerous, olivaceous warbler (*H. pallida elaeica*), or the larger olive-tree warbler (*H. olivetorum*), which has very rarely been reported, both of which birds have whitish underparts tinged with pale buff and cream respectively.

It was not until 1956–57 that the icterine warbler was discovered to be an irregular passage migrant at both seasons, and has since been found to turn up in variable numbers, especially in spring during a rush of migrants, while in other years almost absent, appearing mostly from late April to mid-May. In autumn from late August to mid-October, but mainly in September.

BALKAN OLIVACEOUS WARBLER

Hippolais pallida elaeica

Rather smaller than the last species, some 5 ins (13 cm) in total length, the olivaceous warbler is uniform pale grey-brown above, without a trace of olive-green. Below it is white suffused with buff. The throat is almost white. A small ring of feathers round the eye is whitish and there is an ill-defined creamy-white eye-stripe. The shape of the bill will alone proclaim the genus in which this warbler is placed: very broad at the base with exposed nostrils and a flattened under-mandible.

This is a very numerous summer visitor which arrives early in April, exceptionally in early or mid-March, and spreads all over the island, wherever there is plenty of cover in which to build its nests. We recorded it in our previous book as extending from the plains to 6,500 ft altitude, in the mountains of the Southern Range, it being very plentiful also in the foothills wherever there was plenty of cover. The birds which remain in Cyprus to nest – for it is also an abundant passage migrant until mid-May – do so in May and early June, in all types of environment, gardens, acacia thickets, in *maquis*, by streams and in all the woods. Altitude is no barrier to it, for it has been found breeding right up to 6,100 ft on Mount Olympus. Describing its breeding haunts in Cyprus, a writer in the *Oological Record* XXXV, 1961 wrote that its nests were found in a variety of small shrubs, mainly cistus, thorns and brambles – and occasionally in the Troödos mountains in a small pine or golden oak. Varying considerably in size, structure and materials, all were works of art, combining lightness and elasticity with concealment. Of eleven nests examined in the Troödos mountains, nine held eggs, seven with C/4. The highest nest was 3 ft from the ground, the lowest 14 ins. Eggs vary from two to four and in colour are pale lilac-white spotted with dark brown. This warbler is double brooded.

Birds begin to leave their breeding ground in the higher altitudes in late July. The autumn migration sets in from early to mid-August and continues to mid-September, stragglers passing sparsely thereafter with the late-comers to early October, rarely late October. Spending its summer in the Balkan Peninsula, Crete, Cyprus, Asia Minor, Iraq and Turkestan the olivaceous warbler winters in tropical Africa; great numbers are reported passing through Sinai in the autumn from mid-August onwards.

NOTE

Another member of the genus *Hippolais* – the **olive-tree warbler**, *H. olivetorum*, greyer and larger (6 ins (15 cm) in length) than the above, has been reported on several occasions. Between 1961 and 1969 eleven birds have been recorded in April and May, and four in August and September, details of which occurrences are given in the latest Check-List, in which publication some of the earlier records have been discarded as doubtfully correct. See Appendix p. 220.

BLACKCAP

Sylvia atricapilla

There is no difficulty in recognising either male or female blackcap in Cyprus for of all the warblers that have been recorded now from this island – some thirty-three species to date – only the male Sardinian might be momentarily mistaken for it. Sombrely coloured, the body-plumage is greyish-olive above, paler on the rump and tail-coverts. Wings are grey-brown and the tail blackish. The underparts, including the throat, are pale grey, washed on the flanks with pale olive; only the middle of the belly is white. The character which enables the blackcap to be instantly recognised is the very crisply defined crown, glossy black in the male, bright reddish-chestnut (or chestnut-brown) in the female.

Renowned for its beautiful notes the blackcap has few rivals as a songster in

spring, pouring forth a variety of rich melodious notes surpassing in their sweetness those of any of its family.

Recorded as the commonest of all passage migrants to Cyprus, literally arriving in thousands, this unfortunate little bird pays a heavy toll in numbers for the privilege of resting awhile on this Island. It falls victim to the limers more than any other, as the number taken during the Smithsonian Institute inquiry of 1968 proved. Quite apart from those captured *in the autumn* or in other villages which practise the liming business – for a thriving lucrative business it is – the blackcaps taken at Paralimni village and nearby on lime-sticks between 5 March and 11 May 1968 numbered, 3,946 out of a grand total of 25,000 birds belonging to 100 species [official figures]. Such captures speak for themselves of the immense hordes of blackcaps which must visit Cyprus every spring, the main passage occurring from mid-March to mid-May. The practice of liming, and the capture of thousands of birds to be plucked and pickled in jars, and widely exported as "Beccaficoes" to neighbouring countries, is as old as the hills. It flourished in 1553 and is as easy to eradicate in Cyprus as would be bull-fighting in Spain. It is in the Cypriot's blood.

No doubt wisely, the blackcaps elect to pass on to countries where their voice and benefits to agriculture are more widely appreciated, where they can rear their families in peace before once more running the gauntlet *en route* to their winter quarters in Africa.

In the latest Check-List of Cyprus birds prepared in 1970 by officers of the C.O.S. the blackcap is said to be especially common on the *autumn* passage from late September to early November. If, as we should, we put faith in the writings of the early ornithologists who paved our way, there have been spasmodic instances of pairs remaining to breed, when several nests, one containing young, were found in the hills above Kyrenia in May.

Some modern recorders, who have themselves failed to discover signs of breeding, are inclinded to doubt the truth that blackcaps have ever bred in Cyprus, but we are glad to see those responsible for the new Check-List are not among them, and accept the old statements. Certainly there are no recent records, but blackcaps are still occasionally, though rarely, seen in summer.

BARRED WARBLER

Sylvia nisoria [Plate 23, facing p. 145]

This is one of the largest of the warblers and may be likened in size to the Orphean. Both measure 6½ ins (17 cm) from bill to tail tip. The adult male is easy to recognise, in colour brownish-grey above and on the wing, with white tips to the secondaries. In some birds the tail appears quite grey with white tips and inner margins which are very noticeable when the tail is spread. Both mantle and rump are barred. The underparts are white, barred everywhere with crescentic grey markings except the middle of the abdomen. Bill horn above, yellowish-flesh colour below; legs and feet grey-brown. The eye (in adults only) is bright yellow.

The female is browner and not nearly so noticeably barred as the male. Immature birds, in Autumn dress, are very difficult to name in the field. Then there are no bars on rump or underparts. The white sides and flanks are washed with pale ochreous-buff, this colour also appearing on the breast.

Formerly believed to occur in Cyprus only during the autumn passage – for prior to 1958 there were no spring records – it is now proved to visit Cyprus at both seasons. As many as six have been seen in one day at Paralimni, caught on the lime-sticks on 28 April. The barred warbler is never really numerous and must rank as one of the least common, though in autumn a regular bird of passage, mostly in August and September. Its spring migrations are less regular, mainly in early May, but it has occurred from mid-April.

ORPHEAN WARBLER

Sylvia hortensis

This large, robust warbler measures 6½ ins (17 cm) in total length and has a superficial resemblance to the male blackcap, which has a much slimmer figure. The male orphean has also a black crown, but it is not clearly defined like a cap as in *S. atricapilla*, nor is it glossy, but much duller. In addition the orphean has a pure white throat and the underparts are much whiter. The upperparts are greyish-brown, the wings darker. The tail of the orphean is brownish-black tipped with white and the *outer feathers are almost all white*. The blackcap has no white in the tail. Thighs and under tail-coverts are pinkish-buff as are the sides and sometimes the breast. *The eye is cream* an unusual colour among the warblers; bill black; legs and feet slate-colour. Ear-coverts and lores are nearly black – a feature to note. The adult female closely resembles the male when in *winter dress*, but the crown is greyish-brown. In summer the crown of the female becomes darker brown.

Those who are familiar with the song of the orphean warbler consider it more powerful than that of the blackcap, but not to be compared with it in sweetness. Some care is required to avoid confusing the female orphean with the immature barred warbler in autumn dress, but the very dark lores and ear-coverts of the orphean should betray it.

A passage migrant in March and April and again in early August to mid-September, the orphean is then much scarcer than on the spring migration; when it first arrives in mid-March and from later in that month to early April, it is fairly common.

GARDEN WARBLER

Sylvia borin

Another regular passage migrant at both seasons this warbler is an even brown colour on the upperside and dull white on the underside, washed with pale buff on the sides. The pale eye-stripe is poorly defined and does not attract attention; nor in fact does the bird itself as it moves quietly about in a tree, diligently searching for insects and occasionally uttering a very sweet song – a series of warbles with little or no phrasing as in the blackcap. It is a large one-coloured warbler, 5½ ins (14 cm) in length, and combined with its subdued colouring is not to be confused with any of the smaller Phylloscopine warblers like the chiffchaff and willow warbler.

The garden warbler comes to Cyprus in April and May and soon after arrival spreads over the woodlands. We stressed in our previous work that it appeared to arrive later than many other passage migrants, early May being a more usual date for their arrival than early April. The dates of passage provided by the C.O.S. confirm that late April to mid-May is the height of the spring migration and that mid-September to early October sees the main autumn passage, the late migrants occasionally to the end of October. In some years the garden warbler is scarce.

There is a considerable autumn passage

Garden warbler

in the eastern Mediterranean, large numbers passing regularly through Sinai, Palestine, Arabia, Egypt and the Red Sea before entering tropical Africa by way of Eritrea, Ethiopia and the Somalilands to reach the country of the East African lakes where many spend the winter.

WHITETHROAT

Sylvia communis

The male common whitethroat has a slate-brown to dark grey cap and rust-brown mantle and underparts. A very conspicuous white throat, especially in the breeding season gives way to a duller white breast and belly, the breast flushed with pink, the sides and thighs with buff. A noticeable feature is the chestnut fringe on the wing feathers (secondaries and coverts) which immediately distinguish the whitethroat, both male and female, at all seasons from the lesser whitethroat. When it flies there is a lot of white visible in the tail on the outer rectrices. Its total length is 5½ ins (14 cm). Feet and legs are pale brown. The female is duller and has a browner cap but shares the wing and tail features with her consort.

It is a perky-looking bird with a favourite habit of perching on top of bush or hedge, the male often puffing out its white throat. The usual note is chattering and vigorous, the song a subdued warble.

Whitethroats pass through Cyprus in both spring and autumn and are most in evidence from late March to early April continuing to mid-May. We have seen them from shore level up to 2,000 ft in the spring, mainly in the west. In autumn the migration last from mid or late August to mid or late October, chiefly September to early October.

It has once been reported to nest (*Ibis* 1909 p. 594) but the eggs had been wrongly identified, and were later shown to be those of the Cyprus warbler. There is no genuine record of either the whitethroat *or* lesser whitethroat having bred in Cyprus. We unfortunately quoted the erroneous breeding record from the *Ibis* in our *Birds of Cyprus* p. 104. This should now be deleted.

The latest information concerning the whitethroat's movements through the island are quoted above, from the statistics supplied by the officers of the C.O.S.: a large number fall to the lime-sticks on the spring passage but nothing to be compared with the loss suffered by the next species which is quite staggering.

LESSER WHITETHROAT

Sylvia curruca

Only slightly smaller in appearance than the common whitethroat, the present species also measures about 5½ ins (14 cm) in total length. It has no chestnut on the wing and shows less white in the tail. The upperparts are grey-brown, greyer than in *S. communis* while the underparts are whiter. Legs and feet are bluish lead colour. A feature to note is the dark ear-coverts which show prominently against the grey head.

The male has a distinctive song ending with a rough rattle on one note. It is not uttered on the wing. Of the two white-throats which visit Cyprus the lesser is by far the most numerous. It migrates through Cyprus in both seasons but especially in spring. Our first personal record was on 18 March and after that it was seen every day in increasing numbers on the lower ground.

The lesser whitethroat heads the formidable list of birds captured on lime-sticks by the Paralimni limers *for the largest number taken in a single spring migration*. If the year 1968 was in the nature of an average capture, the numbers destroyed in this island must soon reach millions, if the 5,415 taken that year at Paralimni is multiplied by the other Cyprian villages which – admittedly to a much smaller extent – participate in this trade.

It passes through Cyprus in the spring when it is most conspicuous from late March to mid-April but early arrivals can be seen from late February onwards and the passage continues to early or even mid-May in smaller numbers. In autumn first arrivals are seen in early August and from late August to early or mid-October, the passage never ceases, some birds even to late October or early November.

It has a wide European distribution except in the S.W. Northern populations migrate in a S.E. direction to winter largely in the Sudan where they occur from mid-October to mid-April to about 8° south.

RÜPPELL'S WARBLER

Sylvia rüppelli [Plate 21, facing p. 129]

The male of this smart and conspicuous warbler has been beautifully portrayed in the accompanying plate and little description is needed. The black cap terminates below the crown, the upperparts are grey, the tail of a darker shade has the outer feathers white. A broad white stripe separates the dark head from the black chin and throat, passing over the ear-coverts. The rest of the underside is white. The female lacks the ornamental plumage of her consort, the crown and cheeks being all grey with dark middles to the crown feathers, the throat is white dappled with black. Both sexes have red-brown eyes and legs. The length is about 5½ ins (14 cm). The alarm note is a harsh rattle.

Many of these warblers pass through Cyprus on the northern spring passage on their way from the Sudan, where many winter in the bush as far south as 13° N. For some reason unexplained they are much scarcer in the autumn from mid-September to early October when on the way to their winter quarters. In spring we have seen them mainly in April, but they have been reported from mid-March to the first week in May. From late March to early April the passage is at its height.

There has been some difference of opinion over its local status. In *Birds of Cyprus* p. 105 we wrote "may occasionally breed", in view of a definite statement sent to us in Cyprus by a recognised naturalist that he had found nests in the Karpas Peninsula, admittedly he did not say eggs had been found. The compilers of the latest Check-List prefer to ignore that possible record, since no-one has ever been able to confirm that Rüppell's Warbler breeds in the island.

Rüppell's warbler is a bird of the low maquis country in our experience commonest in the Karpas Peninsula but widely spread when on passage. Its nesting habits as observed in Crete are described in *Birds of Cyprus*. The Karpas country is ideally suited for a nesting environment. It winters mainly in eastern Africa, notably in Sudan.

Plate 26

1. Goldfinch ♂
2. Goldfinch ♀
3. Mediterranean greenfinch ♂
4. Mediterranean greenfinch ♀
5. Syrian linnet ♂
6. Syrian linnet ♀
7. Serin ♂
8. Serin ♀
9. Corn bunting
10. Brambling ♀ (Jan. bird)
11. Brambling ♂ (June bird)
12. Cyprus chaffinch ♂
13. Cyprus chaffinch ♀
14. Reed bunting ♂ (winter bird)
15. Reed bunting ♀ (winter bird)
16. Rock bunting ♀
17. Rock bunting ♂
18. Ortolan bunting ♂
19. Ortolan bunting ♀

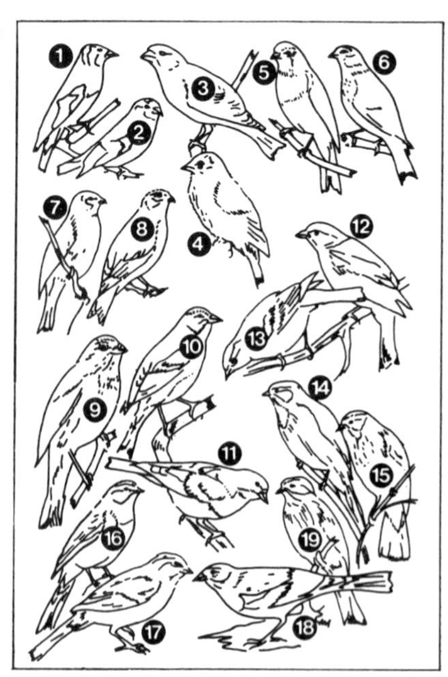

C.E.Talbot Kelly '70

We may point to the fact that for years the nest of the spectacled warbler remained undiscovered in Cyprus and today at least four different colonies of breeding birds have been located! There is still hope for Rüppel's warbler to claim Cyprian nationality.

CYPRUS WARBLER

Sylvia melanothorax

[Plate 22, facing p. 144 and plate 27, facing p. 192]

Cyprus is the real home *and only breeding place* of this warbler, despite the fact that earlier writers named it the Palestine warbler, from which country it was originally described. Its status in Palestine appears to be that of a casual winter visitor from its homeland, and our suggestion in 1958 that it more properly be named the *Cyprus* warbler, has been accepted as the more appropriate colloquial name. We were able to devote a lot of space to this interesting warbler in our larger book. Here we have room only for a summary. As we give three figures in colour of the bird in this Handbook, word-description can be brief.

Very like the Sardinian warbler, it is darker grey on the upperparts, with the underparts ashy-grey; the throat and breast are black with whitish-grey margins to the feathers, giving a flecked appearance. The legs are fleshy-yellow, the iris reddish and there is a red ring round the eye. The head of the female is flecked with blackish; the underparts are white, the flanks washed with greyish-brown and the throat and breast usually with black crescent-shaped makings. Its length is 5¼ ins (13 cm).

The appearance of the cock-bird changes with the seasons, the dark bases to the feathers of the underparts becoming increasingly conspicuous with abrasion, so that it appears largely pale below in autumn, and largely dark with pale "moustache" by the following summer. These extremes are exhibited in the male birds depicted on Plates 22 and 27.

It is a fairly common bird in Cyprus both on the scrub-covered plains such as the Karpas Peninsula, in the maquis country of the foothills and again in the more mountainous areas where it has been found nesting in both mountain ranges up to at least 4,600 ft in the Troödos area. Breeding begins in the low ground, Karpas etc., at the end of March, nesting in isolated thorn bushes among the cistus; in the middle zone many nests can be found with eggs in the last half of April, such as on the slopes near St. Hilarion. A completed clutch of slightly incubated eggs was found at Platania, 3,700 ft on 15 May, probably an average date for the altitude. The most favoured sites were low bushes of various kinds and cistus, but nests are also placed in bushes of Salvia and even in a sapling pine. The cup of the nest is deep, obliging the sitting bird to hold its tail cocked up and may be lined with fine grasses, the exterior of soft bents and grasses and strips of juniper bark, usually a fairly massive construction. Strips of juniper bark are nearly always included among the nesting materials, even in cases where this bark must be brought a considerable distance.

Four or five eggs is the usual clutch. The eggs show only a small range of variation and are described as having a greyish-white or pale greenish ground colour, generally speckled with brown or olive-green spots, over ashy shell-marks, having an indefinite zone at the big end.

Elsewhere *loc cit* we have given a full description of clutches of three, four and five eggs as written for us by a distinguished oologist (see pp. 107–111 of our larger book). Several clutches in his collection had the ground clear white, which showed up the brown surface markings much more distinctly, as also the underlying grey blotches. More detailed notes on the Cyprus warbler will be found in *Birds of Cyprus* (1958) and further nesting data in *Oologist's Record* XXXV 1961 p. 38.

The Cyprus warbler moves to higher altitudes to some extent in late summer and downhill partially in late autumn and winter. Migration from Cyprus takes place to an unknown extent, but it is still found commonly on the southern coast and on foothills on the Southern Range below 4,000 ft and in the whole Northern Range.

On spring passage in March it occurs on the Mesaoria plain when later it is more or less absent. There must be a considerable influx in the spring as in 1968, when a census was taken, no less than ninety eight Cyprus warblers were limed after 5 March at Paralimni alone.

SARDINIAN WARBLER

Sylvia melanocephala

The adult male, about 5½ ins (14 cm) in length, has the forehead, crown, lores and ear-coverts jet-black, the mantle and back dark slate but the wings brown. Chin and throat are *pure white* – a feature to bear in mind – while the rest of the underside is white washed with slate-colour. Very noticeable is the *brick red eyelid* (sometimes orange-yellow), duller in the female. The outer tail feathers show much white when the bird flies.

The female has no black cap and is brown, with white chin and throat, but may be recognised by the orange ring round the eye; like the male it has white on the outer tail feathers and the tail is graduated.

A restless little bird, fond of dry hillsides and scrub-covered country, *it has never been found nesting in Cyprus* but is often to be seen in the Karpas Peninsula and we met with it ourselves constantly from our first meeting with it on 20 February right up to the Stavros forest station in the Southern Range in mid-April, where we saw it up to 4,600 ft. We expected to find it a resident species, but in that we were mistaken. The C.O.S. list it (1971) as a winter visitor and passage migrant in variable numbers, usually fairly common, but numbers fluctuate, returning to Cyprus more generally in late October and remaining in the island until at least the third week of April, frequenting the then deserted areas of the Cyprus warbler, including the Mesaoria plain where dense vegetation grows.

It is one of the species caught in small numbers by the Paralimni limers in spring when the birds must be *leaving* (not entering) the island. Twenty-one were captured this way in 1968.

SUBALPINE WARBLER

Sylvia cantillans albistriata

An exceptionally small bird even for a warbler, the male of this species is easily identified in Cyprus. In size it is but 4 ins (10 cm) from bill to tail tip. Mouse-grey above from the crown to the upper tail-coverts, with a distinct white moustachial stripe extending from below the base of the bill to just beneath the earcoverts, this skulking little bird would easily escape detection were it not for its bright terra-cotta (or sometimes pinkish-brown) underparts. There is a good deal of difference in the colour of specimens some being much brighter than others. In flight, the white on the outer tail feathers is a prominent feature and at close quarters the red ring is discernible round the eye. The female subalpine is difficult to distinguish from the lesser whitethroat, the underparts being buffish and the upperparts drab brown. The orbital ring is possibly the best distinction to look for, and the tail is browner than in the male with less white.

First recorded from Cyprus in 1888 it has erroneously been recorded in a standard work on Palaearctic birds as breeding in the island, but there is little doubt a mistake has there occurred, and has been copied in other works. The subalpine warbler is in fact a fairly common spring migrant in variable numbers from early March to mid-April. Most records are from south coast locations. Unless 1968 was a phenominal year, huge numbers must pass through the island, for in that year, when the Smithsonian Institute made its valuable census, 654 of these birds were caught on limed foliage at Paralimni village alone. In the same year flocks of fifties were not uncommon on the Akrotiri Peninsula, pointing to a spring migration on a large scale. There are *no summer or autumn records*, which may be explained by the birds using a different course from their breeding quarters in the Balkans to winter on the fringe of the Sahara in a circumscribed area. They return in spring by an eastern route which brings them, periodically, within the range of Cyprus. 1968 was such a year.

SPECTACLED WARBLER

Sylvia conspicillata [Plate 23, facing p. 145]

The male has a grey crown tinged with brown, a rufous-brown mantle and paler rump and upper tail-coverts. The wings are brown with broad rufous fringes. Tail brown but outer feathers white. Throat white, breast and flanks pinkish-brown, belly white. Legs and feet pale straw colour. A feature to note is the narrow white eye-rim. It is 5 ins (13 cm) in length. The female is paler above, less grey on crown and less pink on the underparts than her consort.

Writing of this little bird in our larger work we suggested that it was perfectly *possible* a nest would be found in Cyprus in due course. A nest was eventually found on 22 April 1958, containing five heavily incubated eggs in a well-concealed nest, some nine inches off the ground, in an isolated tuft of *Poterium spinosum*. This was near the village of Akromeritis in the Troödos foothills. More intensive search has brought to light other breeding stations, the best known of which are situated at Kouklia reservoir, the Dhekelia area and below Buffamento in the Northern Range. There have also been breeding records from Larnaca Salt Lake, Athalassa reservoir, and from the environs of Nicosia. Its precise status is not well known. Birds have been seen showing display flight in January and February and fledglings have been found in mid-April. Undoubtedly the bird is resident but the Cyprus population is evidently partly migratory. In spring outwith the breeding sites, most birds have been seen in March, pointing to an influx from overseas at this time which is supported by the spring liming at Paralimni in 1968, when sixty-two birds were taken between 5 March and early May. Most records are from the eastern part of the island.

Eggs have been found between 7 and 24 April. Nests are described as untidily built of various lengths of grasses, dead flowers and a few leaves. They have a wide base and small but deep cup. The Cyprus eggs are described (*Oologist's Record* 1961) as quite typical with pale greenish-blue ground lightly flecked with pale olive-brown and a few ashy shell marks. The normal clutch is five. The race in Cyprus does not differ from the typical subspecies.

RUFOUS WARBLER

Agrobates galactotes syriacus

[Plate 23, facing p. 145]

The eastern race *syriacus* may be distinguished by having the crown and mantle wing-coverts and most of the middle pair of tail feathers brown. In this race there is a distinct contrast in colour between the back and the rump, the rump being foxy rufous as in the west European bird. The underparts are whitish or cream colour and there is a conspicuous cream streak over the eye. The long, broad, fan-shaped tail is strikingly patterned. In colour it is bright rufous, with broad white tips to the four or five feathers and a black subterminal band to all but the middle pair. The rufous warbler is a large member of the warbler family, 7 ins (18 cm) in total length, the males rather larger than the females. It stands high on its greyish-flesh coloured legs and spends much of its time on the ground. It has a characteristic habit of elevating its tail above its back and flicking its wings. Its song is described as particularly beautiful.

The Syrian race breeds in Bahrain, Asia Minor, northern Syria and the Balkan Peninsula migrating through central Arabia to Somaliland and eastern Africa (Kenya). Its migrations do not normally take it through Cyprus, but rufous warblers have been identified on rare occasions, and it must be classed as an uncommon accidental visitor.

First obtained in August 1901, there have been some seventeen records between that date and 1970, all single birds except on two occasions when five were limed at Paralimni. August and September in autumn, March, April and May in spring, are the months when records have been accepted as valid by the C.O.S., details of which are in the latest Check-List. No two systematists seem to agree on the genus name and I prefer to retain that where it was placed for ages by Hartert and others. Meinertzhagen in *Birds of Arabia* preferred *Erythropygia*, but if ever a bird deserves a monotypic genus surely this does?

FAN-TAILED WARBLER

Cisticola jucidis [Plate 23, facing p. 145]

This prolific small warbler is a resident in Cyprus – one of the few warblers which breed in the island – in comparison with the many who pass through on passage only. Once given a subspecific name it was later shown to be inseparable from the birds in Sicily, which is the type locality of the species.

The upperparts are dark brown streaked with reddish-buff and it has a rufous rump which is a conspicuous feature. The underparts are unstreaked and whitish with a rufous wash on the flanks. The tail when spread like a fan has dark webs and a white tip which is succeeded by a black subterminal spot. It is very distinctive.

When seen in its breeding area it draws attention to itself by mounting high in the air to 100 ft or so, with feeble rather undulating flight, where it remains cruising around above its mate with dipping flight, uttering the while what have been described as sharp resonant little scratchy squeaks *zit zit*, and staying in the air for some minutes before dropping down again to earth to perch on reed or stem.

The fan-tailed warbler is commonly found in Cyprus on low ground, in high growing vegetation wherever there are marshes or sometimes apparently in fields of standing corn. For nesting it is practically restricted to its own particular swamp. Its nest is unique in shape and has the entrance at the top. It was fully described in our previous work. One nest found 8 ins up in dead vegetation among *salicornia*, near Akrotiri Salt Lake on 12 May, was 6 ins deep and almost transparent, made of vegetable down lined with fine grass. It held three nearly fledged young. Another nest in an open cornfield near Nicosia held a complete clutch of five eggs on 6 May and a nest at Akrotiri Salt Lake held five young which were fledged by 8 June.

Eggs are white with very fine light brown spots. Some dispersal takes place in winter when it has been found up to 1,500 ft.

WILLOW WARBLER

Phylloscopus trochilus

Both races of the willow warbler – the typical *P. trochilus trochilus* and the northern willow warbler *P. trochilus acredula* must pass through Cyprus on passage but their distinctions are fine. To quote from my *The Birds of the British Isles* vol. iii (after Ticehurst): In fresh spring dress *acredula* is paler on the upperparts, more yellowish and brighter olive-green than *trochilus*; the yellow on the underparts paler and less of it on the breast. In fresh autumn dress upper and underparts also paler than similar plumage in *trochilus*.

The plumage of the willow warbler and the chiffchaff is so close that the two birds are always being confused and it is to the song we must turn for the surest guide to identification. A comparison between these two birds is given under the heading of the chiffchaff. Only *when handled* the willow warbler may be distinguished by the fact that *no emargination is present on the outer web of the sixth primary* (the same applies to the wood warbler). In the chiffchaff the outer web of the sixth primary is emarginated.

Unlike the chiffchaff the willow warbler is only a passage migrant. It does not, like the former species, winter in the island, other than odd birds, but hastens on its way to Africa. The main passage in autumn is from the middle of September to mid-October some arriving in August and stragglers passing to late November. The spring migration is on a smaller scale, usually from mid-March to late April or early May. During the spring liming in 1968, 673 willow warblers were caputed by this method between 5 March and 11 May – but compare these figures with those of the chiffchaff!

CHIFFCHAFF

Phylloscopus collybita

Compared with the willow warbler the chiffchaff is a little darker on the upperparts; also the legs are darker. It has more buff on the flanks and the size is a little smaller.

When handled the chiffchaff may be told by the emargination of the outer web of the sixth primary – a sure way of determining the bird for the ringer – but of no use for the field observer, who must, when possible, rely on the distinctive song *chiff-chaff, chiff-chaff* to settle the question of specific identity.

The chiffchaff is a very small warbler which on first arrival in the spring has the upperparts buffish-olive, tinged with light yellowish-olive, especially on the rump. A dirty-white supercilium is ill-defined. Cheeks and ear-coverts are buffish-olive, mixed with paler olive. The underparts are whitish tinged with buff on the flanks and streaked with yellowish on the breast. Under tail-coverts are yellowish-white. Wings and tail are brown washed on the edge with light yellowish-olive. No wing-bar is present. In autumn the flanks and breast are more suffused with buff.

This little bird passes through in spring and returns in autumn, when many remain to pass the winter and are then found up to 4,000 ft. It is to be seen in shrubs and trees and usually works its way along a bough seeking food. It moves about swiftly and gracefully, very often with neck stretched out, which gives it a graceful slim appearance. Sometimes it hovers in front of a twig for a few seconds before flying on. This fluttering examination for insects is common to this bird and the willow warbler, which it so closely resembles.

It arrives in Cyprus in the autumn in enormous numbers and three distinct subspecies have been identified by the aid of trapping: *P.c. collybita* (November to mid-April), *P.c. abietinus* (late November to mid-March) and *P.c. tristis* (in winter to early February). *Abietinus* is the commonest, *tristis* the rarest. Main passage occurs in November to early December, but birds begin to arrive in mid-September and are abundant by late October, reaching peak numbers in the first half of November. Chiffchaffs are plentiful in winter all over the island until the main departure in March when the spring migrants are coming through on their way north. Huge numbers have been recorded passing in that month, the migration falling off in April. The Paralimni limers secured 4,646 Chiffchaffs in 1968 between 5 March and 11 May – appalling damage to an insect-destroying species which requires no stressing, but liming permits of no discrimination.

WOOD WARBLER

Phylloscopus sibilatrix

From the other Phylloscopine warblers – willow warbler, chiffchaff, Bonelli's, the present species may be recognised by its larger size, 5 ins (13 cm) in total length, yellow throat (seen only at close quarters) and *all white underparts*. A yellow supercilium is well marked: a line passes through the lores and is continued backwards under the supercilium. Cheeks, ear-coverts and bend of the wing are yellow like the throat, with the yellow wash extending to the breast. Wings and tail are dark brown, the feathers edged with green. No wing-bar is present. It is all green above from the crown to the upper tail-coverts.

The wood warbler is greener above than the willow warbler and the yellow breast contrasts more sharply with the rest of the white underparts, but the "wood wren" is best recognised by its distinctive song – a softly uttered *pee pee pee* followed by a noise like the jingling of a bunch of keys. While uttering these notes the little bird "shivers" its wings. Unfortunately on migration it is seldom heard, and then the wood warbler keeps to low bushes.

This warbler is a very common spring migrant in variable numbers, less numerous in autumn. It is mainly recorded in April and May, mostly in the latter half of April. None remain to nest. In autumn the passage lasts from mid or late August to mid-October, once caught in late November. Odd birds have been reported to over-winter but the evidence is inconclusive and dates of sightings lacking. It is to be found from the coast to mid-altitude pine forest.

Its summer breeding range embraces most of Europe but it is locally distributed, occurring only in wooded areas and avoiding tangled growth. In winter it is found in Africa north of the Equator.

BONELLI'S WARBLER

Phylloscopus bonelli orientalis

A dull coloured warbler with the crown and cheeks, mantle and back greyish-brown, the feathers of the back shading terminally into yellowish. Above the eye a whitish-buff superciliary streak; ear-coverts dusky-brown and the lores buffish. Rump and upper tail-coverts are more strongly washed with yellow than the back. Tail brown with narrow yellow outer edge. Wings and coverts brown, bordered outwardly with greenish-yellow. Axillaries lemon yellow and under wing-coverts white washed with pale yellow. Entire underparts silky-white, the chin and throat having a faint yellowish tinge in Autumn only. It is 4¼ ins (11 cm) in length, a very small bird.

In our previous work we briefly compared this warbler with the chiffchaff and willow warbler which are about the same size. Bonelli's is very like the latter bird but has more yellow on the rump and on the edge of the wing. The best distinction is in the all white underparts of Bonelli's, when these can be seen. In habits there is also a distinction in the field, Bonelli's having a more buoyant flight and preferring the tops of trees from which it darts out after insects, instead of searching the leaves as do the other two. The song of all three are distinctive, but one requires to know them.

The main passage of Bonelli's warbler through Cyprus is in the spring, in variable numbers, normally fairly common and rarely abundant. Some years relatively scarce. The usual passage occurs from mid or late March to late April or early May but mainly during the whole of April. Autumn records are scanty and all have been in the period between early September and early October.

NOTE

Three additional members of the genus *Phylloscopus* have been found as stragglers in Cyprus: the typical race of *P. bonelli*; a **dusky warbler**, *P. fuscatus*, and a **yellow-browed warbler**, *P. inornatus*. Details of their capture are given in the Appendix p. 221.

Family REGULIDAE

We retain the goldcrests and the firecrests in this family – the smallest representative of the bird-world in the Palæarctic Region which modern taxonomists now include in the Sylviidae, but which for years, have been given family rank. Minute in size 3½ ins (9 cm) in total length, the two species occupy different habitats. The goldcrests inhabit coniferous forests of cedar and pines, more rarely in broad-leaved forests, whereas the firecrests are mainly inhabitants of deciduous woods or mixed broad-leaved forest and conifers and in the Mediterranean countries – as Dr. Voous has pointed out – mainly forests of evergreen oak and tree-heaths, and in some cedar woods. Goldcrests winter in the tree-tops of dense coniferous forests, firecrests preferring the lower growth, they do not gather into flocks in direct contrast to the goldcrests which wander through the forests in flocks and often associate with tits (Paridae) in foraging expeditions. Both these minute birds seem to have a very different way of life from the warblers, and as they have a very wide, though discontinuous, distribution, especially the firecrests, which are both holarctic and oriental, we are loth to fall into line with those naturalists who wish to reduce them from family rank. Wherever they occur together the goldcrest is infinitely the more numerous of the two species.

In Cyprus the goldcrest is an inhabitant of the Troödos forest in the winter months whereas the firecrest is but an occasional visitor.

Both are resident in Turkey from which country Cyprus is most likely to receive its winter guests.

GOLDCREST [Plate 23, facing p. 145]

Regulus regulus

Greyish-olive above, especially on the hind neck, and rather dull white below, washed with buff to a varying degree; a white bar across the wing caused by the pale tips to the major-coverts and the distinctive head-colouring are all features easily seen, for the tiny bird, 3½ ins (9 cm) in total length, is unafraid of human beings and is easily approached and watched at close quarters. The crown of the head in the male is brilliant orange and in the female yellow, bordered on each side with black. When the wing of the little bird is spread the cream bar spreads right across the secondaries and is bordered with black both above and below. The tail is black without any markings, the long rump-feathers, if disarranged, exhibit dark grey bases with white tips, producing a marbled effect. The short fine bill is black; the legs and feet brown.

A very close relative the firecrest, *Regulus ignicapillus* has very rarely (see Appendix p. 221) been observed in Cyprus and so care must be taken not to take for granted that every sighting is a goldcrest. The distinctions are very slight, the similarities great. The firecrest has a brighter green back and mantle and above the eye is a broad white eyebrow extending towards the nape.

Goldcrests, and an occasional firecrest, must presumably reach the forests of Cyprus from the north, braving the sea-passage from Asia Minor in the same way as these diminutive bundles of feathers cross the North Sea to reach the shores of Britain. They are strictly winter visitors to the island, arriving in early November and leaving again by early March or at latest before that month is out. Many seen in mid-winter.

Family MUSCICAPIDAE

When in our *Birds of Cyprus* we attempted to enumerate some of the salient features by which the Muscicapidae – using the family name in its original sense – could be recognised, we then restricted our remarks to those flycatchers which habitually occur in Cyprus and the surrounding areas of the Middle East. They may be typified by the spotted flycatcher of the Old World. The flycatchers of the Palæarctic Region are all rather small birds and all display the same manner of capturing their insect prey, selecting a prominent perch – the dead leafless branch of a tree is popular – from which they dart after their victim, returning with it to the same stance or one close by. Flycatchers have wide gapes assisting the capture of flying prey, and the mandibles are flattened. Rictal bristles are present. Very swift in their flight and quick in their reactions the birds seldom return empty beaked! Plumage is usually subdued in the Middle East members of the family which breed in Europe and winter in tropical Africa, for they cannot exist where insect life is no longer available in the colder countries. Consequently Cyprus and all the neighbour countries are visited twice in every year. The four species which come to Cyprus are common to all.

Like the Turdidae, flycatchers have spotted young a character which should at least influence taxonomists to keep them separate from the Sylviidae (warblers) who have unspotted young. As now grouped by some modern workers the family Muscicapidae is indefinable: a very good reason why we restrict the name to the group of birds for which it was intended.

SPOTTED FLYCATCHER

Muscicapa striata

The adult bird is uniform hair-brown except for the crown which is streaked; underparts white, washed with pale brown on the breast and flanks, the throat white streaked (*not* spotted) with brown. Wings and tail are brown, not relieved with any white markings. The bird gains its trivial name from the plumage of the *juvenile* in which the whole of the upperparts are darkish brown with cream or buff middles to the feathers, the underparts white with dark fringes. Its graceful flight as it darts after an insect and returns to the same vantage point time after time, is likely to betray the adult bird.

The spotted flycatcher is an abundant passage migrant in spring and autumn, some remaining to nest. The passage migrants arrive in the island in the early days of April, arriving mainly in mid-April to early May. The autumn passage lasts from mid-August or early September to late October, occasionally to mid-November.

To which race the breeding birds belong has not been satisfactorily settled and the suggestion that it is *M.s. neumanni* seems to rest on guesswork, though birds approaching that subspecies have been taken in Cyprus. A bird ringed in Heligoland on migration presumed to be *M. striata striata* in mid-September was recovered the same autumn in Cyprus.

Breeding fairly commonly above 3,000 ft nests were not found or eggs described until the years 1957–59 when five fresh eggs were discovered in a nest under the eaves of a cottage at Troödos on 8 June and several nests were found in the same area two years later, either built against the trunks of Troödos pines or in a knot of an overhanging bough. Another pair whose nest was against the trunk of a pine was incubating five eggs on 23 May in a rather scanty nest constructed of dark brown bents and bits of paper, all beautifully concealed by the background. The eggs are described as rather small with greenish ground, not boldly marked but rather evenly suffused with ashy shell marks and reddish-brown spots. c.f. *Oological Record* 1961 p. 49 where first described by a member of the C.O.S. The C/5 found in 1957 by another member was said to be more typical.

Well-grown young were reported seen in the Troödos mountains on 4 July, 1929 but not till the account quoted above were the eggs discovered and described by the young Serving Officer who has so successfully filled in many blanks regarding the breeding habits of many Cyprus birds.

PIED FLYCATCHER*

Muscicapa hypoleuca

[Plate 23, facing p. 145]

This is a passage migrant in spring which does not stay to breed.

---

*An unfortunate error for which we were not personally responsible crept into our *Birds of Cyprus* (1958) in connection with this bird. It was recorded (p. 83) that two pied flycatchers ringed respectively in Latvia and eastern Russia had been captured in Cyprus and the rings returned to the British Museum. The record was sent to us in all good faith for publication in *Birds of Cyprus* and it was not until too late for correction we learned they had not been recaptured in Cyprus after all.

Except for a small white patch on the forehead and a mottled grey and white rump, the whole of the upper surface of the body from crown to upper tail-coverts is sooty black. Only on the wings is a large white area which is very conspicuous. When closed the tail appears all black and dark brown, but when open the two outer feathers have a white outer margin. Underparts from chin to vent are white. Female pied flycatchers are uniformly brown above except for a white band parallel with the closed wing; the underparts are white washed with buff. There is great difficulty in distinguishing the female pied and female collared flycatchers which few but an expert can determine.

The migration dates through Cyprus of this flycatcher will be given in a final paragraph but one very interesting fact has emerged after a two year study of mist-netting to which the recorder of the C.O.S.'s fifteenth *Bird Report* draws attention. In 1967 thousands of pied flycatchers passed in spring. From those caught at the Akrotiri ringing station, it appeared that they passed in the ratio of one male to eight females. This was a general feature over the island. In the spring of 1968 pied flycatchers were few and far between and then were predominantly males.

In normal years these flycatchers are fairly common on the spring migration from late March or early April to the first week of May (rarely till mid-May). Very abundant in some years in the latter half of April. Pied flycatchers in Cyprus are the typical subspecies, but on one occasion a male caught at Akrotiri on 2 May 1968 had a wing-length pointing to its being an example of the Siberian race (*F.h. sibirica*) whose presence in the island had not been suspected.

Cyprus is missed to all intents on the return journey and only two autumn occurrences have been recorded: two trapped 13 September 1966 at Troödos and one male seen 17 October at Episkopi.

COLLARED FLYCATCHER

Muscicapa albicollis [Plate 23, facing p. 145]

This is a spring passage migrant.

In summer dress the *adult male* of this flycatcher is distinguished from the pied flycatcher by the broad white collar surrounding the neck and the broader white forehead. There is also more white on the rump, the tips as well as the bases of the feathers being white. In *breeding dress*, with its glossy black upperparts, white collar, forehead and underparts and the wing speculum, the male collared flycatcher cannot be mistaken. The winter dress of the male collared can be distinguished with certainty, *when handled*, by the following points. It is greyer above than the pied, not so brown, and the bases of the feathers of the hind neck are white. There is considerable difference in the size of the wing. *M. albicollis* males have wings 80–87 mm as against 76–82 in *M. hypoleuca*. Females of *M. albicollis* have wings 79–84·5 mm as against 75–80 in *M. hypoleuca*. The wing formula is also slightly different. In *albicollis* the second (i.e. first *long*) primary is longer or as long as the fifth primary, in *hypoleuca* it is almost invariably shorter. These tiresome figures may be of considerable use when attempting to determine ringed or limed birds. In the field the females are practically indistinguishable, unless both species are seen at once, when the collared flycatchers greyer plumage may be remarked.

To Cyprus the collared flycatcher comes in variable numbers in the spring from late March or early April to early May, rarely seen to the middle of the month. The main passage in the latter half of April is sometimes on a large scale. Autumn passage is negligible, only four records in recent years in September and October.

An example of the subspecies *M.a. semitorquata* is reported to have been collected on 9 April 1958 at Cape Greco and may well be present in the island unrecognised. Mist-netting may confirm.

RED-BREASTED FLYCATCHER

Muscicapa parva [Plate 23, facing p. 145]

This is the smallest of the European flycatchers, the upperparts are light brown, the crown shaded with grey, the cheeks and the side of the neck pure grey; chin and breast orange-red. The underparts are white, shaded with orange-buff immediately below the breast and on the sides. Wings light brown, the tail feathers darker brown. The basal half of all but the central feathers in the tail white. The eye, large for the size of the bird, has a white ring. The female has entirely brown upperparts and no grey on the cheeks or crown. The tail has the same pattern as that of the male. Its length is 4½ ins (11 cm).

The red-breasted flycatcher has been recorded in autumn in most years in the island and very seldom in spring. It is far the rarest or least-often seen, of the *Muscicapa* group. We were lucky to meet with it once on 16 April 1954, at 1,900 ft altitude, immediately below the village of Stroumbi, and later saw four together on a ploughed field during a rush of migrants. These were apparently the only *spring* records available up to 1963, when the first Check-List of the C.O.S. was issued. At that date there were eight or nine autumn records between mid-September and early November. The latest figures relating to the passages through Cyprus show that it is probably a regular passage migrant in autumn in small numbers but rare and irregular in spring. Since 1963, when the first Check-List was issued to cover observations up to that year, only one additional spring record has been made, on 18 April 1965, at Nicosia, in comparison with at least twenty-two in the months September to November, up to 1969 inclusive. Individual dates and localities of these records are too numerous to detail here, but are to be found in the second C.O.S. Check-List (1971).

Family PRUNELLIDAE

In which are placed the accentors, or to mention the best known members in the Palæarctic Region the dunnock or hedge sparrow (modularis), but embracing also the Alpine accentor (collaris) three of which are included in the list of Turkish birds but not yet recorded from South of Asia Minor. The dunnock however occurs in both lists. Accentors are Palæarctic species – a near relative living in Japan. The family is not represented in the New World and the species to be described hereafter may be taken as typical of this very small family. Its relationships seem still to be obscure but Dr. Wetmore places it next to the wagtails and pipits and Dr. Voous next to the Turdidae. A very retiring quiet little bird, with most unobtrusive habits and equally unobtrusive colouring. It is usually sedentary except in the more northerly areas subject to severe climatic changes. The main population winters in central and western Europe south to the Mediterranean. It can only be rarely met with in the Middle East.

HEDGE SPARROW or DUNNOCK

Prunella modularis

Although very subdued in appearance the hedge sparrow's plumage is not unattractive on close inspection. The male has the head and neck slate grey streaked with brown, the back and wings rufous-brown streaked with umber; the wings and tail brown, the former with a distinct buffish-white bar across the wing-coverts. Throat and breast are slate-grey, fading into the whitish abdomen. Sides and flanks are yellowish-brown streaked with rufous-brown. The bill is fine, broadening at the base and black in colour. Legs and feet pinkish-brown; the eye reddish-brown.

The female is duller in colour and has a browner, less grey breast, than the male. Total length 5¾ ins (15 cm).

No-one appears to have collected a specimen of this bird in Cyprus, and the race to which the casual winter visitors belong has not been determined.

It is reported to be scarce and irregular, in some years seen frequently, in others not at all. When observed, which is usually in the mountains, it has been from early November to late February, rarely to mid-March.

The description above is that of the north European race from which the Cyprus birds are said to be darker but to ally them with *obscura* as has been suggested with the type-locality Oporto(!) seems to be very far from satisfactory. The race to which the Cyprus birds belong requires more study when material is available, in the meantime we believe they are better allied with the typical race than any other described form.

Family MOTACILLIDAE

The association of the wagtails and the pipits in the same family, despite their outwardly different appearance is owing to their having many points in common both structurally and in habits. As an instance, in both groups the inner secondaries of the wing are abnormally lengthened and are as long as the primaries. Both groups are mainly terrestrial, though some species will perch on trees e.g. the tree-pipit and, in the Motacillinae, the white wagtails in particular, but the habit is not restricted to these two. The two groups are of world-wide distribution. The Motacillinae may be distinguished by their relatively longer tails which they are fond of vibrating, and by their more distinct and brighter colour patterns (many have bright yellow underparts and more noticeable head pattern) which catch the eye, compared to the more sombrely clothed pipits in the sub-family Anthinae. The latter exhibit colours on the uppersurface toning with the ground: brown, tawny or grey relieved with darker streaking. Both groups live on an insect diet and are found on variable terrain: arable, stony hillsides and grassy plains. Pipits are attracted by marshland and the wagtails by water. Like the larks the male pipits soar in the air while singing.

The Motacillinae are represented in Cyprus by white, grey, black-headed and yellow wagtails, the last named (in the species *flava*) exhibiting extraordinary variation in their head patterns, known as the blue-headed, grey-headed and ashy-headed wagtails with which some authors include the blackheaded wagtail (*feldegg*) in the same association. We keep the last as a full species however. All are regular migrants in the Middle East, passing through Cyprus in very considerable numbers.

We are among those authors who place the wagtails of the *flava* and *lutea* groups with yellow underparts and shorter tails in the genus *Budytes*, restricting within our limited area the genus *Motacilla* to the white wagtails and the grey wagtail. Of all eight wagtails on the Cyprus list only one: the grey wagtail is possibly a breeding bird in the mountains but if so, very locally. We treated it in our larger work (1958) as a winter visitor, a status which it shares with the far more numerous white wagtail.

Eight species of pipits are on the Cyprus list, all entirely migratory, six seen regularly on passage; some, like the red-throated, exceedingly common, but two rarely encountered, one about which the identification has been queried. An interesting record if correct, it is of little consequence if not accepted by the C.O.S. referees. We included it in brackets having been the observers! See *Birds of Cyprus* p. 55.

Every one of the pipits and wagtails dealt with here are passage migrants through Asia Minor, and figure on Dr Kasparyan's *List of Turkish Birds*, only one species is there listed which is not yet recorded from Cyprus indicating how completely the avifauna of Cyprus, and the neighbouring countries of the Middle East, correspond, particularly as regards their passage migrants and more especially, perhaps, among the passerine groups of birds.

Sub-Family MOTACILLINAE

WHITE WAGTAIL

Motacilla alba [Plate 24, facing p. 160]

This is the wagtail most frequently encountered in Cyprus in the winter months. The forepart of the crown and ear-coverts are white, the hind crown and nape black. The rest of the upper-parts grey, but blackish tips to the upper tail-coverts. There are *two white bars on the wing*. In summer plumage the chin and throat are black, but in winter these parts are white, except for a broad crescent, or bib of black spots across the lower breast. The total length is 7 ins (18 cm) of which the tail takes up 3½ ins. When the white wagtail is walking, only a white edge to the outer feathers can be seen, but when the tail is open more white is exhibited, and is then very noticeable.

As a winter visitor this wagtail is very numerous. From September onwards the birds are seen on passage, the numbers increasing from early October to early November. It is then to be seen everywhere in the island till departures in mid-March at the same time as the passage migrants are arriving from Africa.

The white wagtail is stated to have nested in 1962 near Kyrenia c.f. Stewart's Check-List, (1971) but this is the only possible record known to us.

The subspecies *Motacilla alba personata* has been recorded on one occasion, on 22 September 1966 at Akrotiri, but how frequent it is on passage remains for future investigators to discover. It is very like the typical subspecies but the black area of the throat and neck are not separated by white and the ear-coverts are black. It is an inhabitant of S.W. Asia.

GREY WAGTAIL [Plate 19, facing p. 113]

Motacilla cinerea

In most parts of the Old World where it occurs the grey wagtail is a universal favourite. To Cyprus it comes as a winter visitor and passage migrant. Very dependent on fresh water, it disappears from Cyprus in the spring from all the lowland areas when the lakes dry up but a few single birds, or perhaps pairs, remain in the Troödos area *throughout the year*. It must, therefore, be classed as a partly resident species restricted *in summer* to the highest elevations where its haunts are those formerly frequented by the dipper, now believed exterminated. Up to date there is no actual evidence of breeding in the Cyprus highlands but it may be expected to do so. There is still plenty of field work to be accomplished in the higher altitudes of this island.

The grey wagtail is one of the easiest birds to recognise. The surest character at all seasons is the grey back. Its underparts are bright yellow in summer, paler in winter. In breeding dress the male has a black throat, the female a mere indication of blackness. After the autumn moult the throat is white tinged with buff. The long tail is blackish, with the three outermost feathers white. Its length is 7½ ins (19 cm), of which the tail is 4 ins.

In the winter of 1957–58 and on later visits, we found single birds at intervals at many localities from the sea-shore to 2,500 ft. along the mountain streams. Our first record was an early one, 19 February at Bellapais in the garden of the tea shop where the Cypriot owner assured us it remained *there* all the year! Whether he was correct in that observation we were unable to prove. If there is running water which does not dry up it has small reason to leave the area. In 1969 we saw a pair in the dirty little stream in Kyrenia in the middle of the town.

The autumn migrants arrive occasionally as early as August, but normally in mid-September and become generally distributed from October to March when departure takes place from all but the highest elevations, the last stragglers leaving in April. It was reported again in the Troödos mountains in the summer of 1968–69 but still without evidence of breeding.

THE YELLOW WAGTAILS

Budytes flava [Plate 24, facing p. 160]

There are three races, if we retain the Blackheaded as a full species as we prefer. The following are their chief characteristics:

1. Blue-headed wagtail (*B. flava flava*) pronounced white eye-stripe; well developed white chin; yellow throat; grey ear-coverts.
2. Grey-headed wagtail (*B.flava thunbergi*) no eye-stripe; much reduced white chin; sometimes dark yellow throat; black ear-coverts.
3. Ashy-headed wagtail (*B. flava cinereocapilla*) ill-defined white eye-stripe, sometimes absent; chin and entire throat white; ear-coverts black.

All three have grey crowns, No. 1 is decidedly paler than No. 2 to which the crown of No. 3 closely approaches.

We do not include the Black-headed Wagtail (*Budytes feldegg*) as a race of *B. flava* and have dealt with it separately on p. 190.

Immature birds of all three yellow-breasted wagtails can only be determined in well-prepared cabinet specimens and then need the closest inspection by experts; it is useless and dangerous to try and name them in the field!

The C.O.S. has paid considerable attention to these yellow wagtails and from the notes which have been made on the four birds enumerated, it is evident that No. 1 the Blue-headed, is the commonest of them all. We have given much fuller diagnoses of each species and each race in our larger volume (p. 56) for which we have no space here.

The following is a summary of the observations made by members of the C.O.S. on the yellow wagtails *since* the publication of *Birds of Cyprus* (1958) when we gave a very full account of the species up to that year. Since then the status, as migrants to Cyprus, has been determined as follows:

1. Blue-headed: The commonest race in autumn mid-August to late October. Spring early March to late May.
2. Grey-headed: Tolerably common in spring, early April to early May, more scarce in autumn: late August to late September, few reported.
3. Ashy-headed: Possibly the least common, often reported in April

and again from late August to late September but numbers relatively small.

In the Cyprus Check-List (1971) the author goes into much more detail than we have space to quote. The above is a summary of the dates of passage. These Wagtails are always a problem for the field observer and equally for the taxonomist to unravel.

After severe gales yellow wagtails literally pour into Cyprus as we witnessed for ourselves on 16 April 1954, when the whole plain between Yialia and Polis was alive with wagtails of various kinds – the occasion when we established the ashy-headed wagtail (*cinereocapilla*) as a new record for Cyprus. All the other yellow wagtails on the Cyprus list were identified on that memorable day when the air was thick with Sahara dust and the sunlight nearly extinguished in a tearing southerly gale.

BLACK-HEADED WAGTAIL

Budytes feldegg [Plate 24 facing p. 160]

This bird is a full species. We do not consider that it should be listed as a subspecies of *B. flava* as was done in the 1963 Check-List of Cyprus birds issued by the C.O.S. in that year.

This is the most easily identified of the wagtails with yellow underparts, especially in summer plumage when the whole crown and nape is jet black and the underparts from chin to vent a rich yellow. As the ear-coverts, lores and the area beneath the eye are black, the bird appears to have a tight-fitting black cap on its head. It has no eye-stripe, though very occasionally there is the faintest indication of a yellowish marking. The back is darkish olive, the rump a more yellow olive. The tail is black except for the two white outer feathers. The wing has a double bar formed by the creamy-yellow tips to the secondary feathers. The head of the female is less black than the male's. In winter the crown is greenish but there are usually a few blackish feathers.

This very distinct wagtail is a migrant to Cyprus both in spring and autumn, the dates of whose passage will end these notes. It has also been proved *to breed*. It was not realized that it nested in the island until two members of H.M. Forces, serving in Cyprus in 1957, both members of the C.O.S., found two pairs breeding at Akrotiri in April, May and June of the year cited: a new breeding record for the island. It has since been recorded as nesting at the Karpas Peninsula (2nd Check-List 1971).

Spring passage takes place from early March to early May, mainly late March to mid-April. The autumn movement from mid-August to late October, mainly September to early October.

NOTE

A typical example of *Budytes lutea* finds mention in the second Cyprus Check-List for the first time; a bird at Akrotiri recorded on 15 September 1969 and another trapped at the same locality on 12 May 1970. This is the Russian species, the true yellow wagtail, of which our British bird is a race *B. lutea flavissima*, and which is distinguishable from all the other wagtails with yellow underparts by having the crown yellowish-green (yellow in breeding dress); a well-defined yellow eye-stripe, chin and entire throat yellow, and olive or olive-brown ear-coverts. (See Appendix p. 221).

Sub-family ANTHINAE

MEADOW PIPIT

Anthus pratensis

There is always a danger of confusing this bird with the tree-pipit, to be described hereafter, unless the longer and *less* sharply curved hind-claw of the meadow pipit can be clearly seen. In fresh autumn plumage the meadow pipit has darker and more heavily striated upperparts and a richer and more intensely spotted undersurface, but the richness soon wears off as winter approaches. When birds can be compared in a museum series – a very different matter from examination in the field – the meadow pipit is distinctly more yellowish-olive on the upperparts, the tree-pipit browner, lacking the yellowish tinge, a character of no use in the field. Of the two species the tree-pipit has the underparts whiter, the ground colour of the meadow pipits undersurface being more buff. Both are heavily spotted on breast and sides. Total length 6⅝ ins (17 cm).

The meadow pipit is an abundant winter visitor and passage migrant – the commonest pipit in the island – which we have encountered in small parties in many places on the low ground during the winter months. It arrives in autumn in October between the beginning and middle of the month, rarely in September and departs mainly in March, the last of the winter residents leaving before April is out. There is also a passage movement through Cyprus from early March of birds on their way to their breeding areas.

The clutch of eggs taken in May 1910 (c.f. *Birds of Cyprus* 1958 p. 52) at first assigned to this bird by a writer in the *Ibis*, were later shown to be those of a short-toed lark. There is therefore *no breeding* record for the island.

TREE PIPIT

Anthus trivialis

A passage migrant in both spring and autumn but no record of breeding has been established. Buffish-brown on the upperparts with dark streaking on the back and an unspotted rump. The breast is bright yellowish-buff with heavy black streaks. The belly white. In flight the outer tail feathers exhibit a good deal of white. Legs and feet are flesh-colour and in total length it measures 6 ins (15 cm).

Tree pipit

A point to notice is the *short hind claw*, immediately separating it from the meadow pipit, the hind claw of which is notably long, but this is best seen when handled and far from easy to note in the field. The tree pipit loves to perch on the topmost twig of a tree from which it rises to give forth its pretty little song before planing down to the same perch. Under the heading of *meadow pipit* we have given some further points of distinction between these two birds which were for many years confused by the older naturalists.

From the records kept by the C.O.S. the tree pipit arrives in March, usually from the middle of the month up to mid-May. It is most often seen in mid-April when it has been described as abundant. The autumn passage lasts from mid-September to mid-October, a few to the end of the month or to mid-November.

Singing birds have been heard in the high Troödos area on 14 June but as yet no nest or eggs have been found and those birds which cross the Southern Range on migration are most likely to be late arrivals in the island on their way to Europe where it breeds up to 70° N.

TAWNY PIPIT [Plate 24, facing p. 160]

Anthus campestris

This is a pale-coloured pipit whose colour is very uniform: upperparts pale sandy-brown, indistinctly streaked on the crown. Above the eye a well-marked cream stripe. This is the only pipit with practically *unstreaked breast*, its colour is buff with the rest of the underparts creamy-white. The outer tail-feathers show a pattern of black and white but the rest of the tail is blackish. It stands high on its yellowish flesh-colour-ed legs and can run with great speed. In total length it is 6½ ins (17 cm).

The tawny pipit is a regular passage migrant at both seasons but its numbers are small, even in spring. When in Cyprus it seeks the drier areas for it is a lover of dry countries many wintering in southern

Arabia. We found it on open spaces sparsely covered with scrub – we usually saw two or three at a time, but occasionally a small party of up to 15 birds has been recorded. Sometimes a number of single birds scattered over the area are observed denoting a small passage on their way from their winter quarters. It breeds over the greater part of Europe but so far as we know has not done so in Cyprus.

The dates of its arrival in the island in spring range from mid-March to mid-May, normally fairly common throughout April. In Autumn usually from early or mid-September to mid-October. It is scarce and irregular in winter when there have been odd individual records between December and early March.

RICHARD'S PIPIT [Plate 24, facing p. 160]

Anthus richardi

This is the largest of all the pipits on the Cyprus list, only the uniformly coloured tawny pipit approaching it in size. It stands high on flesh-coloured legs and in total length it approaches 8 ins (20 cm). The plumage is brown streaked with blackish-brown on crown and mantle, the rump more uniform; a pale buff to white streak passes over the eye extending almost to the nape. The breast is buff with dark spots on either side of the throat. The tail is very conspicuously marked when open, almost black with white tips to the rectrices and a white edge to the outer feathers. We were the first to record this pipit from Cyprus when on 30 March 1954, we found it at Patriki; another sight record was reported on 26 April 1957 from Nicosia. Three years later a small flock was observed on 14 December which appeared to us very grey on the upperparts rather than brown, due probably to recent moult, the breast boldly streaked and the rest of the underside white. A feature of this bird is the very long hind claw but not easily observed in life. On freshly ploughed ground at St. Hilarion where we saw this flock on 14 December 1957, they were running about like mice in all directions feeding as if ravenously hungry.

There have now been a number of sight records of Richard's pipit in Cyprus from which it can be regarded as an occasional visitor. Its visits have been in March and April and again in late October, November and December, usually on the coast or plains, once (by ourselves) at St. Hilarion as noted above. In the second Check-List to be issued on 1971 by the C.O.S. individual occurrences are all listed.

It is a bird which prefers open ground upon which to forage and can be looked for from sea level to about 2,500 ft. Its summer home is in central and eastern Siberia, the main body wintering in India, but it wanders considerably in the off-season.

Richard's pipit

Plate 27 (opposite)

Cyprus warbler
Black-headed bunting
Cretschmar's bunting

Plate 27

RED-THROATED PIPIT

Anthus cervinus [Plate 24, facing p. 160]

A very numerous passage migrant, wintering in small numbers and often consorting with meadow pipits on the plains and cultivated ground, but on occasions in winter in much increased numbers, even in hundreds, as reported in the latest Check-List of the C.O.S. In autumn on passage from late September or most usually early October to early November, numbers being variable. Spring passage from mid or late March to late April or early May.

Compared with either the tree pipit or meadow pipit, this is a much darker bird on the upperparts. Crown, mantle and back are all heavily marked with black, the warm brown fringes are narrow, and much of each feather black. In the other two pipits only the centres of the feathers are blackish. Another point is that in the red-throated pipit the rump and upper tail-coverts *are streaked with black*, whereas in the tree and meadow pipits these parts are uniform. The boldly spotted underparts in both winter and summer invite confusion with the tree pipit. Indications of the fawn-coloured throat are usually apparent but in winter the pinkish-fawn throat is often lost and the differences are then very fine. By far the best and surest way to distinguish the red-throated pipit is by its unique note, described as a high pitched metallic squeak, both louder, fuller and richer than that of the meadow pipit. In summer its rich fawn-coloured throat is unmistakable. Its length is 5¾ ins (15 cm).

In its summer quarters the red-throated pipit occurs in the tundra and damp cultivated land in the far north from Finland eastwards; many migrate to eastern Africa in the winter months and the passage through Cyprus must be on a very large scale. Birds can be seen in Cyprus in their summer dress with quite red throats en route to their northern breeding grounds but on the autumn passage are not so easily recognised.

WATER PIPIT

Anthus spinoletta

In plumage this is very like the rock pipit which we retain under the specific name *Anthus petrosus*. Modern taxonomists consider the two birds conspecific. The habits of the two are very different in their breeding area, and if compared in life the water pipit is the more slimly built. In appearance the water pipit is a larger bird than the meadow pipit, it measures 6½ ins (17 cm) in length. The upperparts are dark olive-brown with some streaking; the underparts are mottled on a creamy white ground, the marking being stronger on the breast. There is a whitish-buff eye-stripe which extends towards the nape. The outer tail-feathers are pure white, *not* grey as in the rock-pipit group.

The water pipit is a frequent winter visitor to the fresh water lakes of Cyprus, first arriving in late October or early November, but more usually from late November remaining until the spring passage commences in late March, lasting until early May. Never in any strength. Odd birds, or two or three, are the rule and they are said to be partial to particular spots where they can usually be found. Specimens collected in earlier days were found to be of the typical subspecies.

NOTE ON THE OCCURRENCE OF THE ROCK PIPIT IN CYPRUS

In 1958 we wrote (*Birds of Cyprus*) that on one occasion when making our survey of the island's birds for the then Cyprus Government we identified to our complete satisfaction rock pipits *Anthus petrosus* probably *littoralis* at Cape Plakoti but this had not been confirmed until 1970 when, in the second Check-List attention is drawn to *littoralis* as a bird "new to the island"! See Appendix p. 221. Not being in the fashion, the writer has always considered the rock and water pipits specifically distinct, close as they are in appearance – and shall continue to do so.

Family BOMBYCILLIDAE

The Waxwings have only obtained mention in this book by the chance visit of one of this family to Cyprus within recent years. The family finds no mention in our *Birds of Cyprus* (1958) for that reason. Nor is there any reference to the family in *Birds of Arabia* (1954). It does however find mention in Dr Kasparyan's *List of the Birds of Turkey*, though no details of its status in that country are available. It must surely have been from that area that Cyprus is able to claim it as a vagrant? The family Bombycillidae is of Holarctic distribution and the species *B. garrulus* is known for its very erratic distribution and what are truthfully named "invasions" in certain years, to which we who live in Great Britain have become almost accustomed, so frequent have the visitations become. There are waxwings in North America and Northern Asia as well as in Northern Europe. The genus extends right through the holarctic from North America to northern Asia. It very rarely leaves the cold and temperate regions and is a characteristic breeding bird of the taiga. Its occurrence in the Mediterranean area must be entirely fortuitous but as already noted its migratory movements are very irregular. It has been recorded in the past from Corsica and Malta and now from Cyprus (see Appendix p. 221) when such visits are likely to occur at the same time as its periodic eruptions.

Noted for the very remarkable wax-like red tips to the four inner secondaries it has a prominent crest on the crown and bright yellow tips to the tail-feathers. The bird named *Bombycilla garrulus* is about the size of a starling with wonderfully soft mouse-coloured plumage.

Family LANIIDAE

This is a nearly cosmopolitan family widely distributed in the Old World and in North America and its members – at any rate those of the true shrikes in the genus *Lanius* are not difficult to recognise having well developed characteristics. All shrikes are furnished with powerful bills ending in a sharp hook which has a notch at the tip. Rictal bristles are prominent. Wing is comparatively short, often rounded. The tail is a more variable feature: in some long as in the great grey shrike whose rare presence in Cyprus is still disputed. Feet and tarsus are strong, scutelated in front, lamellated behind. Food is mainly insectivorus and some species – the red-backed shrikes in particular – have a habit of impaling their victims on thorns, hence the term "butcher-bird" which they have earned by maintaining a larder, the latter displaying a goodly assortment of hard-scaled beetles which are possibly otherwise difficult to kill. The masked shrike is probably exclusively an insect feeder and is the least aggresive of its family, the larger shrikes and even the woodchat (*L. senator*) will kill small birds and the larger species will attack small mammals and reptiles besides.

Four species in the genus *Lanius* – incidentally the only genus represented in the eastern Mediterranean (we have not heard of the bush shrike *Tschagra* nearer than Arabia or Tunisia) have for certain been found in Cyprus, and as noted above possibly one other. Of these only the attractive masked shrike is a summer visitor to breed. The others are passage migrants and well known visitors in spring and autumn to all the Middle East countries. The dates of their passage and individual characteristics will be discussed under the species headings which follow.

LESSER GREY SHRIKE

Lanius minor [Plate 24, facing p. 160]

This is a passage migrant at both seasons but whereas it is to be seen in spring in relatively small numbers, the autumn migration is on a vast scale from mid-August to the end of September during which period very large numbers are shot. Details will be given later in these notes from statistics furnished by the C.O.S. The spring passage appears to be irregular.

The birds are not difficult to recognise in their grey dress and habit of perching in prominent positions. Apart from the broad black frontal band and ear-coverts, the rest of the head, nape and upperparts are pale grey; cheeks and chin are white, the breast and sides of the body with a strong pink suffusion. The wings are black, with a conspicuous white wing-patch. The tail is fairly long, the middle feathers black, the outer feathers white. In total length this shrike measures 8 ins (20 cm). A feature of all the shrikes is a strong powerfully hooked bill. In the lesser grey shrike it is black.

This shrike occurs from mid-France through all Mediterranean countries, and is found east through Persia to the Altai. Its winter range extends to eastern tropical Africa. It passes through Egypt from early August and stays in the tropics from October to April. The passage is on a narrow front and subject to some irregularity. The latest summary of its migrations from C.O.S. records, shows that it arrives early to mid-April, sometimes in numbers to mid-May when the last birds are usually seen. The autumn passage covers the period early August to late October, subject to considerable variation from year to year, the main passage occurring from mid or late August to early or mid-September. The autumn migration, when the birds are often abundant, is much more in evidence than the spring migration.

NOTE

On the strength of records supplied by earlier naturalists, we included the **great grey shrike** *Lanius excubitor* in *Birds of Cyprus* for which see the Appendix in this volume p. 221.

As the lesser grey shrike is fully described, it will only be necessary to give here the differences between it and the great grey shrike. This bird has no frontal band; often, but not always, it has a double white wing-patch. The broad black band through the eye extends only to the lores. The upper surface is dark grey, the underparts white washed with vinous pink. Its length is 9½ ins (24 cm).

WOODCHAT SHRIKE

Lanius senator [Plate 24, facing p. 160]

The woodchat cannot be confused with any other shrike on the Cyprus list; handsome birds, they are conspicuous with their bright reddish-chestnut crowns and nape, the black band across the forehead being continued through the eye to expand over the cheeks and ear-coverts to form a blackish patch. The blackish upperparts, with *white scapulars* contrast with the cream-coloured rump. The tail is black with a white border and there is a whitish area at the base of the tail. The whole underparts are white, washed with buff on the flanks.

The female is much duller, it has no black frontal band or black through the eye; crown duller chestnut, the back brown and scapulars creamy-buff instead of white; the pale buff underparts are crossed with narrow crescentic bars on the breast and sides.

In flight a large white patch across the middle of the wing, not to be confused with the white scapular, is a conspicuous feature. The woodchat possesses a fierce-looking toothed bill which, like the legs and feet, are black. Total length 7½ ins.

On the spring passage from winter quarters in Africa, to breed in central and southern Europe, the woodchat is fairly common, arriving regularly from early April for the rest of the month; in some years from mid to late March, but the majority in mid-April. There does not appear to be a return passage through Cyprus in autumn, when the island is virtually missed. Only some six records are available between mid-August and late September. On their way south the birds evidently take a different route. A passage of these shrikes was reported in 1962 but has since been discounted. There is one certain summer record in early July, 1965.

RED-BACKED SHRIKE

Lanius collurio [Plate 24, facing p. 160]

An uncommon breeding bird in Cyprus in the higher altitudes in insignificant numbers, this shrike is a common passage migrant from early April to mid-May and in autumn from mid-August to late October. In the lower coastal areas the male is one of the more conspicuous migrants, with its light grey crown and nape, rufous-chestnut back and scapulars, pearl-grey rump and black band through the eye. The whole of the underparts are buffish with a strong rosy blush, the under tail-coverts white. In flight a narrow white bar is exposed on the wing, and the tail exhibits a great deal of white on the basal two-thirds. The black bill is not nearly so powerful as in the woodchat but is sharply decurved at the tip. Total length 6¾ ins (17 cm). The female has heavy crescent-shaped black bars on the breast and sides on a creamy-buff ground. Crown and upperparts are mostly brown, including wings and tail. A dark band below the eye extends to the ear-coverts.

The red-backed shrike migrates from its European breeding grounds in autumn in a south-easterly direction and is then numerous in Cyprus, Syria and Palestine, Transjordan and Egypt. It returns in the spring via the Red Sea, and those birds which breed in the west turn in that direction after passing through Asia Minor. Dates of its passage through Cyprus, where it is common on both migrations, are as follows: sometimes in spring it arrives in great numbers in mid or late April, but more often in early May. In autumn the first migrants appear in mid-August, rarely earlier and are common from the end of the month or early September until mid-October, the last arrive from late October to mid-November. It is never so numerous in autumn as it is in spring.

As a breeding bird it is evidently rare, but that it does breed in Cyprus we proved ourselves. We have watched this shrike building a nest at Kantara in the Northern Range in a cistus growing on rough ground 1 May 1957. In other Mediterranean islands it is known to nest freely in cistus, wild rose, olives and diciduous bushes. Eggs show a great variation in colour, the commonest have a pinkish ground with spots and sometimes blotches forming a zone at the broad end. The first circumstantial breeding record was in 1909. In the previous year young were reported in early June from Troödos and adults collected, pointing to nesting in that area. We are of the opinion it may breed more often than records suggest.

MASKED SHRIKE [Plate 18, facing p. 112]

Lanius nubicus

A common and attractive summer visitor

which remains to breed. Smaller than most of its family and more graceful in appearance, especially in flight, the masked shrike is not difficult to recognise. The male has the underparts mainly glossy blue-black with white markings on the forehead, over the eye, and on the scapulars and rump. The black wings have an ornamental white patch. The tail is black in the middle, the outer feathers white. The throat and belly are white; the rest of the underside washed with rusty-buff. Total length is 6¾ ins (17 cm), the tail taking up half. The female resembles the male but is duller, being ash-brown where the male is black and with less bright underparts.

Arriving at first from mid-March and leaving before mid-September, it soon repairs to the more mountainous interior to breed and is then absent from the plains until broods have flown. In the Southern Range, the majority nest from 3,000 ft to 5,000 ft or even more. It breeds also in the Northern Range at considerably lower altitudes around 2,000 ft. The breeding season is protracted being later in the high Troödos area where fresh clutches can be found in early June. Mid-May is the height of the egg-laying season at lower elevations. Most nests are built far out on branches of Aleppo pines, occasionally of Juniper. We gave the description in *Birds of Cyprus* p. 77 of one nest found by a friend in an ancient almond tree, built almost entirely of grey *gnaphalium* stalks, only a few bits of grass being used, and lined with strips of pine and juniper bark, flower-heads and fine grasses.

Another naturalist who examined ten nests in Cyprus described them as "beautifully built of flowering plants, down, grey twigs and sometimes pine-needles and lined with fine grasses"; nests were rather small, always neatly and compactly built with a deep cup usually cited on a lateral branch. The clutch varies from four to six. The description of the eggs given in *Birds of Cyprus* is misleading and requires amendment; green in the ground colour is evidently more uncommon than we realized and more often noted in clutches from Palestine. The ground usually varies from cream to yellowish-brown, occasionally stone colour, and very rarely white. The shell markings vary, some having different shades of brown spots, others blotched with dark brown and ash-grey, and all with ashy shell-marks. A series of Cyprus-taken eggs is described in detail in the *Oological Record* 1961, p. 50.

It has been observed that when the young are fully fledged they disperse to lower ground, as do *some* of the adults, taking up territories there for the rest of the summer. Departure overseas takes place from mid-August to early September. The curious scarcity of adults in the hills in July, August and September has raised the interesting point whether there is an earlier departure of the parent birds to their winter quarters in Africa leaving the juveniles to follow later. This scarcity of adults was especially noted in the Northern Range, and the possibility of early departure was first raised in the new *Check-List of Cyprus Birds*.

This shrike has a comparatively small breeding range outwith Cyprus extending from Macedonia to S.W. Persia, Bulgaria, Turkey and Palestine. Its main winter quarters are in the Sudan.

Family STURNIDAE

This is the family of starlings which, in the Palaearctic Region, is represented by many racial forms of the common starling (*Sturnus vulgaris*) and by its close relative in the western Mediterranean, the spotless starling (*S. unicolor*). The latter does not occur in the Middle East, but the common starling is abundant, fortunately not as a breeding bird in Cyprus. Another member of the family, more closely connected with Middle East countries, especially those which were periodically invaded by locusts, is the rose-coloured starling or rosy pastor, *Pastor roseus*, a very interesting bird which rarely appears today in Cyprus but is well-known in Asia Minor and Syria and from the countries which border the Black Sea. It is from these sources that an occasional visit is paid to Cyprus. The rose-pink of its adult body plumage and black head with short crest will at once betray it. All the starlings mentioned are the same medium size, about 8½ ins (22 cm) from bill to tail. They have powerful legs and bill and are very strong on the wing; the population of northern and central Europe and Asia being migratory to a high degree. Much of their life is spent on the ground in their search for food but being omnivorous and often in large numbers, so far as *Sturnus vulgaris* is concerned, they can become a serious menace.

The various species of Sturnidae in tropical Africa which belong to other genera than *Sturnus* are highly decorative with marvellous iridescent plumage and are known as glossy starlings, but only the amethyst starling reaches S.W. Arabia where it has spread from the eastern Sudan. None of these brilliant birds are ever likely to stray to the eastern Mediterranean. At least four different races of the common starling have been found wintering in Cyprus but their status needs more study.

STARLING

Sturnus vulgaris

The common starling of Europe is probably the best-known of all birds and for its vast numbers, both in towns and country, it is not universally popular. It is doubtful if the typical *Sturnus vulgaris vulgaris* has occurred in Cyprus, as those which have been critically examined in museums have been assigned to at least four of the many starling races which have been described – the Siberian starling *S.v. poltaratskyi* in particular, which differs from the typical subspecies in having the head invariably purple and the ear-coverts with purple reflections; the back green with golden-brown spots, the breast and flanks purple. The other races recognised are mentioned in our larger work but there is no space to discuss them here. To that list *Sturnus vulgaris tauricus* from the Crimea has now been added. See Appendix p. 222.

Starlings are very handsome in their breeding plumage when the bill turns yellow and the feathers are shot with green and amethyst reflections. At a distance the starling looks uniformly black, its plumage iridescent with purple and green is only obvious on closer inspection. In winter it becomes speckled, the feathers with terminal buff and white spots. The beak in winter is dark.

In a recent Report of the C.O.S. the recorders state that a roost of *circa* 2,000 birds is situated 8 miles S.E. of Nicosia. How interesting it would have been to have known their origin and their correct subspecific name.

Starlings are very numerous in winter, sometimes in thousands, arriving usually in October and remaining until the end of February; the last departures taking place in March or even early April, only odd birds being met with occasionally in May and June, or before October. Three birds seen at Cape Andreas in 1967 on 22 September were exceptionally early arrivals.

NOTE

The **rose-coloured starling** *Pastor roseus* formerly visited Cyprus when locusts occurred in the island; today, very rare visitors: see Appendix p. 222.

Family PLOCEIDAE

Sub-family PASSERINAE

The family Ploceidae is that in which all the weaver birds are placed and it is only within very recent years that taxonomists have removed the sparrows (Passerinae) from their association with the finches (Fringillidae) to include them as a sub-family of the weavers. The last-named are not represented in Europe, but if we are to include the sparrows in the weaver family the range of the latter is enormously increased, for sparrows are practically of world distribution. There is much in favour of retaining the sparrows in a separate family Passeridae and we note that Professor Voous has already preferred that course in his *Atlas of European Birds*.

When people think of "sparrows" they usually have the common house-sparrow or the Spanish sparrow in mind, but while those birds may be considered typical, the family embraces many other species as well, rock-sparrows and desert sparrows and tree-sparrows for instance. There is one group, which embraces *Passer domesticus*, characterised by the male having a black throat and chin and a black stripe through the eye; they can adapt themselves to any built-up area in which man is present. The sexes are dissimilar, the females are brown streaked with black on the mantle. Sparrows are everywhere gregarious and like to build their untidy nests in company, but not to the extent the weavers do in almost closed colonies.

There are only two species – the common and Spanish sparrow on the Cyprus list, both locally abundant. In a manner the two birds are complementary to each other, the common sparrow being the town dweller and the Spanish sparrow more of a country dweller, but in some of their breeding areas it does not always work out like that. Being voracious grain eaters sparrows can do a great deal of damage to the crops and from no point of view, other than perhaps for their extraordinary lack of fear, can they be welcomed. Sparrows being very prolific, breeding two or three times in the season and laying large clutches of eggs, soon establish themselves and increase out of all proportion, at the expense very often of the local birds of other species. Both *P. domesticus* and *P. hispaniolensis* can be very agressive neighbours.

PALESTINE HOUSE-SPARROW

Passer domesticus biblicus

The resident sparrow of Cyprus belongs to the same race as those of the mainland named as above. The cock has a grey crown, chestnut-brown upperparts streaked with black, white cheeks and blackish throat. The hen has no grey on the dull brown crown, no white on cheeks and no black on throat. The general colour is dull brown and buff. Both cock and hen have a slight wing-bar formed by some white tips to the median coverts.

This is an all too numerous bird in Cyprus found at all levels and particularly in the towns and villages where it is resident throughout the year, rearing at least two broods within the year. Beyond the built-up areas colonies of these sparrows occur in isolated pockets in the country far from any village. It has now been found nesting from shore level to at least 4,000 ft in the Southern Range. To what extent the resident birds have their numbers reinforced in spring no-one appears to know, but the fact that 358 *Passer domesticus* were reported by the Smithsonian Institute observers to have been taken in the spring of 1968 by the Paralimni limers surely must point to house sparrows arriving from overseas; whether on passage or to remain and breed, has not yet been determined. There are no figures for other liming centres available.

Breeding on the plains begins early; there are numerous records of eggs in the last week of March. On the other hand house sparrows found nesting at 4,000 ft were still carrying nest material on 28 May pointing to a prolonged breeding season and more than one brood. Eggs are described (*Oologists Record* 1961) as mainly having white or greyish-white ground, the shell handsomely blotched sienna brown, dark brown, violet or brown and violet. The feature of the Palestine house-sparrow's nesting seems to be the large size of the clutches so often found, sets of seven and eight being not uncommon. Young birds are general after April, and second broods are to be seen abroad in May in the lower elevations.

SPANISH SPARROW

Passer hispaniolensis

The male of this sparrow is a very handsome fellow with a chestnut crown, black throat and breast and large white cheek patches. The back appears streaky from above; below, the white belly, with streaked sides only, is very noticeable. Like all sparrows it is a pugnacious, noisy little bird especially in the breeding season. The female is almost exactly like the hen *P. domesticus*. The bright chestnut crown of the cock is the character which at once enables this sparrow to be distinguished from the house sparrow. In size there is nothing between them.

Since we wrote the article on this sparrow in *Birds of Cyprus* a great deal more has been learned about its status and migrations in Cyprus and the fact has emerged that it is not only a passage migrant in huge numbers, and a winter visitor but – what had escaped all naturalists prior to 1958 – that it is *a breeding bird* as well, nesting locally in large and small colonies all over the Karpas peninsula and westwards to Famagusta. One colony of twenty-five to thirty pairs was found nesting alongside *Passer domesticus* in bushy pines at 500 ft in the Karpas in April, where a clutch of four eggs was found at the end of March, and many other pairs on 30 April had incomplete sets, large, young or abandoned nests. On 19 April another huge colony of 250–300 pairs was located in the forest of Salamis; the nests still under construction were 45–50 ft up in tall stone pines – on 6 May. This colony contained young or hatching eggs, including one C/5 and a hatching C/6. One tree had fifty-one sparrows nests and a raven's, the raven perhaps providing some protection against kestrels, hobbies and hooded crows seen near the colony. Eggs examined had a whitish ground and were lightly spotted with brown and ashy-grey, resembling some paler examples of the house-sparrow. (*Oologists Record* 1961 p. 55).

It is today a locally abundant resident in the eastern part of the island with another large breeding colony at Kouklia. Autumn migrants occur from the end of September, the numbers increasing to thousands in the first half of October, with wintering flocks of hundreds up to March when departure takes place. Only a small spring passage has been recorded in late March to late April. Thousands of Spanish sparrows are captured on lime-sticks every year, especially in the Kapvounos valley. In the autumn they have been seen coming in from Turkey over Morphou Bay and passing through the Xeros valley.

The breeding birds are reported to be *Passer hispaniolensis transcaspicus* and passage migrants are believed to be both of that race, which breeds in Asia Minor, and the typical subspecies, *P.h. hispaniolensis*, of southern Europe.

Spanish sparrow

Family FRINGILLIDAE

The finches are one of the largest family of birds in the Palaearctic Region and as many of them are forced to migrate during the colder months there is a heavy autumn migration of the family seeking a more salubrious climate in the Middle East. Seed-eaters in one form or another, almost without exception, the birds have to go where they can feed and the Mediterranean basin is a much favoured area for many in the colder months. In this Handbook we have, contrary to our treatment in *Birds of Cyprus*, divorced the buntings from the Fringillidae, but even so the finches are now represented in Cyprus by eight genera, one of which *Loxia* includes the insular race of the crossbill.

The finches usually have very short thick bills capable of dealing with the dry husks of seeds, but the bill of the crossbill is very different, the mandibles being curved and crossed which in some way assists the birds in their efforts to deal with the seeds of the fircones. The field naturalist usually learns to distinguish members of the "finch family" by sight, either by their voice or their flight or by identification marks of individual species, but to define characters on paper which are applicable to the family as a whole is really impossible. Wing-formulas are of no assistance unless the wing can be examined. Mostly small birds of the chaffinch size they have a dipping rather than a direct flight, but that is a feature of other birds beyond the family, as for instance the wagtails and pipits; wings are mainly pointed; the legs fine and feet in most genera, delicately formed. Tail is of medium length in the true finches: greenfinch, goldfinch, chaffinch, serin, brambling etc. but in the hawfinch with its huge thick bill and stumpy tail we have an example of the other extreme. With the perusal of the following pages the very diverse nature of the finch family will be appreciated. Thirteen different species have now been recorded from Cyprus, at least four of which are rarely encountered and relegated to the Appendix. The buntings are *not* here included with the Fringillidae, but dealt with separately.

HAWFINCH

Coccothraustes coccothraustes

It was a surprise to us to find the hawfinch in Cyprus as a winter visitor. Its appearances are however irregular and it is not a bird that the ordinary visitor is likely to see during his rambles in the island.

The hawfinch is the largest and the most stockily built of any finch to be seen in Cyprus. It has an enormous bill and a bullet-shaped head on a very thick neck. These features, with the short, broad and square tail, give it a heavy, stumpy appearance, although its over-all length is only 6½ ins (17 cm). The crown is orange-brown, separated by a grey nape from the darker brown mantle and back; the underparts are vinaceous-brown. Features which catch the eye are the white on the wing-coverts and the broad white border to the tail feathers, the white under the tail, the jet black lores joined by a narrow line at the base of the bill, and the black throat. The hawfinch is only seen in Cyprus in the winter and its bill is then pale yellowish-horn with darker tips. Seen late in the season, the bill might have its summer colour, leaden blue. The flight is undulating. The wings beat quickly and the short tail is at once noted. It utters a clicking tzik-tzik as it flies and this attracts attention.

Surprisingly the hawfinch is one of the bird visitors taken by the Paralimni limers, two were caught on lime-sticks on 10 November 1967. The bird does not figure in the Smithsonian list of spring migrants caught by the limers in 1968 – a list which must be a fair sample of the species captured annually at this well known liming centre.

The latest information we have of its status in 1970 is that it is an irregular and rather scarce visitor from early November to early April; in some years quite numerous. Such an invasion took place from January to March in 1911 and was occasioned by abnormally severe weather on the continent. One was caught in a mist-net 10 November 1969 and another trapped 23 May 1970, both at Akrotiri Peninsula.

NOTE

The tree-sparrow and the rock-sparrow have been reported, once each, from Cyprus but the records are rejected by the C.O.S. and must be deleted from any list in which they figure.

MEDITERRANEAN GREENFINCH

Chloris chloris aurantiiventris
[Plate 26, facing p. 176]

This well-known winter visitor to Cyprus is a handsome bird, olive-green throughout with a yellower rump and both the wings and the basal half of the black tail are bordered with bright yellow. The yellow markings are most conspicuous in flight. The bird has a thick bill capable of opening the strongest seed-pods; it is a pale flesh colour, as are the legs and feet. The female is much duller in plumage, altogether browner and with the yellow markings paler. The male has a characteristic wheezy note – a long drawn out nasal *dwee*. The length is 5¾ ins (15 cm).

The bird described is the Mediterranean race of the greenfinch *aurantiiventris* and is the breeding resident. We have however seen greenfinches in Cyprus which could not be assigned to this race or to the nominate subspecies which were in a mixed flock on 27 March, possibly new arrivals. They stood out from the rest of the flock for their very pale green plumage possibly *C.c. turkestanicus*, which also breeds in Iraq.

When we wrote our *Birds of Cyprus* (1958) there had been no breeding record confirmed. Whether that had been overlooked by the earlier naturalists or whether the greenfinch has only of recent years established itself as a breeding species must remain in doubt, but today it is a resident bird, breeding locally.

First recognised nesting at Akrotiri and Phassouri in 1963, since 1967 at least it has bred at Polemidhia and was seen in June 1969 at Famagusta.

Winter visitors arrive from late October or early November but are not common until late November or early December and remain so until departure from Cyprus in late February onwards, the last winter visitors leaving in March to mid-April. As a breeding bird it is evidently expanding. It is to be hoped some ringed birds from Europe or Asia will be recovered in Cyprus to give a clue to the country of origin of the winter flocks.

GOLDFINCH [Plate 26, facing p. 176]

Carduelis carduelis niediecki

The breeding bird in Cyprus is the Asia Minor subspecies *C.c. niediecki* to which the following description and field-notes belong: The bright colours of this little finch, the most common in Cyprus, make it easy to recognise. The crimson mask bordered with white contrasts with the black on the crown and on the sides of the neck; the black wings with broad yellow band and white terminal spots on the primary and secondary wing feathers, the white-tipped tail, are all conspicuous features against the brown back and light upper tail-coverts. The underparts are white, with a brown wash on the flanks. The two sexes are exactly alike. Total length 4¾ ins (12 cm).

This has been truly described as an abundant resident except in the highest part of the Southern Range, it is also a winter visitor, considerable numbers coming in to the island from overseas; the subspecies to which these "other visitors" belong can only be determined by the capture of ringed birds or critical examination of birds caught in other ways. Both *brevirostris* of the Caucasus and *loudoni* of N.W. Persia (if valid races!) have been mentioned by Hartert in this connection, and also *balcanica* as in the latest Check-List.

The spring passage is noticeable in March and early April and autumn passage in October and early November, many birds remaining to winter. It is very abundant then on the low ground, when the winter flocks have arrived and the birds which have bred in the mountains have descended with their broods. Some of these may migrate, as a ringed Cyprus juvenile has been recovered in Egypt.

Before nesting begins in April goldfinches can be seen in large and small flocks all over the island, but are especially fond of waste land. They start to nest in the first half of April, seldom earlier, mainly on the plains, the earliest record for eggs, (which were highly incubated) is 23 March, while a late clutch, taken at Halefka of six eggs on 11 May, proves that the breeding season is protracted. We do not have dates of any clutches obtained from the higher elevations. The nests are usually placed fairly high between 10 and 20 ft up in the branches of various trees: poplars, olives, eucalyptus, cypress, wattles and fruit trees. One nest, described in our larger volume, was well built of graphalium and fine roots as well as 100 anthemis-like flowers mostly on the outside, the cup lined with soft yellow vegetable-down: inside diameter 53 and depth 26 mm, external diameter 80 mm and from top to bottom 40 mm. Other nests are described as usually built of flowers, grasses and wool, with a lining of fine hair. The clutch consists of four to six eggs, normally four or five. They have a ground colour of greyish or bluish-white, spotted and streaked sparingly with reddish or mauvish-brown, with ashy shellmarks.

SISKIN

Carduelis spinus

Mainly olive-yellow in colour relieved with black, the siskin is a very pretty small finch some 4¾ ins (12 cm) in total length. It has a yellow breast and rump, yellow basal half of the tail and a conspicuous yellow band on the wing. The crown, throat and tip of the tail are black, while the yellow wing-bar has a black band on either side. The white belly has black flank streaks. The female is grey-brown above streaked with blackish-brown, and has no black on head or throat. She has the same yellow markings as the male. The shrill clear note may be rendered *tsuu*, on the wing often prolonged and not so sharp. It has an agreeable song of very rapid modulated notes.

Winter visitors to Cyprus sometimes seen in flocks numbering thirty individuals, we encountered it first on 3 March 1954 on the Paphos-Polis road. They ascend to the higher elevations and are recorded from near Troödos in November. Their visits are evidently irregular and as we know in the British Isles there are "siskin years" when the birds are unusually abundant as in others they are scarce. The statistics of the C.O.S., and notes kept by the earlier band of naturalists, show that Cyprus too has invasion years which have been listed as 1907–8, 1937–38, 1947–48, 1953–54, 1959–60, 1961–62.

There has been no breeding evidence but birds have been reported in the island as late as mid-June when "large parties" were seen around Troödos. "Large parties" do not usually imply breeding but the date is unusually late for a bird which has generally departed by the early days of May.

SYRIAN LINNET [Plate 26, facing p. 176]

Carduelis cannabina bella

We believe the breeding birds of Cyprus to belong to the Syrian form *bella* and refuse to agree that they are of the "nominate race" whatever the latest American authorities may say. This is not the place to argue the point but we challenge those who say all the breeding birds of the Mediterranean islands are *C.c. cannabina*, to produce a single skin of a *breeding* Cyprus linnet collected prior to 1970. Many of the winter flocks are also *bella* which breeds extensively in Asia Minor, Palestine and Syria.

The male may be succinctly described when in fresh plumage as having dull red on breast and forehead, this changing to scarlet in spring. Mantle chestnut, feathers with dark brown centres; rump and upper tail-coverts whitish, streaked black. Wing black, outer edge of primaries fringed white. The female resembles the male but has no red on forehead or breast, wing 78–81 mm (after Meinertzhagen). Length 5 ins (13 cm). *C.c. cannabina* from continental Europe is larger and darker; *C.c. mediterranea* extending from Spain and northern Africa to Crete is paler and smaller.

The linnet is a common breeding bird at

all levels frequenting especially the rough hill ground, the mountain population descending to the lower levels in winter and returning in February according to the weather. The wintering birds have their numbers greatly augmented in the autumn by visitors from Europe, among which must be flocks from Europe and Asia Minor.

Passage migrants pass north from late February or early March to early April. Breeding begins in early April at coast level; an exceptionally early brood of five is on record (*Birds of Cyprus* p. 20) found in a neat nest, well lined with hair and feathers, a foot above ground in a genista bush on 13 April; but even at Nicosia, which stands on fairly high ground, nests are seldom completed before May. Other Cyprus nests have been described in the *Oologists Record* 1961 p. 51: one of which was built of dead flowering plants and lined with vegetable down, fine grasses and hair. The pretty blue eggs in this nest had typical spots of purplish-red and liver; one of the eggs being exceptionally blue.

NOTE

The **redpoll**, *Carduelis flammea*, has been taken on three occasions in Cyprus of recent years. See Appendix p. 222.

SERIN [Plate 26, facing p. 176]

Serinus canarius serinus

A breeding resident which has extended its nesting area since our larger book appeared, the serin is recognisable by its lemon-yellow rump, so conspicuous in flight, but duller in the female. Forehead and nape are yellow, the remaining upper-parts pale brown streaked with sepia. Wings and tail dark brown; throat and breast lemon-yellow, belly white. It is 4½ inches (11 cm) long and the bill is short and stumpy.

First reported to breed in Cyprus in 1877, a completed nest remained to be described for ninety years, when one was at last found with four eggs on 1 July 1967 at Troöditissa and several other pairs seen in the neighbourhood. Nests, still under construction, had already been found in 1959 by a C.O.S. member on 21 and 29 May, 20 and 30 ft up respectively in an Aleppo pine, near Troödos, at 3,500 ft but no eggs were found that year. It has been generally believed to be restricted for breeding to this Highland area in Cyprus, and great was our surprise to learn that serins had bred "abundantly" in a plantation near Akrotiri in June 1969. This extraordinary occurrence is confirmed in the latest Check-List (1971), where the locality is named as Phassouri. Normally breeding only takes place about 2,500–3,000 ft.

Nests are usually very small and have a characteristic lining of hair. Four eggs is a normal clutch. Eggs in Europe are streaked with purplish- and reddish-brown on a pale bluish ground-colour. Cyprus eggs remain undescribed. When breeding is over, the birds descend to the lower ground, when flocks of forty and up to 200 have been reported – the latter at Polimedhia on 12 December 1968. To what extent overseas migration takes place requires further investigation, but a flock of 200 points to the resident serins having their numbers greatly implemented from Europe in the winter months. In the new Check-List the Serin is described as a "common winter visitor from the north" (presumably meaning from Turkey) with large flocks arriving in December–January and remaining abundant until late February especially in towns and lowland park-like areas.

GUILLEMARD'S CROSSBILL

Loxia curvirostra guillemardi

[Plate 25, facing p. 161]

Crossbills at reasonably close quarters are unmistakable birds by reason of their peculiar bills, the mandibles of which are crossed and very powerful. The relatively large head, thick neck and short tail give this finch a rather stocky appearance. The Cyprus cross-bill has less crimson in its plumage than the typical subspecies, yellow often taking the place of the bright crimson usually found in Scandinavian birds which have many of the body feathers so coloured, especially bright on the rump. Wings and tail are brown. In winter the colours are duller. The female is yellowish-green with a mottled mantle and grey belly. Juvenile birds have streaked upperparts, the dark brown feathers having whitish borders; the underparts are then heavily streaked with sepia. The mandibles are not crossed until the birds are at least three weeks old. Before the birds are fully adult, a variety of intermediate plumages are to be seen. In total length the crossbill is 6½ ins (17 cm), remembering that it has an unusually short tail.

In Cyprus it is found only in the high Troödos pine-forests above 5,000 ft where the trees are of ancient growth, but of recent years crossbills have been seen elsewhere. Three such unusual appearances are mentioned in the latest Check-List i.e. One at Akrotiri 11 November 1961; three also at Akrotiri 25 October 1964, and four or five at Salamis 1 September 1969. Could these coastal sightings have been of overseas visitors from Turkey? Had they been of midwinter date, they might have been forced by severe conditions to lower ground, but the dates: September to early November, do not support that view. They rather point to overseas immigration, but of which race?

The crossbill is normally a very early breeder laying its eggs in January or February even in Tunisia, but Cyprus eggs have not been described and still await discovery. In other breeding areas – there is a well-established race in northern Africa well-known to the writer – crossbills build a compact nest with a foundation of twigs and a lining of moss, hair and feathers. The normal clutch is four and the female sits very tight. We give no description of the egg until those laid by Guillemard's crossbill have been found for the first time.

NOTE

A specimen of the **two-barred crossbill** (*Loxia leucoptera bifasciata*) was reported from Mount Olympus on 24 Feb. 1965 and its identification accepted by the Recorder of the C.O.S., but see Appendix p. 223.

CYPRUS CHAFFINCH

Fringilla coelebs cypriotis

[Plate 26, facing p. 176]

That several races of the chaffinch occur periodically in Cyprus there can be no dispute, and it is all the more desirable to retain the name *cypriotis* for the *resident breeding birds* which were separated on their noticeably dark mantles in the *Bulletin of the British Ornithological Club* 1945, p. 4. *Fringilla coelebs cypriotis* was named by a British ornithologist with an extensive knowledge of European-Asiatic birds, familiar with the Cyprus chaffinch both in Museum series and in the field. It is restricted when breeding, to altitudes above 2,000 in the Northern Range and up to 5,200 ft in the Southern Range where nests have been found. The chaffinch is too well-known by everyone to require a written description. We have included a good picture of the bird in this Handbook which should suffice. It is not known to what extent the breeding population moves down to the lower levels in the winter, but the chaffinch is a hardy bird and many are present in mid-winter on the snow-covered Troödos mountains. Further study by resident ornithologists is needed to decide this point.

A long account of the chaffinches in Cyprus appeared in our larger work, and a valuable paper which appeared in the *Oologists's Record* (1961) has greatly implemented (pp. 51–52) what we wrote about the nesting habits. In the Southern Range where the investigation was made by a military member of the C.O.S. – eight nests were examined at altitudes between 3,000 and 6,000 ft between 19 May and 5 June. Nests were typical, built of moss, bents and pine-needles encrusted with lichen and lined with wool, hair and feathers. Eggs were brownish-stone colour with spots and striations of brown and dark purple. The nests cited held three or four young, and one, three eggs. All were built between 12 and 35 ft from the ground. Most were on lichen-covered boughs of pines, one in a wild cherry.

So far as overseas migration occurs we believe the breeding population to be resident subject to some extent to local movements not yet understood. There is in addition a considerable immigration of winter visitors to the lower ground occurring from the mid- to late October, with passage migrants from late October to early November most noticeable on the south coast. The spring migration is mainly observed from mid- to late February to the middle of March when considerable numbers are to be seen on the plains, the females predominating. The wintering birds disappear between February and late March, a few remaining on into April.

We believe these wintering flocks to be mainly of the chaffinches from central Europe which we have always considered rightly named as *F.c. hortensis** but the latest American revisionist unites both *hortensis* and *cypriotis* with the nominate *F. coelebs coelebs*. His opinion is open to correction.

BRAMBLING [Plate 26, facing p. 176]

Fringilla montifringilla

The brambling closely resembles the chaffinch in size, flight and behaviour. In winter the male has a dark head, buffish breast, orange lesser wing-coverts and a white rump. The crown and cheeks have a mottled appearance after the autumn moult, but this diminishes until in spring the glossy blue-black of the head and shoulders contrasts vividly with the chest-nut-buff breast and shoulder patches and the snowy-white rump and belly. The female changes less and is altogether a duller version of the male. The bird's length is 5¾ inches (15 cm).

In *Birds of Cyprus* we described this bird as an Accidental Visitor to Cyprus as at that date (1958) only three records of the brambling were known. Since then, with the increase in observers, about a dozen more have been seen and it is reasonable to conclude the bird visits Cyprus every year in winter but is very rarely seen. Definite records accepted in the new Check-List since the formation of the C.O.S. between 1956 and 1965 cover all years but two, and fall between 23 October and 4 March. A small number of sight records were not sufficiently established. Numbers seen at one time varied from one to six birds, the latter small flock on 2 December 1963 at Larnaca.

Breeding widely in northern Europe and Asia it is known to undertake mass movements to southern Europe in certain years subject to conditions in their summer quarters, and at such times a small number may reach Cyprus. We expect that many pass un-noticed for they have been seen at widely separated localities i.e. Nicosia, Larnaca, Kornos, Dhekelia, Paphos, Saittas and even Troödos. They appear sometimes – an odd bird or two – in the midst of a flock of visiting chaffinches with which they are likely to have migrated from the continent. The white rump should at once betray the species under such conditions.

*As we wrote in a footnote in *Birds of Cyprus* (1958) we were indebted to the late Colonel R. Meinertzhagen, to Dr. Keve of Budapest and to Dr. James Harrison of England for examining Cyprus specimens and for their opinions as to the races which occur in the island, in particular the endemic race. Could they all have been wrong?!

Family EMBERIZIDAE

The buntings are another large family of grain-eaters which were formerly included in the Fringillidae with the grosbeaks and finches. Professor Voous among others has raised them to family rank and in this we are in agreement. They form a very large assemblage in the Palaearctic Region and in the Middle East are a prominent feature of the avifauna with many interesting species present. Vaurie has agreed that the buntings, of the old World at anyrate, differ clearly from the finches and do not present a taxonomic problem . . . the genus *Emberiza* in which so many buntings are grouped, has twenty-nine species restricted to the Palaearctic Region alone, according to the article he contributed to the *New Dictionary of Birds*. Of these, eleven species have reached Cyprus, five of which can only be classed as vagrants. Of the remaining six the well-known European bird, the yellowhammer, is an occasional visitor, the black-headed bunting and Cretschmar's bunting are summer visitors to breed, and the corn bunting also breeds locally but is mainly a passage migrant, the reed bunting is a winter visitor but naturally local in Cyprus and the ortolan – another favourite species (especially of the gourmet) – is an abundant migrant mainly in the spring. All the members of this family suffer tremendous persecution in the Middle East and their numbers are diminishing alarmingly in consequence.

The bunting family lay eggs of a particular pattern, so-called "worm-lines" or scrolls being a special feature on the shell. Their migrations are dealt with in the sections which follow, that of the black-headed bunting being especially worthy of notice.

YELLOW BUNTING or YELLOW-HAMMER

Emberiza citrinella

In summer dress easily identified by its bright canary-yellow head, neck and underparts. It is indistinctly striped on the yellow face and throat, and the flanks and breast are streaked with chestnut-brown. Mantle and back are chestnut, streaked blackish but the bright chestnut rump is unstreaked. The amount and intensity of yellow on the head varies considerably. In winter the streaking of the crown and generally duller plumage give the bird a more subdued appearance. The hen is duller than the male in any case, less yellow on the underparts and more streaked with brown.

Yellowhammers had never been recorded from Cyprus before 1957 when seven birds were seen at Troödos in December and a party of twenty-five at Platres in the following year, confirming as do more recent sightings, that the bird is evidently a rare winter visitor to the higher elevations. It seems to be sufficiently regular in its visits to be dealt with in this part of the Handbook. Whether it is restricted to the high ground is doubtful as one was reported from the low ground on 9 March 1962.

There is no evidence of breeding to date in Cyprus, but a pair were seen in the Troödos area in 1967 at the end of May which is a curious date, if the birds are only winter visitors.

The records accepted by the authors as valid in the new 1971 Check-List, in addition to those mentioned above, are: one obtained Ayios Athanasios 5.9.58; one Dhekelia 13.4.60; one Cape Greco 9.3.62; eight Episkopi 5.1.65; one near Nicosia 17.1.65. The race to which these visitors belong has not been determined.

CORN BUNTING [Plate 26, facing p. 176]

Emberiza calandra

The general colour of this bunting is not unlike that of a skylark but the bunting has no trace of white on the outer tail feathers and is a much plumper looking bird. About 7 ins (18 cm) in total length, it possesses a decidedly heavy bill and head and its dark "bib" is very noticeable. The hair-brown plumage is streaked with dark brown on the head, back and breast; the eye-stripe, chin and throat are paler and the feathers of coverts, wings and tail have pale edgings. A dark moustachial stripe runs obliquely downwards from the base of the bill – the afore-mentioned "bib". Bill is brown above, yellow below, the legs brownish flesh-colour and the eyes hazel.

This is presumably a resident bunting breeding in the island and subject to large increases in numbers in the autumn, a huge influx having been observed in October. It must therefore be considered a winter visitor as well as a passage migrant. In autumn it is mainly seen from early or late September into November, considerable numbers remaining over the winter. The spring movement is less marked from early March to early April. Huge flocks have been seen at Kouklia in mid-June. For some reason not clearly understood the corn bunting becomes very scarce or even absent in July and August but whether it disappears from the island for these very hot months needs further investigation.

In 1958 its status as a breeding bird was doubtful, but we have since learned that it is quite a common bird in suitable localities on the plains. The nest is described as a large compact grass structure; one was found on 20 April in a dense patch of dry reeds by Morphou river, another on 10 May 10 ins up in a dead tamarisk, juncus and *salicornia* undergrowth. Both nests contained five eggs, which had the ground colour light sienna, handsomely smeared with violet, with bold streaks and blotches of liver and black.

BLACK-HEADED BUNTING

Emberiza melanocephala

[Plate 27, facing p. 192]

The male is a very striking bird. The entire underparts bright canary-yellow; a yellow collar almost surrounds the neck; crown and forehead black; remainder of upperparts bright chestnut. Wings dark with pale tips to the coverts. Tail uniform brown. In fresh autumn plumage the crown and mantle become much duller. The female is a sparrowy-looking bird, brown above, finely streaked with darker brown. The underparts are pale fulvous washed with sulphur-yellow; in some stages of plumage the breast is suffused with buff. Bill lead blue, legs and feet dark flesh-colour. Yellow is the dominant colour when a flock of these birds is encountered.

From several viewpoints this bunting has an exceptional history, it is one of the very few species which does not winter in Africa but comes to Cyprus to breed from its winter quarters on the plains of India. The migration to their summer breeding places via Syria and Mesopotamia, to S.E. Europe and Asia Minor, the sexes flying separately, is briefly traced in *Birds of Cyprus*. The birds arrive in flocks, the males first, about mid-April and the pairs take up their territories soon after, which they guard rigorously against intrusion. Nesting up to at least 4,000 ft and widely dispersed in the island, these brightly coloured birds with their brilliantly yellow breasts, are conspicuous in the early days of their arrival as they perch on high branches from which they take short flights to parachute down to the same spot singing all the while. They do not at first occupy the higher elevations in the Southern Range, May is well on the way before they begin nesting in the upper zones. Building, entirely by the hens, which alone incubate, has been watched at about 4,000 ft near Amiandos between 25 and 28 May. We have on the other hand seen full clutches taken in the hills between 6 and 15 May, which is presumably normal for the lower and mid-elevations. Observations taken at Kakopetria (2,200 ft) in 1948, and 1954 showed that the birds arrived at the same place each year almost to a day: 13 May, over three weeks later than on the slopes below St. Hilarion Castle. Kakopetria is situated on the northern slope of the Troödos range, N.N.E. of Mount Olympus.

Nests are typical bunting structures of stalks and dried grass lined with fine material and hair. A favourite site is in thick clumps of tall thistles, in bramble-clumps and in deciduous bushes. Those recently discovered at a high elevation are described as follows: one nest 30 ins up in a cistus, another 8 ins from ground in the main stem of a grape-vine and yet another in green herbage and blue *Salvia* growing on the edge of a stone terrace. Eggs which number from three to six, normally four or five, are laid every 24 hours, and no male bird has ever been found on the nest.

In *Birds of Cyprus* we described the eggs on good authority as having a greyish or greenish-white ground with spots and streaks and as lacking the usual scrolls on the eggs laid by the bunting family. Two clutches taken in 1959 at Kyperounda were described *Ool. Record* 1961 p. 52 as having a *blue* ground; in one clutch with a zone of small black spots at the big end and in the other, which showed much blue ground, with flecks and spots of violet and light brown, mostly at the big end.

After breeding the buntings gather into flocks and depart with their broods during the month of August. A late record is of one ringed at Akrotiri on 12 September, the last birds normally leave before August is out.

ORTOLAN BUNTING

Emberiza hortulana

[Plate 26, facing p. 176]

Ortolans are not difficult to recognise, the male has the head, neck and chest grey tinged with olive, a heavily striped black and chestnut back and a diagnostic yellow patch on the throat, with distinct malar stripes on each side. The chest is greyish-olive, below which the underside is cinnamon-buff. In flight the white outer tail feathers are conspicuous. Bill, legs and feet are brownish-red. In length it is 6¼ ins (16 cm). The female is similar but duller.

This attractive member of the bunting family is a fairly common passage migrant in spring, mainly from late March to May with largest numbers on passage the second half of April. We have seen it from the coastal area to the mountains but to what height it ascends no observers have stated. It is common all over the Northern Range in spring, and there is an interesting record of two ortolans seen in the Southern Range at Platres, on 1 July 1967, both the place and the date being unusual. Another late record of a female ortolan seen on 24 June 1969 at Ayios Chrysostomos, confirms that individual birds or a pair may remain in the island long after the others have gone, but there is still no evidence of breeding occurring.

They begin to leave their winter quarters in the Sudan and Abyssinia in March and comparatively small numbers then pass through Cyprus on their way to breed in Europe, where they have a wide but interrupted range. On their long journey *thousands* are shot, netted or limed in Mediterranean countries every year, as it is a favourite article of food and considered a delicacy even in France. That the numbers which pass through Cyprus annually are diminishing is not surprising, as few birds are *more* persecuted. In the census, taken in 1968 by a team of scientists from the Smithsonian Institute of Washington, of birds captured on lime-sticks at Paralimni village, between 5 March and 11 May, only thirty-eight ortolans were caught that year as against seventy Cretchmar's buntings and seventy-four corn buntings. Surprisingly only twenty-three black-headed buntings fell victims in the spring.

The autumn return passage is on a much smaller scale than the spring, and takes place from late August till about 20 September, occasionally till the end of that month.

When we wrote our larger volume (1958) we believed the ortolan might *once* have nested in Cyprus many years ago (*Journ für Ornithologie* 1929 p. 35) and noted "some may remain to nest". Breeding has never been substantiated and had ortolans nested in Cyprus since the formation of the C.O.S. in 1957, with the greatly increased interest in birds now evident, the fact would surely have come to light.

CRETSCHMAR'S BUNTING

Emberiza caesia [Plate 27, facing p. 192]

The male has the crown, nape, ear-coverts and a line on each side of the throat blue-grey. Lores, chin and throat pale chestnut. A pale eye-ring is distinctive. Below the throat, underparts are chestnut. Mantle rich brown, streaked dark brown. Rump and upper tail-coverts rich chestnut, wings paler brown, the greater coverts with rufous fringes. Tail brown with some white on the outer feathers. The female is paler than the male with only a suspicion of grey on the crown and on the sides of the breast which is pale chestnut. Bill pale reddish-brown, legs and feet pale brown, eye brown, in both sexes. Total length 6¼ ins (16 cm).

This most attractive bunting is a summer visitor to Cyprus in considerable numbers which arrive in the island in March, when there are records of "huge influxes" in the middle of the month at Akrotiri. It is also an abundant passage migrant both in spring and autumn. The records, kept so carefully by the C.O.S., indicate that the birds arrive on the low ground from early or mid-March with migrants to that area to at least mid-April. The main passage is in late March and early April.

In autumn the main passage is noted from late August to early September, a few coming in late July, numbers increasing through August; the last birds leave from late September to early October, with stragglers up to mid-November.

The summer visitors begin nesting on the low ground in April and can be heard singing zee zee zee zee in every direction but unlike the black-headed bunting they choose to sing from low elevations and are consequently much less conspicuous. We gave *very full* data in *Birds of Cyprus* of dates and places where full clutches had been taken with detailed description of nests. Egg-laying is not restricted to the plains and foothills in April, for we listed six nests from Kakopetria which lies at 2,200 ft in the Troödos Range, five with young and one with five eggs, between 9 and 18 April. Breeding continues throughout May when fresh eggs have been found up to 5,500 ft on 29 May near the Forestry cottage, Troödos.

Nests are built on, or even *in*, the ground in scrapes under cistus plants or salvia, or by the tufts of *Pterocephalus* and similar low-growing vegetation. Slopes sheltered by cistus are perhaps the most favoured site. The nest material is rather loosely put together of bents and grasses, the rather deep cup usually but not always, lined neatly with various coloured hair, probably goat; the whole structure supported by grasses, thistles or plants, or built into the roots of the cistus. Some nests are very ill-concealed, others cunningly hidden and perfectly in harmony with the background. The clutch is usually four or five, exceptionally only three. No C/6 has been recorded.

Eggs have a ground-colour of greyish or yellowish-white to russet or reddish-grey; exceptionally with ground of delicate blue-grey, a few ashy shell-streaks and a few dark brown spots and streaks. Normally the shell is rather glossy, with almost black spots and streaks and violet-grey underlying spots and "worm lines". (c.f. *Ool Record* 1961).

REED BUNTING [Plate 26, facing p. 176]

Emberiza schoeniclus

In winter plumage, when the reed-bunting appears in Cyprus, the bird is not so easily recognised as it is in its summer dress. In breeding plumage the head and throat are black, and a white collar passes below the ear-coverts. The back is rufous-brown streaked with black, the rump bluish-grey, and the underparts white. There is much white visible on the tail, in both sexes.

In winter the male's black head is obscured by buff tips to the feathers, and the striking white collar turns to buff and is then much less noticeable. The female is a sparrowy-looking bird at both seasons; the head reddish-brown streaked with black; a dark malar stripe is a feature. Chin and throat are buff, but no white or buff collar is present. Total length 6 ins (15 cm).

The typical reed-bunting has a fine pointed bill, a feature which separates it immediately when near enough to see it, from the thick-billed reed bunting which has also been recorded from Cyprus (see Appendix p. 223.

The European reed-bunting comes to Cyprus in some numbers, when it is to be found in any marshy ground. Dates of its arrival and departure, from observations by the C.O.S. indicate that in a normal year it may be expected in late October or early November, common from the middle of November to the middle of February at least; departure of these winter visitors begins in early March and the last birds have left before the month is out. We believe that most of the wintering birds are of the nominate race.

NOTE

In addition to the **thick-billed reed bunting** mentioned above, the **rock bunting** (*Emberiza cia*) has been definitely recorded from Cyprus and also the **cirl bunting** (*E. cirlus*) on less satisfactory evidence, for details of which see Appendix p. 223.

APPENDIX

List of Rarely-recorded Visitors to Cyprus including some exceptional occurrences*.

Because a bird figures in this list does not necessarily imply it is of rare occurrence. Species which *appear* to be rare may quite possibly be regular passage migrants in small numbers which pass un-noticed and unrecorded.

The List is based on the records (with latest revision) already enumerated in *Birds of Cyprus* and, since 1958, on the second *Check-list of the birds of Cyprus* (1971) prepared with exemplary care from the annals of the Society by Sergeant PETER F. STEWART of the Royal Air Force assisted by Mr. Steen Christensen. The first *Check-List* appeared in 1963 in Bulletin 15 of the C.O.S. in which the Editor collated all records which covered the difficult teething years since the Society's foundation. With the experience of the intervening years it has been found necessary to delete some of the records then accepted, and to add many new ones. The observation particularly applies to the List of "Rarely recorded Visitors" which follows.

Individual records are NOT listed by us other than exceptionally but can be traced primarily in the revised *Check-List*† and in the Annual Reports and Bulletins of the C.O.S. All records in the new check-list, and other matter which the List contains has been placed unreservedly at our disposition, in advance of its publication, for inclusion in our Handbook, by Mr. Stewart and with the full approval of Mr. George Savvides, President of the Cyprus Ornithological Society, a privilege of which we are very sensible and for which we have expressed our gratitude in The Preface.

For the convenience of those who possess our original work a page reference is given to *Birds of Cyprus* (1958) in which *every* species, which

---

*When a bird in this list is enclosed in square brackets, there is a doubt of the record being accepted, even though included as valid in previous publications. An explanation is given in most cases.

The Senior author is responsible for the acceptance or otherwise of the birds in this list when they deviate from the new *Check-List of the Birds of Cyprus* 1971, prepared by Mr. P.F. Stewart and Mr. S. Christensen, but in general we agree very closely. A page reference to that list would have been given had it been in print at the time of our *Handbook* going to press.

†*A Check-list of the Birds of Cyprus* 1971, by Peter F. Stewart and Steen. J. Christensen.

had occurred in the island up to the date of that publication, *is fully described.* That volume is still obtainable at the time of writing from leading booksellers in Cyprus. It contains much additional information for which space could not be found in the much smaller and lighter book now issued.

The following list may be used in conjunction with *Birds of Cyprus* 1958. Page references to English headings are to the text in this Handbook.

HYDROBATIDAE

Storm Petrels see p. 3

Storm petrel: *Hydrobates pelagicus.* Accidental rare visitor. B. of C. p.273. A single example collected on 13 March, 1903 at Larnaca, seen on a number of occasions in Cyprus waters during July 1956.

PROCELLARIIDAE

Shearwaters see p. 4

Mediterranean shearwater: *Calonectris diomedea.* Occasional visitor. B. of C. p. 273. An example of this large shearwater was killed at Kyrenia in August, 1961. In that year several were seen offshore in July and August.

PELECANIDAE

Pelicans see p. 6

White pelican: *Pelecanus onocrotalus.* Occasional visitor Autumn and Winter. B. of C. p. 269. Records now accepted on 23 November 1957, Akrotiri, previously wrongly identified as *P. crispus*; one 2 December 1959, Episkopi; one juvenile 1 December 1962, Akrotiri; three adult 11/12 December 1962, Akrotiri; 24 juvenile and 34 adult 24/25 November 1964, Akrotiri. A party of 4 adults visited Akrotiri Salt Lake on 23 July 1970 and remained in the vicinity two or three days.

A dark-marked underwing is diagnostic of *P. onocrotalus.* In *P. crispus* the wing is all white. Feathers of forehead terminate in a *point* at base of culmen in the white pelican, but in a *concave line* in the Dalmatian pelican.

SULIDAE

Gannets and Boobies see p. 7

Gannet: *Sula bassana.* Rare visitor. First seen off Salamis 2 May 1965. Six seen off Curium headland 27 February 1969 and several off Episkopi between 14 and 16 March of the same year.

ANATIDAE

Swans, Geese and Ducks see p. 23

Whooper swan: *Cygnus cygnus.*
[Plate 3, facing p. 5]
Rare Winter visitor. B. of C. p. 247. Recorded twice only, one shot near Famagusta 28 December 1910, others reported same time; three again on 27 January and 2 February 1963.

Bean goose: *Anser arvensis.*
[Plate 3, facing p. 5]
Rare Winter visitor. B. of C. p.250. We see no reason to discard either as doubtful records.

Brent goose: *Branta bernicla.* Rare accidental visitor. B. of C. p. 251. No reason to disbelieve identity of one *shot* December 1908 at Kyrenia.

Red-breasted goose: *Branta ruficollis.* Rare accidental visitor. B. of C. p. 251. Larnaca Market 1928.

Scaup: *Aythya marila*.
[Plate 4, facing p. 12]

Rare accidental visitor. B. of C. p. 264. Record substantiated.

Goldeneye: *Bucephala clangula*.
[Plate 4, facing p. 12]

Rare visitor recorded in Spring only. B. of C. p. 265.

Common scoter: *Melanitta nigra*.
[Plate 4, facing p. 12]

Rare accidental visitor. B. of C. p. 265. *Bull*. 15 p. 21: In view of this assurance we accept this as the only identified scoter. The **Velvet scoter**: *Melanitta fusca*, is more likely to occur among several older records, where specific identity was not established, but no *certain* record to date.

Smew: *Mergus albellus*.
[Plate 4, facing p. 12]

Rare accidental visitor. B. of C. p. 266.

Goosander: *Mergus merganser*.
[Plate 4, facing p. 12]

Rare accidental visitor. B. of C. p. 268 and 15th *Bird Report* 1968 p. 7.

AEGYPIIDAE

Vultures see p. 36

Bearded vulture: *Gypaëtus barbatus*.
(*aureus* is the Turkish race). Rare accidental visitor. B. of C. p. 229. Two records only, (1) A pair in the Kyrenia mountains in early March 1909, (2) one seen at Akrotiri on 16 October 1966. The bird passed overhead in S.E. direction. The somewhat thin tapering wings and diamond pointed tail were outstanding, and the uniformly dark plumage pointed to a juvenile bird.

ACCIPITRIDAE

Eagles, Buzzards, Kites, Harriers see p. 39

Short-toed eagle: *Circaëtus gallicus*.
Occasional on passage. B. of C. p. 225 where fully described. There are nine records considered valid up to end 1970, late September to mid October; and one mid-April which remained into July 1962. Last record was 11 April 1965.

[**Tawny eagle**: *Aquila rapax*.
No satisfactory record until a specimen can be examined, then most likely to be the steppe eagle *A. rapax orientalis*. B. of C. p. 205. This species is omitted purposely from the latest 1971 Check-List of Cyprus Birds issued by the Society as *no records are considered valid*].

[**Golden eagle**: *Aquila chrysaëtos*.
No satisfactory record. See Note under white-tailed eagle in main text. This species has been listed in the latest Check-List (1971) among the rejected species].

Rough-legged buzzard: *Buteo lagopus*.
An accidental visitor. B. of C. p. 213. Underside of wing exhibits bold contrasts, sharply defined black carpal patches and black tip to primaries. Conspicuous light tail with broad dark terminal band. Tarsi covered with white feathers. 20–24 in. (51–61 cm) in length. The compilers of the latest *Check-list of Cyprus Birds* believe that the only satisfactory records of the Rough-legged Buzzard are as follows: The one mentioned in *Birds of Cyprus* seen on 24 November 1957 and two earlier ones which have recently come to light in a Swedish Museum, dated respectively 27 and 28 December 1946, both juvenile females; their correct identification has been verified by the Swedish Museum authorities. All other reports of this north Scandinavian buzzard in Cyprus have proved unsatisfactory.

Long-legged buzzard: *Buteo rufinus*.
Two phases of plumage: dark chocolate and reddish-brown. Former with conspicuous white patch on underwing. Larger and heavier on wing than *B. buteo* but difficult to recognise unless obtained. B. of C. p. 212. A scarce visitor in Winter. Apart from three specimens *shot* and recorded in *Birds of Cyprus* there is only one satisfactory *sight* record (also mentioned in our book) seen on 9 December 1957 at Famagusta. All other supposed occurrences are based on characters equally applicable to the Steppe buzzard.

Almost certainly this bird *was* seen in the Autumn raptor movement between 27 August and 15 September 1967, and 26 September and 6 October 1968, seven birds in all, but such records can only be placed in square brackets.

Levantine sparrow hawk: *Accipiter brevipes*. Occasional visitor on passage; recorded Spring and Autumn. B. of C. p. 219. Distinguished from *A. nisus* by grey cheeks. Eight records accepted, but only one bird handled, caught on limestick, Paralimni, 22 September 1967, definitely established the species. Other records between early September and early October and from early to late April.

Red kite: *Milvus milvus*.
Rare autumn visitors. B. of C. p. 220. There have been very few records of the red kite in all. The C.O.S. recorders accept a female shot near Larnaca 22 September 1901 and several sightings in 1957 viz. one Xeros 24 September, one Dhekelia 5 October, one Akrotiri 6 October, four Akrotiri 9 October. How many birds were involved in 1957 is not clear, possibly only four. There have been no records since.

Black-winged kite: *Elanus caeruleus*.
Accidental, one sight-record: Pissouri, 20 November, 1960. About the size of a rock-pigeon. Dove-grey above, white below, a large black patch on each shoulder; bill black, feet and unfeathered legs yellow. Long pointed wings, buoyant graceful flight. Care needed in field not to confuse with pallid harrier. Inclined to hover like kestrel.

FALCONIDAE

Falcons see p. 50

Sooty falcon: *Falco concolor*.
Very rare accidental visitor in autumn. Entire plumage pale slate-grey in normal phase, but has also an almost black phase. In size like eleonora falcon, but tail shorter. Feet and tarsi bright lemon yellow. Both sexes alike in plumage. May accompany *F. eleonorae* on return from East Africa. Flight described as swift and Hobby-like. The only record accepted as valid was a single bird seen at Cape Gata on 22 September 1962.

RALLIDAE

Rails, Crakes, Moorhens, Coots, Gallinules etc. see p. 62

Greater purple gallinule: *Porphyrio* ? *species*. Accidental in January 1968 an example new for Cyprus was identified in the Paphos district and recorded in the 15th *Cyprus Bird Report* for that year as *Porphyrio porphyrio*. Its large size, 17 ins in length, forehead covered with red horny shield and brilliant plumage of turquoise blue, purple, green and black and with white under tail-coverts, red bill and legs all point to this reed-hen being *Porphyrio poliocephalus seistanicus*, (*Vögel Palaearktishen Fauna* p. 1847) a native of the Caspian Sea area, Persia, Mesopotamia and Syria, rather than the bird of South West Europe and North Africa which it so closely resembles.

Allen's gallinule: *Porphyrula alleni*.
Accidental. Much smaller in size (9½ inches, 24 cm in length) than the bird described above, it is also brilliantly coloured. The upperside of wings green instead of blue, horny shield greenish-blue instead of red are the main colour differences. Olive-green above. Rump and tail blackish, underparts of body lilac, middle of belly blackish, under tail-coverts white. Young birds more often encountered on migration are brown above with buff or greenish margins, underparts pale cinnamon brown to white. An example new for Cyprus was *obtained* at Nicosia on 25 December 1968 and another believed to be of this species seen two days earlier near Episkopi, probably the same bird.

OTIDIDAE

Bustards see p. 67

Great bustard: *Otis tarda*.
Very rare visitor in abnormal winters, B. of C. p. 329, including four examples seen in 1925.

Houbara bustard: *Chlamydotis undulata.* Rare accidental visitor. B. of C. p. 331 (under subsp. *macqueenii,* i.e. Macqueen's bustard), which race definitely once identified.

CHARADRIIDAE

Plovers see p. 69

White-tailed plover: *Vanellus leucurus.* One shot by local hunter, present at Akrotiri Salt Lake 15 to 21 March 1970. Skin preserved.

Lesser sand-plover: *Charadrius mongolus.* Rare accidental visitor, one record only. on 9 April 1958.

Dotterel: *Charadrius morinellus.*
[Plate 11, facing p. 49]
Rare visitor in winter. B. of C. p. 317. May be less rare than records suggest.

SCOLOPACIDAE

Sandpipers, Godwits, Curlews etc. see p. 74

Slender-billed curlew: *Numenius tenuirostris.* Accidental. B. of C. p. 293. Distinguished by its smaller size and paler plumage (total length 15–16 ins, 38–41 cm, bill 3 ins) whiter underside with bold heart-shaped spots, and higher pitched call. Had been reported without satisfactory evidence.

Since then there have been slightly better established records: One on 4 April 1957 at Famagusta, and two on 22 December 1964 near Nicosia, but none have yet been collected.

It is a native of the Western Asia steppes and winters in S.W. Asia.

Bar-tailed godwit: *Limosa lapponica.* Rare visitor, three records Spring and Autumn.

Knot: *Calidris canutus.* Accidental. A party of three knots in winter plumage recorded from Akrotiri peninsula on 26 September 1967 and all eventually ringed; one retrapped 7 October same year. First established records for Cyprus. (See 14th *Bird Report* for 1967 p. 11. of Cyprus Ornithological Society). Another appeared at Akrotiri Salt Lake 26 September 1969 (16th *Bird Report*) and one was seen at Larnaca lake on 12 January 1970.

Broad-billed sandpiper: *Limicola falcinellus.* Rare on passage in Spring, several records, but difficult to recognise in winter dress. B. of C. p. 304.

More recent records in 1970 from the Salt Lake at Akrotiri are three birds on 27 May 1970, one on 15 July, seven on 29 August, two on 31 August and three on 2 September. The autumn records probably refer to the same birds.

Terek sandpiper: *Terekia cinerea.* The first authentic record for Cyprus occurred at Akrotiri Salt Lake in the autumn of 1970 when a terek sandpiper was present between 29 August and 2 September; seen on three different days.

Features to note are: long black upturned bill, bright orange legs and feet, ash-grey body plumage including rump, ashy sides of breast and throat, white axillaries and under tail-coverts, and blackish shoulders. Breeds from the Gulf of Bothnia (Finland) to Central Siberia. Migrates via S.E. Europe and S.W. Asia to winter in eastern Africa ranging to south of Equator.

PHALAROPODIDAE

Phalaropes see p. 88

Red-necked phalarope: *Lobipes lobatus.* Rare Spring visitor. B. of C. p. 297. A number of sightings took place at Akrotiri in 1970 between 29 April and 5 June, and again between 24 August and 6 September of from one to five individuals. Most of these records refer to the same birds. One was shot at Famagusta on 21 June 1914, but the skin if preserved, cannot be traced.

GLAREOLIDAE

Pratincoles and Coursers see p. 89

Cream-coloured courser: *Cursorius cursor.* Occasional visitor in Spring. B. of C. p. 323. The latest was recorded at Kouklia 27 April 1969 but it can only be considered rare.

STERCORARIIDAE
Skuas see p. 91

Arctic skua: *Stercorarius parasiticus.* Rare visitor in Spring and Autumn. B. of C. p. 355.

NOTE

Two unidentified skuas were present in Limassol harbour on the 22 November 1969.

LARIDAE

Gulls and Terns see p. 92

Sub-Family LARINAE

Great black-backed gull: *Larus marinus.* Rare accidental visitor see B. of C. p. 337 for early recordings. Recently one seen by ourselves: Xeros 11 February 1958 and by another observer at Akrotiri 30 March 1958.

Caspian Sea herring gull: *Larus argentatus cachinnans.* A very likely visitor in Winter from Caspian Sea area, impossible to distinguish from *michahellis*, the Mediterranean herring gull at that season unless handled. Not yet definitely identified. B. of C. [p. 339, but almost certain to occur casually].

Common gull: *Larus canus.* Rare accidental visitor in Winter or early Spring. B. of C. p. 340. Between 1954 and 1965 about 30 birds in all reported between end November and third week April round coast including eight at Zhygi by ourselves.

Great black-headed gull: *Larus ichthyaëtus.* A record on 23 January 1958 Paralimni Lake rests on sight record by a reliable observer. B. of C. p. 344 where given in brackets.

Kittiwake: *Rissa tridactyla.* Rare accidental visitor. Three first noted 1961 Famagusta harbour in February and one at Kyrenia 1 October of same year.

Sub-Family STERNINAE

Terns see p. 99

Arctic tern: *Sterna paradisea.* Very rarely recognised, one present 11 May 1963; also three "positively identified" at Akrotiri 19 May 1966 and on 16 Sep. of same year another was seen.
From 10 to 60 were reported to be present in 1969 on the Akrotiri Salt Lake from 29 April to 17 May (see new *Check-List*).

Sandwich tern: *Sterna sandvicensis.* Rare visitor. Two ringed birds reported recovered Cyprus. Ringed Black Sea. B. of C. p. 354.

Lesser crested tern: *Sterna bengalensis.* The "probable" occurrence of a tern of this species is recorded in the C.O.S. 2nd *Check-List*. The bird was seen at Akrotiri Salt Lake on 24 April 1963, but has not been accepted unconditionally. It would have been of the Red-Sea race *Sterna par bengalensis* (*arabica* auctorum) in all probability, if a valid record.

PTEROCLIDIDAE

Sandgrouse see p. 103

Pin-tailed sangrouse: *Pterocles alchata.* Accidental. B. of C. p. 288. A pair obtained April 1820, preserved in Berlin museum. For other records see our larger work.

COLUMBIDAE

Pigeons and Doves see p. 104

North African turtle dove: *Streptopelia turtur arenicola.* We believe we saw an example of this pale turtle-dove in

Cyprus and only include it in this list as our probable identification has now been confirmed by another record in May 1969. The two specimens, handled and identified by a distinguished ornithologist while on a visit to Cyprus, were unquestionably *arenicola*. Another secured was equally certainly of the nominate race. This is a pale variety of the European bird. It is a common summer visitor to Iraq and Palestine and more than a likely visitor to Cyprus breeding abundantly in S.W. Asia and in northern Africa.

Senegal palm dove: *Stigmatopelia senegalensis*. Status uncertain as also origin. B. of C. p. 285. Has occurred Athalassa irregularly in distant past, and reported still present. No evidence breeding.

[**Emerald dove**: *Chalcophaps indica*. Possibly an escape from ship. One caught on lime-stick, December 1957. A native of the Far East.]

STRIGIDAE

Owls see p. 111

Tawny owl: *Strix aluco*. In *Birds of Cyprus* p. 187 we accepted with some reservation the record of a tawny owl seen on 9 and 10 November at Nicosia (of all places) as the bird is known in Asia Minor, but had never before been reported in Cyprus. This record is *not* accepted by the compilers of the new 1971 *Check-List*, presumably for lack of details supplied by the observer. This decision is open to criticism, in view of the fact that a pair of tawny owls have now been reported to have *bred* successfully at Lefkonico in April 1966, first noticed on 2nd and two fully grown young seen on 30th. This very interesting and unique record calls for further search for this owl in Cyprus whose status is quite unknown in the island. The tawny owl is fully described in our larger volume, together with an excellent line-drawing.

[**Hawk-owl**: *Surnia ulula*. A bird of this species is reported to have been observed in Cyprus (C.O.S. 10th *Annual Report* 1963) at Akrotiri on 6 April 1963, and to have been "well described by the observer". It was considered to be probably correctly identified by the Recorders of that year. This record has again been under review by the compilers of the 2nd *Check-List* to whom it is *not* acceptable, though "possible".

In view of the striking appearance of the European hawk-owl, it is difficult to ignore so positive a record when a description was taken down at the time. A fearless bird given to perching in prominent positions, the plumage shows a blending of brown and white, the upperparts boldly spangled, the breast closely barred. A bright yellow eye is set in a pale grey disc, fringed with a crescent of blackish feathers. Unlike most owls, it has a trim falcon-like outline in flight, when its pointed short wings and long tail remind one closely of the flight of a falcon. It is also known to hover. A native of northern Europe and northern Russia, within the Arctic Circle, a subspecies, *pallasi*, occurs in Siberia. As a straggler it has been reported from Britain and from various European countries, but never before from the Mediterranean, within our knowledge.]

[**Tengmalm's owl**: *Aegolius funereus*. Has been reported seen on one occasion, but is considered a "possible" record *only (Bulletin* 15 p. 30) and should await confirmation before adding to Cyprus list. The record of one caught on a lime stick *Birds* 1970 was very carelessly misnamed. The photograph there reproduced depicts a Cyprian scops owl! The latest Tengmalm's record is worthless].

CAPRIMULGIDAE

Nightjars see p. 115

[**Egyptian nightjar**: *Caprimulgus aegyptius*. Accidental vagrant. We accepted this sight record seen 1st week of April, 1957. B. of C. p. 163. General colour uniform greyish sand-colour, finely vermiculated with black; sand-colour patches on scapulars on outer webs. Primaries barred brown and sandy. No white markings on wings or tail. Throat and breast finely barred and vermiculated. A white patch in centre of throat. Flanks and under tail-coverts finely barred but middle of belly uniform sand-colour. Bill slate, feet grey. Sexes alike. The recorders of the new *Check-List* refuse to accept it as valid "for lack of detail".]

APODIDAE

Swifts see p. 116

[**White-rumped swift**: *Apus affinis* or *Apus caffer*. Three swifts with white rumps which could only be one of the species named were seen consorting with house-martins in the month of April 1968. The first named is the more likely of the two, but field identification mainly rests on shape of tail, square in *affinis* and deeply forked in *caffer* where nearly half total length of bird. *A. affinis* is smaller (5 ins 13 cm) with wing-span 12 ins and has conspicuous white throat as well as rump. *A. caffer* is larger (6 ins 15 cm) with wing span 14 ins and prominent white rump. Both species renowned for peculiar gliding flight in which wings are raised over back.]

ALCEDINIDAE

Kingfishers see p. 118

[**Smyrna kingfisher**: *Halcyon smyrnensis*. Not fully substantiated. Records rest on the credulity of distinguished naturalists believing what they were *told*. No firm evidence but not impossible. B. of C. p. 173; *Bull.* 15 p. 30 Description as follows – Head deep chestnut, mantle blue-green, upper tail-coverts turquoise blue, tail as mantle. Wings turquoise, shoulder chestnut, wing-coverts black. Chin, throat and centre of breast white. Rest of underparts dark chestnut. Bill and feet dark vermilion. Young resemble adults but duller and have crescentic marks on breast.]

Order PASSERIFORMES

HIRUNDINIDAE

Swallows see p. 131

Egyptian swallow: *Hirundo rustica savignii*. In view of the variation shown in European specimens of *Hirundo rustica* we were loth to accept earlier sight records of *H.r. savignii*. The swallows in Cyprus were recognised so far back as 1910, as having the underside "ranging from nearly white to a deep reddish-buff, from *Hirundo rustica* to *H. savignii*. Although one may often see these extremes *in a paired couple*, the differences in colouring do not appear to be sexual." The writer of that sentence was Sir John Bucknill, a leading authority on the birds of Cyprus in his day. (*Ibis* 1910 p. 2.) What could be clearer evidence to refute the presence of the Egyptian swallow in Cyprus in those days of which he was writing? The late F.C.R. Jourdain, who prepared the list of birds in the *Cyprus Handbook* (1930), had obviously, formed the same conclusion. We dismiss the old sight records for the above reason. Whether the record of an "Egyptian Swallow", identified to the satisfaction of several prominent members of the C.O.S. at Bishops Pool, Akrotiri peninsula in late August 1968 (*Cyprus Bird Report* 15 p. 3) can be considered in a different category from earlier recordings must be left to individual judgement but to suggest that the Egyptian swallow has ever been (as quoted) "a regular visitor" is nonsense, and most misleading. It was nothing of the sort.

PARIDAE

Titmice see p. 141

Blue tit: *Parus caeruleus*.
Accidental. One sight record in 1887 on good authority, B. of C. p. 67 which it seems pointless to question at this date. In those days we very sensibly accepted records on the known reputation and experience of the recorder.

SITTIDAE

Nuthatches see p. 144

[**Rock nuthatch**: *Sitta neumayeri*.
An ancient record (1865) with no supporting details has never been corroborated though there is plenty of suitable country in Cyprus, and it occurs in Syria and Palestine under the name *syriaca*. B. of C. p. 64.]

TURDIDAE

Thrushes, Chats, Robins etc. see p. 151

[A thrush seen Akrotiri 10/11 November 1958 assumed to be a **Dusky thrush**, was included in *Bulletin* 15 p. 33 (see also *Bulletin* 6, p. 8). Its correct identification, from the description and argument produced is too complex to accept as a definite record of *Turdus eunomus* as there listed. Even if collected it might have proved a puzzle. An obvious straggler of the Turdidae family its real identity must remain unsolved, other than the possibility there assumed. The record is discussed in the 1971 *Check-List* but no conclusion reached.]

[**Hooded chat**: *Oenanthe monacha*.
Accidental visitor. One pair recorded May 1875. B. of C. p. 131. Not accepted in new *Check-List* "owing to possible misidentification".]

[**Mourning chat**: *Oenanthe lugens*.
An accidental visitor recorded by Schrader in July 1877 and confirmed by Müller. We overlooked this record in *Birds of Cyprus* c.f. *Bulletin* 6 p. 9. where placed in brackets in view of possible error. Named there *Saxicola erythraea* (= lugens). Not accepted in new *Check-List* for same reason as preceding species.]

White-crowned black wheatear: *Oenanthe leucopyga*. An accidental visitor. One on 17 March 1970. identified at Akrotiri.

Red-flanked bluetail: *Tarsiger cyanurus*.
Accidental visitor. One recorded 8 November, 1957. B. of C. p. 140.

Persian robin: *Irania gutturalis*.
Accidental visitor, one recorded Dhekelia 1 April, 1962. *Cyprus Bird Report* 1962 p. 14.

SYLVIIDAE

Warblers see p. 165

Grasshopper warbler: *Locustella naevia*.
An occasional visitor so far as present evidence points. The first definite record was obtained on 22 September by a Cypriot observer in 1968, when a dead specimen was examined and the skin preserved. There were two earlier possible records in 1957, see *Bulletin* 15 p. 34. and 15th *Cyprus Bird Report* 1968 pp. 3 and 16 and *Birds of Cyprus* 1958 p. 92.

Blyth's reed warbler: *Acrocephalus dumetorum*. Accidental visitor, one record 14 August 1962. *Bull.* 15 p. 34., 9th Bird *Report* 1962 p. 15.

Aquatic warbler: *Acrocephalus paludicola*. Accidental visitor, one record 4 April 1956.

Olive-tree warbler: *Hippolais olivetorum*. When we were writing our *Birds of Cyprus* no specimen of this warbler had ever been taken, but from sight records we included it as an occasional passage migrant. Careful re-investigation of the records since our book was published in 1958, by the authors of the new *Check-List of Cyprus Birds* (to be published in 1971) result in the following being considered valid. One, Cape Andreas 7 May 1961, one Akrotiri 5 September and one on 10 September 1962; one Larnaca 28 April 1963; five at Salamis 21 April 1965; two at Kormakiti Forest 10 April 1966 and two "limed" at Paralimni in the spring of 1968; one seen near Buffavento Castle 10 August 1969 and one at Athalassa on 26 August of the same year. Other published records within the years instanced are judged to be invalid by the authors of the new *Check-List*.

East Siberian lesser white-throat: *Sylvia curruca blythi*. One caught in mist-net at Akrotiri peninsula 18 October, 1969.

Desert warbler: *Sylvia nana*.
Accidental visitor. Two records 12 March 1958, April 1961.

Dusky warbler: *Phylloscopus fuscatus*.
Accidental visitor. One record, 30 September 1967, Cyprus Bird Report No. 14 p. 39, bird captured.

Bonelli's warbler: *Phylloscopus bonelli bonelli*. An example of the *typical race* of this warbler was trapped at Akrotiri in Spring of 1970 and identified by its wing formula. First record of subspecies for Cyprus which does not normally occur east of the Adriatic. See p. 182 of main text.

Yellow-browed warbler: *Phylloscopus imornatus*: One caught Akrotiri Peninsula 16 October 1969, and again at Episkopi on 18 and 29 October 1969. See also 1970 Report C.O.S.

REGULIDAE

Goldcrests and fire crests see p. 182

Firecrest: *Regulus ignicapillus*.
Occasional vistor. Status uncertain. Reported on good authority B. of C. p. 72. *Bulletin* 15, p. 36.

MOTACILLIDAE

Wagtails and Pipits see p. 187

The true **Yellow wagtail**: *Budytes lutea lutea* of Russia has been captured twice, one at Akrotiri 15 September 1969 and again at Akrotiri on 12 May 1970. See p. 190.

Yet another new record for Cyprus, in addition to the above in this family, is that of the **Trans-Caspian white wagtail** *Motacilla alba personata* at Akrotiri on 22 September 1966. See main text p. 188.

Two pipits were tentatively recorded by us as probably **Rock pipit** *Anthus petrosus*, and **Petchora pipit** *Anthus gustavi* to remain "on the doubtful list until specimens obtained" in our *Birds of Cyprus* p. 55. There is now evidence that the rock pipit *A. petrosus littoralis* has been found again on 11 May 1970 at Ayia Napa as recorded in the *Cyprus Check-List*. 1971.

BOMBYCILLIDAE

Waxwings see p. 194

Waxwing: *Bombycilla garrulus*.
A rare accidental visitor. First recorded in the new *Check-List of Cyprus Birds*, 1971. Five waxwings were trapped on 2 January 1966 near Myrtou. This record coincides with a large invasion of this species in Western Europe in the winter of 1965–66.

LANIIDAE

Shrikes see p. 194

Great grey shrike: *Lanius excubitor*.
Rare visitor on passage. With the possible exception of the first one recorded (Schrader's), we see no reason to discredit the sight records mentioned in B. of C. p. 75. Authors of the 2nd *Check-List* refuse to admit this species to the Cyprus List as in their opinion no satisfactory details were supplied. We must therefore await the aquisition of a specimen before its occurrence can be assured.

STURNIDAE

Starlings see p. 197

Common starling: *Sturnus vulgaris.*
Several races of the common starling have been recognised in Cyprus, of Asiatic origin. These are the Siberian starling *S. V. poltaratskyi* (see also main text p. 198, the Balkan starling *S. v. balcanicus*, the Russian starling *S. v. sophiae* and the purple-backed starling *S. v. purpurascens.* For details the reader must refer to *Birds of Cyprus* pp. 11–12. To this list has now been added (*Cyprus Check-List* 1971) *S. vulgaris tauricus* from the Crimea. All are probable visitors in the winter months.

Rose-coloured starling: *Pastor roseus.*
Once, when locusts occurred in the island of Cyprus prior to 1910 rosy pastors were irregular summer visitors. Parties of eight and twelve were reported from Paphos in May 1909, probably same flock (B. of C. p. 12). Since then they are only very rare vagrants two obtained Limassol 18 and 19 August 1945 and one seen in the Kormakiti area 22 May 1966.

PLOCEIDAE

Weaver birds

Sub-Family PASSERINAE

Sparrows see p. 199

Tree sparrow: *Passer montanus.*
An early record of this bird, a specimen so identified at first as having been trapped at Morphou on 5 November 1961 was discarded by the Editors of the new *Cyprus Check-List* who there published their reasons. They accept however a more recent occurrence when a tree-sparrow was caught on 12 October 1970 at Bishops Pool, Akrotiri.

Very similar in appearance to the house sparrow the tree-sparrow should be recognised by its chocolate-brown crown (not grey) and by the presence of a black patch on the ear-coverts which stands out conspicuously against the greyish-white cheeks. On close scrutiny a *double* white wing bar is discernible and the black throat of the male is more restricted than in the more familiar kind.

Rock sparrow: *Petronia petronia.*
An ancient record of a rock-sparrow given by Sibthorp in his List was rejected as unproven by the Editors of the new *Check-List.* A patch of yellow on the white throat and the white spots at the terminal end of the tail-feathers is the surest means of identification coupled with a conspicuous broad white eyebrow.

FRINGILLIDAE

Finches see p. 201

Redpoll: *Carduelis flammea.*
An occasional but scarce visitor: one obtained Nicosia, 13 January 1966, was determined as *C. f. flammea*; two others not critically examined for race, were trapped, one at Lefkara 26 November 1966 and one at Limassol 4 January 1968.

Rosefinch or scarlet grosbeak: *Carpodacus erythrinus.* The status of this bird in Cyprus must for the time remain uncertain. There have been three records: an immature collected 19 September 1969 at Akrotiri and one trapped at Akrotiri on 11 November 1969 were the first ever to have been recorded from Cyprus. In the following year another was trapped on 23 May at Akrotiri (where mist-netting for ringing purposes takes place). These occurrences, evidently due entirely to the method of capture, make one wonder if the rosefinch will prove to be more regular in its appearance than three instances suggest. In my opinion, it is more likely to be of accidental occurrence as the main winter quarters of the bird lie in India and not in Africa which would bring it more often to Cyprus. In immature dress it is not easily identified. When adult the body plumage of the male is mostly dull crimson on the head, upper breast and rump. The female is entirely olive-brown streaked with brown and is distinctive by reason of a double whitish wing-bar across the wing-coverts. The shape of the heavy bill is likely to save it from confusion at any age, if clearly seen, from others of the finch family in the island.

Trumpeter bullfinch: Rhodopechys (formerly *Bucanetes*) *githaginea*. One caught on lime-stick at Paralimni 27 April 1969 may have been of the Palestine race named *crassirostris*. First record for the island.

[**Two-barred crossbill**: *Loxia leucoptera bifasciata*. An immature male reported seen 24 February 1965 on Mount Olympus (c.f. new *Cyprus Check-List*) would constitute a new record for the island, but sight-records of immature birds are bound to have an element of doubt and without a bird in this plumage being handled we should be loth to add it to the Cyprus list, although it is a perfectly possible vagrant to occur. Two-barred crossbills are known to wander far afield, and their nothern range is spreading.]

EMBERIZIDAE

Buntings see p. 207

[**Cirl bunting**: *Emberiza cirlus*. Accidental visitor. We discussed this sight record of November 1957 in Cyprus with the *observer* and believed it to be a valid record at the time. B. of C. p. 33. Doubt has been thrown on this identification by others. The military recorder has since sadly lost his life; he was a very good ornithologist, absolutely sincere, and was responsible for several of the more interesting Cyprus bird records while on service in the island. We were prepared to accept his identification. The bunting family are all more or less difficult to identify in the field without handling and a cirl bunting in winter dress is no exception. The record must, we fear, remain unproven.]

Rock bunting: *Emberiza cia*.
[Plate 26, facing p. 176]
We had already, B. of C. p. 37 listed this bird as an irregular scarce visitor summer and winter. Since that publication there have been occasional records. In 1958 several were seen on 15 January in the Northern Range above Ayios Chrysostomos, in 1963 one on 23 April at Episkopi. We had already expressed the opinion that Cyprus specimens would be *E. cia cia* and that appears to have been confirmed.

[**Cinereous bunting**: *Emberiza cineracea*. We place this bird also in brackets. It was identified from descriptions written down *at the time* by a well-known ornithologist who had never seen the species before. See B. of C. p. 31. There were three records in 1929. From Leontari on 7 April (2 birds), from Athalassa 8 April (one only) and from Boghaz 14 April (one bird.) There must always be a shadow of doubt when birds of this complexity are identified by sight alone.]

Thick-billed reed-bunting: *Emberiza schoeniclus tschusii*. This is probably a rare visitor and the races which occur need to be examined. We mentioned these thick-billed birds in B. of C. 1958 p. 38. Reed-buntings with abnormally heavy thick bills have been discussed again in the new *Cyprus Check-List* (1971) but the status of these birds and even the subspecies which occur in Cyprus on occasions require much more study both in the field and the Museum. Only the capture of specimens can help solve the problem these birds present.

[**Little bunting**: *Emberiza pusilla*. The record of a bunting believed to have been of this species appears in the new *Check-List* among birds rejected as not definitely established. Said to have been "probable". Seen Limassol marsh, 20 October 1957.]

INDEX

NOTE: When the species name and the subspecies name are alike, binomials only are used here.

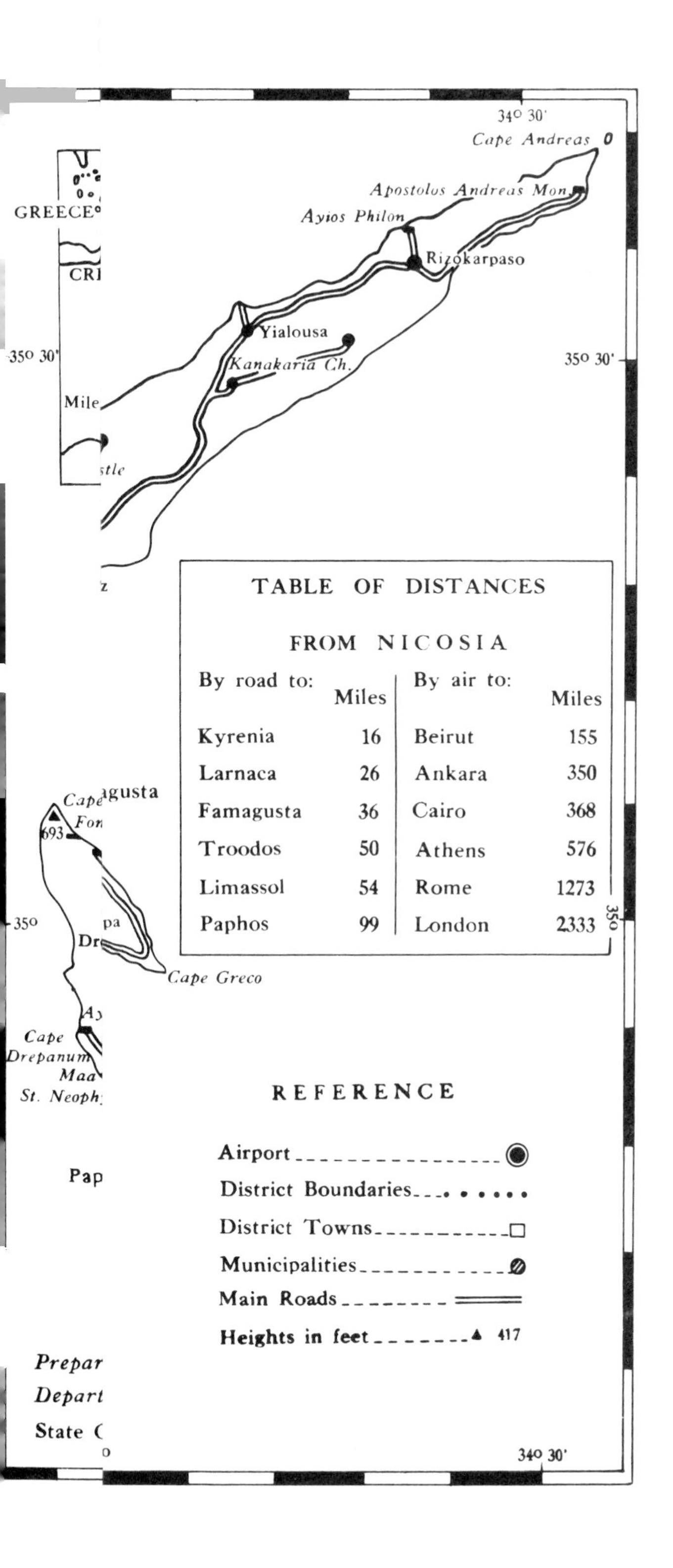

TABLE OF DISTANCES

FROM NICOSIA

By road to:	Miles	By air to:	Miles
Kyrenia	16	Beirut	155
Larnaca	26	Ankara	350
Famagusta	36	Cairo	368
Troodos	50	Athens	576
Limassol	54	Rome	1273
Paphos	99	London	2333

REFERENCE